ADVANCED SERVICING TECHNIQUES

ADVANCED SERVICING TECHNIQUES

VOLUME 2:

Part   I: *Stereo Amplifiers, FM and FM Multiplex*

ORVILLE NEELY
Manager, Product Evaluation Center
Motorola, Inc.

Part II: *Record Changers*

LAWRENCE MASSARO
and
ROBERT S. HARRIS

Part III: *Tape Recorders*

M. P. ROSENTHAL
Senior Member, Technical Staff
RCA CSD N. Y., Systems Laboratory

Part IV: *Home Intercoms*

WILLIAM P. KIST

Part V: *Combination Receivers*

WILLIAM P. KIST

JOHN F. RIDER PUBLISHER, INC., NEW YORK
a division of HAYDEN PUBLISHING COMPANY, INC.

Foreword to Volume 2

While television is the principal product of the electronic home entertainment industry, a service technician today should be equally knowledgeable in the newest techniques of installing and servicing a number of other home entertainment products, including high-fidelity and stereo amplifiers, FM and FM multiplex, record changers, tape recorders, home intercommunication equipment, and combination receivers.

The first edition of *Advanced Servicing Techniques* was devoted entirely to television. When plans were being made for the new edition by the Electronic Industries Association's Service Committee, it was agreed that a number of consumer products, in addition to television, have become important enough to be included in any publication directed to advanced training for service technicians. This volume of *Advanced Servicing Techniques,* therefore, includes the latest information on maintenance, repair, and troubleshooting procedures for these new and important home entertainment equipments and for home intercom equipment.

The increasing importance of these other consumer products is shown by the increase in sales of these products. While television factory sales increased 24% from 1957 to 1963, phonograph sales increased 123% over the same years, hi-fi components 41%, and other consumer products 115%. And, of course, FM stereo did not even exist commercially in 1957.

The original goal of the EIA training program, as stated in the first edition, was "to meet a need of keeping service technicians abreast of new developments and ever-changing techniques," for a technician not only must be adequately trained but also must be readily adaptable to changes occurring after completion of his formal training. Therefore, one of the primary purposes of this book is to expand the technical skill of the practicing technician, especially in the new product areas, and to keep him abreast of new developments.

In addition, recognizing its responsibility to industry and education to help prepare well-trained technicians to enter the television field, EIA has worked with educators in preparing these books for effective use as advanced training material in schools in teaching a systematic, organized, industry-approved troubleshooting procedure, and in utilizing the latest techniques and test instruments.

The experience of the authors insures the same practical, thorough, and clearly understandable coverage of the subjects that has characterized the earlier editions of these books, as well as the other manuals of the EIA-VTI series. And, to insure that the latest industry-wide developments and servicing techniques are included, the authors' manuscripts were reviewed and constructively criticized by a subcommittee of the EIA Service Committee, made up of the national service managers of many of the manufacturers of consumer products.

We believe this text marks another step forward in the efforts of the Electronic Industries Association to enhance the prestige of the service industry by improving the technical skill and proficiency of technicians.

JAMES D. SECREST
Executive Vice President
Electronic Industries Association

Acknowledgments

EIA National Service Committee

CHAIRMAN: Edward J. Gaiden, *Motorola, Inc.*
VICE CHAIRMAN: Andrew Adler, *Olympic Division of Lear Siegler, Inc.*

MEMBERS:

James H. Bradley, *Hoffman Electronics Corp.*
John P. Brocki, *Bendix Radio Division*
Kenneth H. Brown, *Westinghouse Electric Corp.*
Ray Cavalieri, *Capitol Records, Inc.*
Daniel R. Creato, *RCA Service Co.*
John H. Doble, *Westinghouse Electric Corp.*
William A. Ems, *Conrac Division of Giannini Controls Corp.*
Herman Feldman, *Trav-Ler Industries, Inc.*
Kenneth L. Freeland, *Symphonic Radio and Electronic Corp.*
Donald H. Gieb, *John F. Rider Publisher, Inc.*
Charles Golenpaul, *Aerovox Corp.*
Thomas R. Hayes, *Delco Radio Division of the General Motors Corp.*
James B. Hofer, *Arvin Industries, Inc.*

Charles N. Hoffman, *Warwick Electronics, Inc.*
Herbert S. King, *Philco Corp.*
O. H. Lange, *International Business Machines Corp.*
Joseph V. Loiacono, *General Electric Co.*
William N. Maddox, Jr., *General Electric Co.*
William L. Parkinson, *General Electric Co.*
Kermit W. Pietenpol, *ATR Electronics, Inc.*
William D. Renner, *Howard W. Sams and Co., Inc.*
Clifford M. Rigsbee, *RCA Sales Corp.*
Norman F. Schumacher, *Wells-Gardner Electronics Corp.*
Howard Tomlin, *Philco Corp.*
P. Douglas Wexler, *General Electric Co.*
Frank D. Whitten, *Philco Corp.*
Donald E. Winters, *Sylvania Home Electronics Corp.*
Ray J. Yeranko, *The Magnavox Co.*

Subcommittee on Revisions of Advanced Servicing Techniques

CHAIRMAN: P. Douglas Wexler, *General Electric Co.*

MEMBERS:

Andrew Adler, *Olympic Division of Lear Siegler, Inc.*
James H. Bradley, *Hoffman Electronics Corp.*
John P. Brocki, *Bendix Radio Division*
Kenneth H. Brown, *Westinghouse Electric Corp.*
Daniel R. Creato, *RCA Service Co.*
John H. Doble, *Westinghouse Electric Corp.*
William A. Ems, *Conrac Division of Giannini Controls Corp.*
Herman Feldman, *Trav-Ler Industries, Inc.*
Edward J. Gaiden, *Motorola, Inc.*

Thomas R. Hayes, *Delco Radio Division of the General Motors Corp.*
James B. Hofer, *Arvin Industries, Inc.*
Charles N. Hoffman, *Warwick Electronics, Inc.*
Herbert S. King, *Philco Corp.*
Joseph V. Loiacono, *General Electric Co.*
William N. Maddox, Jr., *General Electric Co.*
Kermit W. Pietenpol, *ATR Electronics, Inc.*
Clifford M. Rigsbee, *RCA Sales Corp.*
Frank D. Whitten, *Philco Corp.*
Donald E. Winters, *Sylvania Home Electronics Corp.*
Ray J. Yeranko, *The Magnavox Co.*

Acknowledgment is also made to Donald H. Stover, Service
Coordinator of EIA, for his efforts in behalf of the project,
and to all the many men in each of the member companies
who did most of the actual reviewing and editing.

Contents

Part I

Stereo Amplifiers
FM
FM Multiplex

1 – Introduction

1. High Fidelity

High fidelity is a term originally used by audio enthusiasts to describe a specific type of high quality audio, or sound reproducing system. The term "high fidelity," as used by the relatively few who were fortunate enough to own one of these systems, referred to a system that reproduced sounds with a very high degree of trueness, or realism. Almost all of the early hi-fi systems were monaural systems. They were usually owned by a select few audio enthusiasts, musicians, engineers, and hobbiests. The systems were extremely expensive, cumbersome, and complicated, and, therefore, were not too practical for the average consumer to own, and operate.

Technical Advances

Shortly after World War 2, there were a series of significant advances in several areas of sound reproduction which made possible practical high-fidelity audio systems for the consumer. Today, there are millions of these systems in use in practically every household. Some of the more significant technical advances which made these systems possible were:

1. The development of the ceramic cartridge, which replaced the crystal cartridge. The ceramic cartridge of today has a very wide frequency range. It is small and compact, requires less tracking force because of high compliance, and is also impervious to moisture and humidity, which was the greatest enemy of the crystal cartridge.

2. The use of vinyl for the making of records replacing shellac allowed for many improvements in recorded sound. The smoothness of the new vinyl material produced recordings with much improved signal-to-noise ratio.

3. Because of the improved signal-to-noise ratio, it was now practical to extend the high-frequency response of the record. The grooves were made finer to improve the resolution of the system, improving the high frequency response. Also the high frequencies were boosted 15 decibels (db) in recording, and attenuated in the playback, increasing the signal-to-noise ratio of high frequencies. The frequency response was increased from 5 to well over 10 kc because of these two new recording techniques. At the same time, the speed of the recording was reduced to provide longer playing time.

4. The new playback cartridges with their high compliance allowed lighter stylus pressure. This decreased record and stylus wear considerably. The smoothness of the new vinyl material also lessened record and stylus wear.

5. The tips of the styli were changed from steel to diamond, or sapphire. These harder materials increased the life of the stylus from two or three plays to hundreds of plays. The fact that the stylus retained its shape over long periods of time also reduced record wear due to sharp edges on the stylus.

6. Perhaps one of the more significant advances in recorded sound was the development of the stereo disc recording technique.

Dimension to Sound

All of the advances listed added immeasurably to the quality and convenience of recorded sound, but the advent of the stereo disc added dimension to the sound. Stereo could also be recorded on a standard vinyl disc in a single groove, and could be picked up by a single stylus coupled to a cartridge.

Another development of equal importance was also taking place in the broadcast industry. Although vinyl discs and high-performance pick-ups had been used for many years, AM broadcasting systems did not allow full utilization of the improved performance. The upper limit of the frequency response in the average AM transmitter is approximately 7.5 kc. But, more important, the AM signal is subject to atmospheric noise such as static, which decreases the signal-to-noise ratio. The advent of the FM method of broadcasting allowed for a much improved signal-to-noise ratio, and, at the same time, an extended high-frequency range. Finally, as in the case of the records, a system for broadcasting compatible stereo over standard FM broadcast stations was developed, adding dimension to the already excellent FM sound.

Another significant contribution to the acceptance of high fidelity was the development of the tape recorder with its excellent tonal quality, and its excellent characteristics for reproducing stereo.

These millions of stereo high-fidelity instruments in use today have opened up a new area of servicing for the electronic technician. Although the basic techniques of servicing these instruments are the same as for any audio device, or for that matter, any electronic device, there are new tools required and techniques to be learned to effectively and efficiently service them. The following chapters will examine the various types of high-fidelity systems in use today, and will examine each of the components which make up the systems in detail, outlining recommended service techniques, and then finally will examine practical servicing and troubleshooting methods for the entire stereo system. The systems discussed here will be stereo systems since most systems in use today are stereo. However, I am sure you will recognize that the basic servicing techniques, except for unique instances, apply as well to the monaural systems.

2. Stereophonic Sound

Before we examine the basic sound reproducing systems that are in use today, let us review some of the characteristics of stereo. The human ear determines direction, and the distance to a sound source in much the same way as the eye determines distance and direction. When we view an object, each eye sees a slightly different picture. These pictures are combined in the brain. The brain compares the images from each eye, and then determines direction and distance from the differences between the individual images.

The ear functions in much the same manner. When you listen to a sound, such as a symphony orchestra, each ear hears a slightly different sound. When these sounds are combined in the brain, the brain computes the distance, and the direction of the sound from the difference between these two sets of information.

When all of the sounds of a symphony orchestra are picked up by a single microphone, or group of microphones, and fed to a single amplifier, and this amplifier in turn feeds a single speaker, the ear cannot determine depth or direction. The reason this is so is that the single microphone receives all sound from the orchestra in the same relative phase, and all of the sounds appear to originate from a point source. In other words, the entire orchestra and room are compressed to approximately a two-foot square area. The sound is somewhat similar to what a listener would hear in the room with the orchestra if he listened with only one ear.

If we are to determine depth and direction, the sound system must provide information to both ears.

If the sound from one microphone, one amplifier, and one speaker gives us the sound we would hear with one ear, the use of two separate microphones, two separate amplifiers, and two speakers should give us most of the necessary information to make the sound appear as though we were actually present at the point where the microphones were placed.

We find in actual practice that this is true. If we take two microphones and amplifier systems, record their outputs separately on a tape, or disc, and play back this information over two separate amplifier and speaker systems, we are able to hear the sounds with practically all of the depth and direction characteristics that we would hear if we were actually present at the position where the two microphones were placed when making the recording. This type of sound reproduction is called *stereophonic sound*.

The Stero Disc

The stereo effect is by no means new. The development of a single-track stereo disc recording system has made it a practical consumer item. The stereo disc recording system uses a standard vinyl disc which is pressed in the same manner as an existing monaural record. The disc runs at either 33-⅓ or 45 rpm, which are standard speeds for monaural recordings. The groove widths are essentially the same as those used for standard monaural records. The vertical stylus load required for tracking is essentially the same as that required for the standard monaural long-playing records, and the compensation curves used in recording are essentially the same as those used for most monophonic long-playing systems. The RIAA curve is used.

This adds up to an extremely compatible system. Specifically, it means that the record manufacturers can press stereo discs at approximately the same cost as monaural records, using standard equipment, and methods. The standard monaural disc may be played back on a stereo hi-fi with essentially the same quality as the monaural record. It is not practical, however, to play back a stereo disc using a monaural cartridge. The stylus tip is 0.3 mils larger on the average monaural cartridge, and it can damage the stereo disc, especially the vertical cuts in the groove. Also, considerable loss of high-frequency response will be noted because only lateral components will be reproduced in a monaural system. Most high-frequency information has some vertical component. There will also be some distortion because the larger tip cannot track or follow the smaller stereo grooves properly.

The Stereo Recording System

The ideal stereo system would have an infinite number of channels feeding an infinite number of speakers. It is found, in practice, that the ear can do with much less information with excellent results. With a single channel system, the listener cannot hear depth, or direction. With the addition of the second channel, the illusion of direction is added, and there is a tremendous improvement in the realism of the sound. If additional channels are added, there is only a very slight improvement in the stereo effect. It is more difficult for the ear to determine depth or direction at very low frequencies. It is, therefore, not necessary to provide separation or separate channels at these low frequencies to create a stereo effect.

The term "channel separation," commonly used in stereo, defines the isolation between channels in a system. Ideally, this would be infinite. In other words, if a tone is introduced into one channel only of a stereo recording system, there would be no output from the other channel. In actual practice, 15 db of isolation is sufficient to produce excellent stereo.

Recording Stereo

The compatible recording system is accomplished by cutting two separate sets of information in a single groove on a standard vinyl disc. The recording system consists of

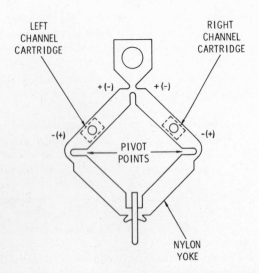

Fig. 1-1. A method used to couple cartridges to a common stylus. The common stylus can move in either a vertical or lateral direction, or in a combination of these directions.

two cutting heads coupled mechanically to a single cutting stylus. The playback system consists of two ceramic cartridges coupled mechanically to a single stylus. These cutting heads and the cartridges are mounted at a 45-degree angle with respect to the surface or plane of the record. For this reason, the recording system is called the 45/45 system. When these two cartridges, or cutting heads, are suitably coupled to a single stylus, the stylus may move both vertically and laterally according to the instantaneous phase and amplitude of the signals fed to each of the recording heads. In most modern monaural recordings, the stylus moves laterally only.

It is a combination of vertical and lateral movement of the stylus which gives the stereo effect, and enables the playback cartridge to separate the sound into two separate channels.

Figure 1-1 shows a method used to couple cartridges to a common stylus. The common stylus can move in either a vertical or lateral direction, or in combinations of vertical and lateral directions, depending upon the relative acoustical phase, and amplitude of each signal reaching the individual microphones. The stereo information is contained in the vertical movement.

The Recording System.   A block diagram of a simplified recording system appears in Fig. 1-2. You will note that the phase of the signal in the left channel is reversed 180° before it is fed into the cutting, or recording head. This is done in recording only so that in-phase signals at the microphones cause the stylus to move laterally. While one head pulls the stylus at a 45-degree angle, the other is pushing at a 45-degree angle, resulting in a lateral movement of the stylus. When signals 180° out of phase are received through the microphone, both heads push the stylus at a 45-degree angle, resulting in a vertical movement of the stylus. The reason for the phase reversal in one channel is that the majority of the power in normal sounds is at the low frequencies. These low frequencies, because of their long wavelengths, present an in-phase signal to each microphone. These frequencies will cause large lateral ex-

cursions of the stylus. It is desirable that these large excursions be in a lateral rather than vertical direction because of the distortions encountered in high-amplitude vertical cuts, and to avoid overcutting of the disc at low frequencies.

Another advantage is that the normal vibration encountered in a turntable, such as from a motor and drive mechanism, imparts more of a vertical movement to the turntable than horizontal. This distortion is known as turntable rumble. The frequencies are usually in the range of 30 to 80 cycles, depending on the type of motor used, and the method of driving the turntable. Bass notes or low-frequency notes, because of their long wavelengths, usually appear in phase at each microphone, and there is no stereo effect at low frequencies. Frequencies around the rumble frequency are recorded laterally, or in the plane where the least rumble vibrations are present.

Two Sets of Information in a Single Groove.   In order to understand how separate sets of information may be recorded in a single groove, let us refer to Fig. 1-3A. We will assume that the signal fed to each microphone is a sine wave of equal amplitude, and of the same phase. Because of the 180-degree phase shift network in channel 1, the stylus will move in a lateral direction only, as described earlier.

In Fig. 1-3B, channel 1 has full output, and channel 2 has zero output; thus, the force on the stylus is at a 45-degree angle with respect to the plane of the disc.

In Fig. 1-3C, channel 2 has full output, and channel 1 is zero. The force on the stylus is, again, at a 45-degree angle with respect to the plane of the disc, but it is 90° removed from the force applied in Fig. 1-3B.

In Fig. 1-3D, the signals are in phase at the microphone, but the output of channel 2 is 50% of that of channel 1. In this case, the force on the stylus is at an angle somewhat less than 45° with respect to the plane of the disc.

In Fig. 1-3E, the signals are in phase at the micro-

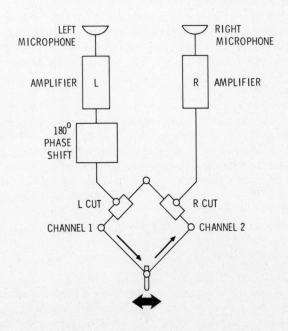

Fig. 1-2. Block diagram of a typical recording system.

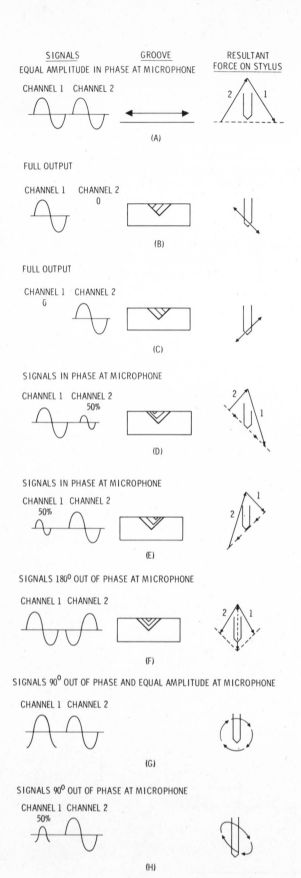

SIGNALS · GROOVE · RESULTANT FORCE ON STYLUS

EQUAL AMPLITUDE IN PHASE AT MICROPHONE

CHANNEL 1 · CHANNEL 2

(A)

FULL OUTPUT

CHANNEL 1 · CHANNEL 2 · 0

(B)

FULL OUTPUT

CHANNEL 1 · CHANNEL 2 · 0

(C)

SIGNALS IN PHASE AT MICROPHONE

CHANNEL 1 · CHANNEL 2 · 50%

(D)

SIGNALS IN PHASE AT MICROPHONE

CHANNEL 1 · CHANNEL 2 · 50%

(E)

SIGNALS 180° OUT OF PHASE AT MICROPHONE

CHANNEL 1 · CHANNEL 2

(F)

SIGNALS 90° OUT OF PHASE AND EQUAL AMPLITUDE AT MICROPHONE

CHANNEL 1 · CHANNEL 2

(G)

SIGNALS 90° OUT OF PHASE AT MICROPHONE

CHANNEL 1 · CHANNEL 2 · 50%

(H)

Fig. 1-3. Signal vs. groove force on stylus.

phones, but the output of channel 1 is 50% of that of channel 2. The force on the stylus is at an angle less than 45° with respect to the plane of the disc, but approximately 90° removed from that in Fig. 1-3D.

Figure 1-3F shows the conditions when signals 180° out of phase, but equal in amplitude are applied to the microphone. The force on the stylus in this case is vertical.

Figure 1-3G shows the force on the stylus when two signals of equal amplitude, but 90° out of phase are applied to the microphones. In this instance, the force on the stylus is in a circular direction, and the resulting groove would be a spiral.

Finally, Fig. 1-3H shows the force on the stylus when two signals are applied to the microphone 90° out of phase, but the output of channel 2 is greater than channel 1. In this case, the stylus, and the resultant groove is an ellipse. If the output of channel 1 is greater, the ellipse would lean in the opposite direction.

It can be seen from this that when a complex wave is being recorded in stereo, such as produced by an orchestra, the point of the stylus may occupy any point within a 360-degree circle, and that the instantaneous position of the stylus is determined by the relative phase and amplitude of the signals being applied to the two microphones during the recording.

The Playback Cartridge

When a device, having the same basic construction as the cutting head, is used to play back the recording described above, it will automatically separate the two signals into right and left stereo signals. Sound from the left side of the orchestra comes from the left speaker, and sound from the right side of the orchestra comes from the right speaker.

The yoke, or mechanical coupling, of the two playback cartridges separates the information on the groove as in the cutting head. Such a playback cartridge is shown in Fig. 1-4. The stylus is coupled to two ceramic cartridges by a diamond shaped piece of flexible nylon. When the force on the stylus comes from the outside of the groove, the right-channel crystal is flexed more than the left-channel crystal. When the force on the stylus comes from the inside or left side of the groove, the left-channel cartridge is flexed more than the right.

There is no 180-degree phase-shifting network in the playback system. A horizontal movement of the stylus produces two equal-amplitude signals in phase, and a vertical movement produces two equal-amplitude signals out of phase. The operation of the playback is identical to that of the cutter used in making the recording, as illustrated in Fig. 1-3.

The diameter of the stylus tip is 0.7 mil, and the vertical stylus load required is 3 to 11 grams according to the type of cartridge used. The vertical stylus load of the standard monaural cartridge is also a nominal 3 to 11 grams. The stylus tip is one mil in diameter. This makes the two systems compatible in that the normal monaural disc may be played back on a stereo system.

The output of the stereo cartridge is slightly lower than that of the monaural cartridge. Also, the recording level in the stereo disc is slightly lower than that on a monaural disc. This is in order to prevent overcutting of the groove. Of course, the frequency response should be the same for both crystals.

The Stereo Record Changer

A good quality changer will function satisfactorily in a stereo system, however, some improvement in performance is possible in a changer designed specifically for a stereo system. The vibration of the motor can be reduced by improved methods of mounting.

Also, the pick-up and the tone arm combination mass has considerable bearing on the turntable rumble. If the tone arm and cartridge mass is resonant at the rumble frequency on a specific changer, the turntable rumble will be high. The tone arm should also move freely in either the lateral or vertical direction. In other words, the vertical and lateral friction should be low.

The motor must have sufficient power. If it is laboring, the vibrations are greater. The tracing error should also be kept at a minimum so that the stylus is essentially parallel to the groove at all points on the record from the inside cuts to the outside cuts. If such is not the case, the stylus may have a tendency to ride the side of the groove, producing distortion, and reducing the channel separation.

It is also important that particular attention be paid to the acoustical feedback on a stereo system. The dual speaker system couples to the air with greater efficiency. This can cause acoustical feedback from the speakers to the cartridge and tone arm.

Typical Stereo Hi-Fi Systems

Perhaps the simplest of the stereo hi-fi systems that are in use today is the small portable system consisting of a record changer, and stereo pick-up device, usually of the

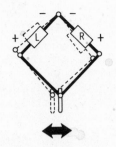

LATERAL MOVEMENT OF STYLUS PRODUCES TWO EQUAL SIGNALS IN PHASE.

(A)

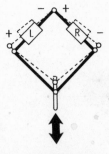

VERTICAL MOVEMENT OF STYLUS PRODUCES EQUAL AMPLITUDE SIGNALS 180° OUT OF PHASE BECAUSE CRYSTALS ARE FIXED IN THE OPPOSITE DIRECTION.

(B)

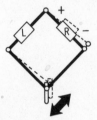

MOVEMENT OF STYLUS AT 45° ANGLE TO PLANE OF DISC PRODUCES OUTPUT FROM RIGHT CHANNEL CRYSTAL ONLY.

(C)

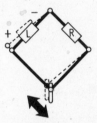

MOVEMENT OF STYLUS AT 45° ANGLE TO PLANE OF DISC (90° REMOVED FROM C) PRODUCES OUTPUT FROM LEFT CHANNEL CRYSTAL ONLY.

(D)

Fig. 1-4. Signal production in the playback cartridge.

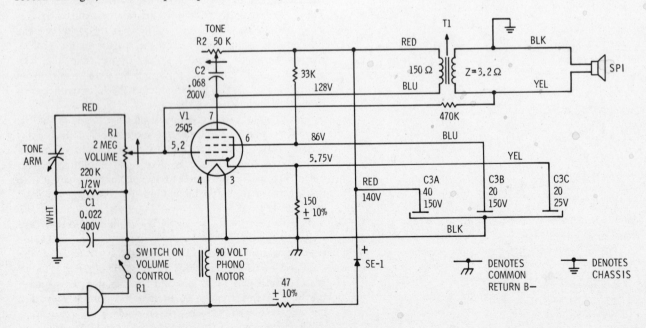

Fig. 1-5. Typical monaural system. (Courtesy of the Zenith Radio Corp.)

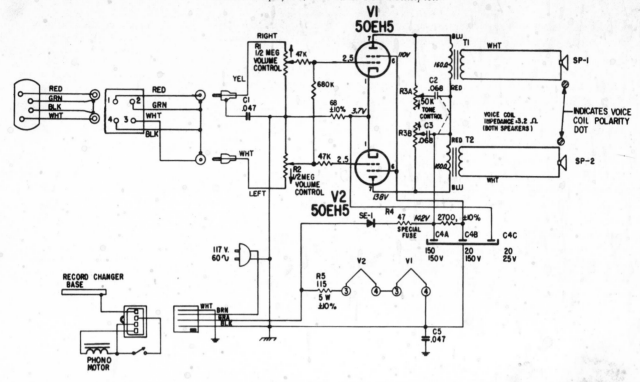

Fig. 1-6. Typical stereophonic system. (Courtesy of the Zenith Radio Corp.)

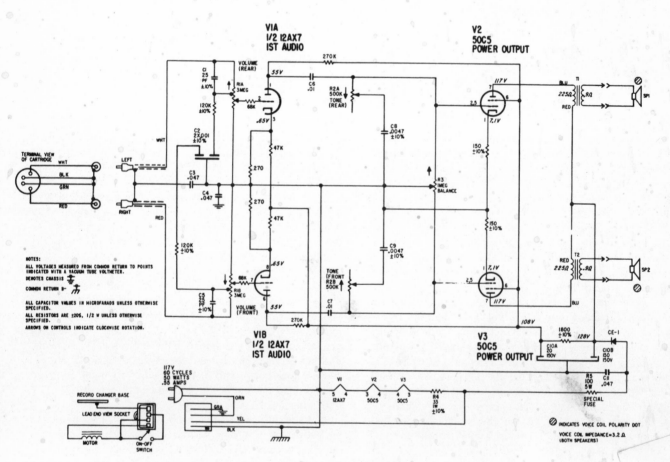

Fig. 1-7. Schematic of a portable hi-fi stereo with a high-performance amplifier. (Courtesy of the Zenith Radio Corp.)

high-output crystal type driving the power amplifier directly. A schematic of a simple system is shown in Fig. 1-5. This system is a monaural system consisting of a high-output crystal cartridge driving a 25Q5 power amplifier stage directly. Note that the phono motor winding is used as a voltage-dropping impedance for the filament of the power amplifier, which is common practice for amplifiers of this type. The B+ supply is obtained by rectifying the line voltage directly. The power output of such a stage ranges from 1 to 1-½ watts, generally, and the distortion is relatively high at normal operating levels, as compared to the higher powered audio systems.

Figure 1-6 is a stereo version of a similar amplifier. In this case, the stereo cartridge drives two 50EH5 power output stages directly. The left-channel output is connected to the grid of V1; the right-channel to the grid of V2. The

The filament power is obtained for the amplifier tubes by connecting them in series through a dropping resistor, R4, across the line. The B+ is obtained by rectifying the line voltage directly. The right- and left-channel tone controls are RC type controls, and are in the plate of the voltage amplifier tubes, V1A and V1B.

The next general class of stereo amplifier usually uses a power transformer to provide more B+ for greater audio output power, and greater efficiency of the power output stage. These amplifiers are used in large portable systems, and in some lower priced consoles. They are available in a wide variation of output powers, and input facilities. They range from systems with two single-ended output channels with a power from 3 to 5 watts per channel with a record changer only, to systems with up to 150 watts per channel with a record changer, AM-FM,

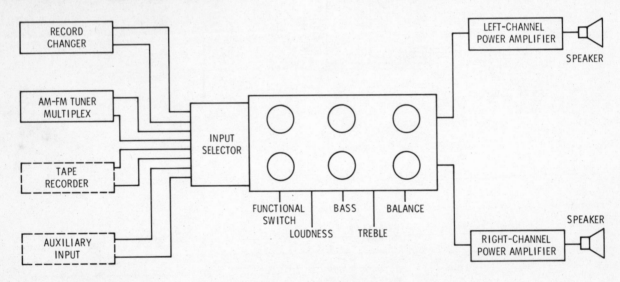

Fig. 1-8. Block diagram of a typical hi-fi system.

left-channel output appears across T1, and the right-channel output appears across T2. B+ power is supplied by rectifying the line voltage directly. The two 50-volt filaments of the power amplifier tube are connected in series through a dropping resistor across the line. The tone controls are ganged, and consist of a variable resistor in series with a bypass capacitor which shunts more or less of the high frequencies to ground in proportion to the value of R3. When R3 is high, all of the highs pass through to the speaker. When R3 is small, the high frequencies are shunted to ground through C2 and C3.

A higher performance amplifier also usually used in portable hi-fi stereos is shown in Fig. 1-7. The higher performance is due to the use of a ceramic cartridge with better high-frequency response, smaller mass, and a lighter stylus pressure requirement. Since a ceramic cartridge has a lower output voltage than the crystal, it is necessary to add a voltage amplifier in each channel (V1A and V1B) to obtain enough voltage to drive the power amplifier (V2 and V3) to full output. As in the amplifier described above, the output power is usually limited to one to 1-½ watts per channel, and the distortion at normal listening level is higher than that on more sophisticated systems.

FM stereo, and stereo tape inputs, as well as other auxiliary inputs and features.

It is in these higher powered low-distortion systems that our main interest lies from a servicing standpoint, for it is these systems that are designed for a very high degree of performance that require special considerations in servicing. The low-power portable systems described up to now are typical of home radio and record player instruments that the service industry is well acquainted with, and service procedures have long been established.

The new series of truly high-fidelity stereo systems about to be described are somewhat different from the technician's viewpoint. They are comprised of many different instruments such as FM tuners, AM tuners, tape recorders, preamplifiers, etc. Each of the individual instruments, and the system must work together comprising an extremely high-performance system with very tight electrical and mechanical tolerances dictating extra care in servicing and adjustment.

A block diagram of a typical high-fidelity system is shown in Fig. 1-8. The various inputs are connected to a function switch. This switch selects the desired input signal; applies frequency equalization, if it is necessary to provide a flat input to the amplifier; amplifies the signal through a series of voltage amplifiers driving the power amplifier. This amplifier is sometimes called the preamplifier. The operating controls such as loudness and tone are usually contained on the preamp. The output of the preamp feeds the power amplifier.

To properly service the high-fidelity system, it is important that we have an understanding of the function and operation of each of the instruments that make up the system, and the proper servicing techniques required for each. It is equally important that we have the proper instruments to efficiently service the system, and to know how to apply them most effectively.

To do the best possible job of servicing, it is necessary to understand how the device you are working with operates, some of the considerations in the design, and knowing these, establish service procedures that allow you to quickly and with confidence determine which section is malfunctioning, and the probable cause of the malfunction.

To accomplish this in the following chapters, we will discuss the power amplifier, the preamplifier, and then servicing procedures, measurements, and test equipment necessary for proper service. We will then discuss the FM tuner, and the proper service procedure and test equipment necessary for proper service. Then we will discuss the stereo FM system, and its proper service, and finally, discuss the servicing and check-out of the entire system.

2 - The Power Amplifier

1. Introduction

The power amplifier is the heart of the high-fidelity system. All other units in the system are then designed to satisfy the requirements of the power amplifier. There are two general types of power amplifiers used in hi-fi stereo systems: the single-ended output stage, and the push-pull type. Usually these amplifiers are class A, however, some push-pull power amplifiers operate class B, or class AB-1 because of the increased efficiency.

The purpose of the power amplifier is to supply audio output power to the speaker system. It is the most critical stage in the entire system. For the most part, it determines the output power, the distortion, the frequency response, and the general sound quality of the system.

The Output Transformer

One of the more important components of the power amplifier is the output transformer, whose basic purpose is to match the output impedance of the tube to the speaker system. In the hi-fi audio output transformer, the primary winding has a large number of turns. The core is large, and is made of a high-permeability, low-loss material. The large core and the large number of turns on the primary keep the primary impedance high, even for very low audio frequencies. If the core area is not large and is not made of high-permeability material, the d-c plate current in the output tubes, especially in the case of the single-ended output stage, can cause saturation of the core, which reduces the effective inductance of the primary, and, in turn, reduces the low-frequency response of the system severely.

Another important consideration of the output transformer is the leakage reactance. If all of the magnetic flux

lines produced by the primary do not link the turns of the secondary, this represents a loss in the transformer. This loss is called leakage reactance. The loss appears as though a small inductance were placed in series with the primary and secondary windings of the transformer, see Fig. 2-1. At low audio frequencies, where the reactances are rather low, they are not important, but at high audio frequencies, the impedances of the leakage reactances cause a loss in high-frequency response. The windings on the transformer must be carefully placed in relation to each other to assure that most of the primary flux lines link the secondary to keep the leakage reactance low.

Another important consideration in power output transformers is the distributed capacitance of the windings, see Fig. 2-2. A high distributed capacitance causes a loss at high frequencies. The higher audio frequencies will be

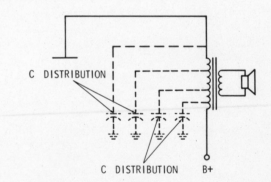

Fig. 2-2. Distributed capacitance in an output transformer.

shunted to ground through the distributed capacitance, will not flow through the primary winding, and, therefore, will not appear in the output. Close attention is paid to the placement of the winding in hi-fi output transformer to keep the distributed capacitance at a minimum. When pentode or beam power tubes are used to drive the power output transformer, which is usually the case, the leakage reactance and distributed capacitance may become resonant at a frequency within the audio range, and cause a hump or rise in the frequency response of the system at the resonant frequency, see Fig. 2-3.

Power Output Tubes for High-Fidelity Amplifiers

The requirement of the power amplifier tube differs from that of a voltage amplifier. In general, the plate dis-

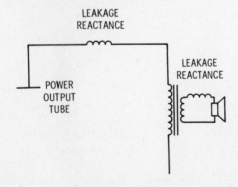

Fig. 2-1. Leakage reactance in an output transformer.

sipation on a power amplifier tube, or the power that can be radiated by the plate without overheating, is higher. The tube is also capable of greater emission, and higher plate current. The pentode and beam power tube is used in most power amplifiers. They normally have a higher plate efficiency than the triode tube, especially when low plate voltages are used, and they require much less driving voltage than the triode tubes. The distortion found in these tubes is generally slightly higher than that found in triodes, but when negative feedback is used, it is negligible.

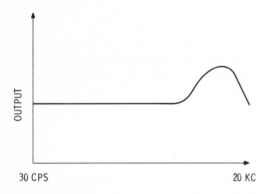

Fig. 2-3. Rise in high-frequency response due to the resonance of the distributed capacitance and the leakage reactance.

A beam power tube generally has slightly lower distortion than the pentode. A schematic of a typical single-ended power amplifier used in a General Electric receiver is shown in Fig. 2-4. The tube used is a 6BQ5, a beam powered pentode, which is capable of five watts of rms power output.

The Left-Channel Amplifier

For purposes of explanation, we will discuss only the left-channel amplifier, since the right-channel amplifier is the same. The power amplifier, V403, is driven by ½ of a 6FQ7 voltage amplifier. The output is applied to the speaker system through T401, which is the audio output transformer. The cathode resistor in the output tube is bypassed by a 20-μf capacitor. The value of the capacitor is high so that it offers a very low impedance to the low audio frequencies. If the capacitor were small, it would bypass the high frequencies around the cathode resistor, but would allow the low frequencies to appear across the cathode resistor. The low-frequency voltage appearing across the cathode resistor would subtract from the low-frequency signal appearing on the control grid, and, consequently, reduce the gain of the amplifier at the lower frequencies. If the cathode bypass capacitor, therefore, should decrease in value for any reason, the low-frequency response of the amplifier will become poorer. This is a rather common malfunction in audio systems.

The cathode bypass is an electrolytic capacitor, and the d-c voltage across it is very low. It has a tendency to decrease in capacitance after long periods of use because there is no appreciable forming voltage present. Another important consideration for good bass response is the

screen bypass capacitor. This capacitor must also be large enough to bypass or offer a short circuit for the lowest bass frequencies. Like the cathode resistor, if it does not, the signal currents induced in the screen will cause an audio voltage to appear across the screen dropping resistor that will subtract from the signal on the control grid, thereby reducing the output of the power amplifier at very low audio frequencies. If the value of the screen bypass capacitor decreases, it may bypass the higher audio frequencies, but allow the bass frequencies to appear across the screen dropping resistor, reducing the bass response.

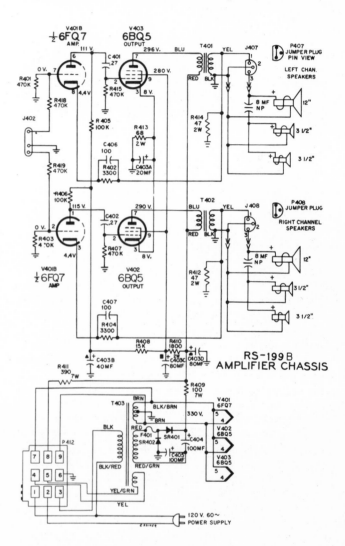

Fig. 2-4. Schematic of a power amplifier. (Courtesy of the General Electric Co.)

Filtering in the Power Supply

Another important consideration in hi-fi amplifiers is the filtering in the power supply, see Fig. 2-5. The filtering in the power supply must be sufficient to reduce the 60- or 120-cycle ripple so that it is a minimum of 30 db down from that of full power output. It must also offer a short circuit to the lowest audio frequencies. So far as the audio signal is concerned, there are two impedances to ground in the plate circuit of the output stage: the primary of the output transformer, and the impedance of the filter system in the power supply.

Usually, the impedance of the filter system is very low at the high and middle audio frequencies, but may offer some impedance at the extreme low audio frequencies. If the filter system does not offer a very low impedance to the low audio frequencies, then some of the low audio frequencies appear across the power supply. This voltage which appears across the power supply is subtracted from the voltage which appears across the output transformer primary, resulting in a drop-off in the low-frequency response of the amplifier.

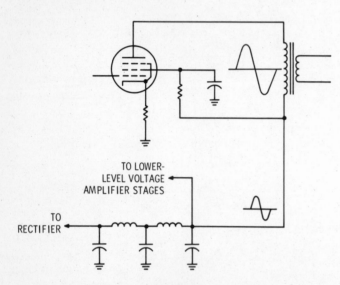

Fig. 2-5. Low-frequency audio signal on the B+ supply due to inadequate filtering.

Another serious problem that can result from insufficient filtering is low-frequency oscillations of the amplifier, which is commonly called motorboating. The lower level voltage amplifier stages are generally connected to the same power supply filter as the output stage. If the power supply filter does not offer a short circuit to the low audio frequencies, the audio voltages appear on the B+ buss of the amplifier, and coupled back to the lower level stages, it causes oscillation or motorboating.

One good method of checking the screen bypass, cathode bypass, and power supply filters to determine if they may possibly have low-value capacitors is to feed a 100-cycle signal into the power amplifier being tested, and connect an oscilloscope across the cathode resistor, screen resistor, and power supply to see if any of the audio signal is appearing across all or either of these. If it does not, it indicates that the value of the bypass capacitors is sufficient. Motorboating, or low-frequency oscillation, is a sure sign of low value or open filter capacitors in the power supply.

Negative Feedback

Most hi-fi power amplifiers employ some form of negative feedback. In other words, some portion of the output signal is fed back to the preceeding stage of the amplifier

in such a manner as to be 180° out of phase with the input signal. Negative feedback offers several improvements in the performance of the hi-fi amplifier:

1. It greatly reduces the distortion generated by the power output stage. Since most of the distortion in the system is developed in the output stage, this greatly reduces the distortion in the system.

2. It stabilizes the amplifier. The gain of the amplifier becomes independent of small variations in the tube and supply voltage. As the feedback is increased, the gain becomes more and more independent of these variables.

3. The frequency response is increased, and the phase distortion of the system is reduced.

4. The speakers looking back into the amplifier see a lower impedance, providing damping which results in a cleaner, crisper sound, and much improved transient response.

A simplified schematic of a power amplifier with negative feedback is shown in Fig. 2-6.

At the time when the grid of V1 is swinging positive, as shown in the solid portion of the input waveform, the

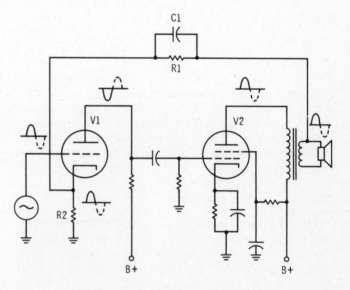

Fig. 2-6. Power amplifier with negative feedback.

signal in the plate swings negative, applying a negative signal to the grid of V2. This signal is inverted in the plate of V2, and induces a positive-going signal in the secondary of the output transformer. This same voltage is sampled in the secondary of the output transformer, and fed back to the cathode of the V1. Since it is fed to the cathode, it has the same effect as feeding that same signal 180° out of phase to the grid. Therefore, so far as the driver tube is concerned, the feedback signal is 180° out of phase with the input signal. As the grid tries to swing positive, the cathode is also swinging positive due to the feedback voltage. This reduces the effect of the positive grid voltage.

R2 and R1 form a voltage divider for the feedback voltage. As R1 is made smaller, more of the feedback voltage appears across R2, the cathode resistor. This applies more feedback, further reducing the effect of the grid voltage, and reducing the gain of the amplifier.

C1 is a frequency compensating capacitor. By varying the value of C1, the feedback voltage can be made frequency selective. The effect of varying the capacity has the opposite effect on the frequency response as might first be assumed. When the high frequencies are attenuated in the feedback network, they cause an increase in the high frequency response of the amplifier because there is less feedback at the higher frequencies. If the value of C1 is reduced, this will increase the reactance of C1 to the higher audio frequencies, and cause less feedback, increasing gain of the amplifier. Conversely, if C1 is increased, the feedback at the high frequencies increases, reducing the gain of the amplifier at higher frequencies. As can be seen, the value of C1 will determine the high-frequency response of the system to a great degree.

Special consideration must be taken when designing the power amplifier using negative feedback. The more feedback used, the more important these considerations become. It is very important that the frequency response be flat over a very wide range of frequencies. If an amplifier's frequency response is not flat, nonlinear phase delays will occur at various frequencies. This means that at certain frequencies near the low-frequency and high-frequency limits of the amplifier, where the frequency response is beginning to roll off, nonlinear delays may be introduced. These delays could shift the feedback voltage as much as 180° so that the feedback signal will be in phase with the input at these frequencies, and cause oscillations. Oscillations can occur at any frequency, but usually occur at the very high frequencies, sometimes above the audible range, or at extremely low frequencies, causing motorboating. Oscillations at very high frequencies usually will cause severe distortion in the system for no apparent reason, and, in severe cases, overheat the power amplifier tubes.

To prevent the possibilty of oscillations due to phase shift at very low frequencies, large cathode and screen bypasses, and large coupling capacitors are used to keep the low-frequency response flat. To prevent oscillation at very high frequencies, the frequency response of the power amplifier is usually extended well beyond the audible range, sometimes to 50 or 100 kc. The amplifier usually will not supply any appreciable power at frequencies above 20 kc, but the response is flat or rolls off very gradually above 20 kc up to 50 or 100 kc. The more feedback that is employed, the wider the frequency response must be.

Feedback is usually expressed in decibels. The average hi-fi power amplifier will have a feedback in the order of 20 db. This means that a one db signal at the input of the amplifier will produce 20 db of negative feedback. Looking at it another way, the feedback reduces the gain of the amplifier, 20 decibels.

In servicing amplifiers with negative feedback, care should be taken to always replace R1 with the proper value. If the value of R1 is not correct, the feedback voltage will be altered. If the feedback is increased by reducing R1, the amplifier could break into high-frequency oscillation. If the feedback is reduced by increasing R1, the gain of the amplifier will increase, possibly causing oscillation or distortion due to overdriving. The value of C1 is also important as it affects the frequency response of the system.

It should be remembered that the adding of negative feedback makes it important that the low-frequency response of the power amplifier be correct. Small changes in the cathode and the screen bypass capacitors and the filter capacitors in the power supply are more important in a stage with feedback. If their value is too low, it may cause motorboating.

Reduction of Distortion by Negative Feedback

Most of the distortion generated in a hi-fi system occurs in the output stage. Considerable improvement in the characteristics can be obtained by the use of negative feedback. Negative feedback will not reduce distortion in the signal fed to the power amplifier. It will only reduce distortion which is generated by the power amplifier stage itself, or the stages within the feedback loop. Distortion simply means that the waveform that was fed into the amplifier has been changed in shape as it passes through the amplifier or that the waveform in the output of the power amplifier differs from the input signal. Suppose one half of the sine wave has a notch in it. This type of distortion normally would not occur in a power amplifier, but is used here for purposes of illustration. At the time when the notch is occurring, the feedback is reduced. This increases the gain of the amplifier during the time of the notch, tending to fill it in or cancel it.

Negative feedback also makes the amplifier relatively independent of electrode voltage, and circuit constants. In an amplifier having 20 db of negative feedback, let us assume that the gain of one of the stages has dropped by 50%. If, before the drop in gain, it required a signal of 20 plus 1 db to produce the desired output, it would now require a signal of 20 plus 2 db to produce the same output, or only a 5% increase in drive signal to maintain the same power output.

2. Push-Pull Power Amplifiers

Schematic

Push-pull power amplifiers are used in a large number of higher power hi-fi audio amplifiers. A schematic of a typical push-pull amplifier is shown in Fig. 2-7. The grids of the push-pull amplifiers are fed with two identical audio voltages 180° out of phase. The plates of the two tubes are connected to the centertapped primary of the output transformer. The signals from the two plates are combined in the transformer in such a manner that they add. To understand how this adding takes place in the primary of the transformer, see Fig. 2-8.

Let us assume that the drive voltage is such that the plate of V1 is at a negative peak. The signal on the grid of V2 is 180° out of phase with the signal on the grid of V1. Therefore, the plate of V2 would have to be positive

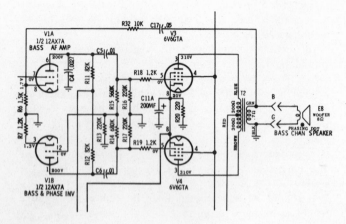

Fig. 2-7. Push-pull power amplifier.

under these conditions. Note that the voltage drops caused by V1 and V2 are in series across the primary of the output transformer, and that they add.

It should be noted that no signal voltages will appear across the cathode resistor, R1, as long as the signals in V1 and V2 are equal. When the plate current due to the driving voltage is increased into V1, it is decreased by the same amount into V2. Therefore, the net change across the cathode resistor, R1, is zero. Because of this phenomenon, it is not necessary to bypass the cathode resistor in a

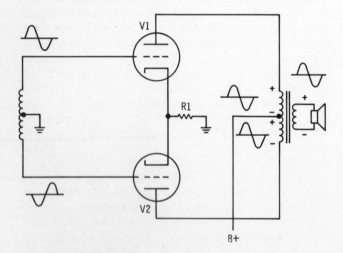

Fig. 2-8. Addition of signals in the power transformer in a push-pull stage.

push-pull amplifier stage since no degeneration occurs. If separate cathode resistors are used for each tube, however, it would be necessary to bypass them to prevent degeneration.

Advantages

Some of the more important advantages of the push-pull power amplifier, besides the fact that it will deliver twice as much output power as a single-ended stage, are:

1. The d-c currents flow in opposite directions in the primary windings. They set up opposite-polarity magnetic fields which cancel, and, therefore, do not magnetize the core, driving it into d-c saturation.

2. As in the case of the cathode resistor, there are no net signal currents appearing on the centertap of the primary of the transformer which is connected to B+. Therefore, no audio voltages appear across the power supply to cause feedback and motorboating. This reduces the filtering requirements of the power supply.

3. Second and all even harmonics that are generated by the output stage, which represent distortion, are cancelled in the output transformer.

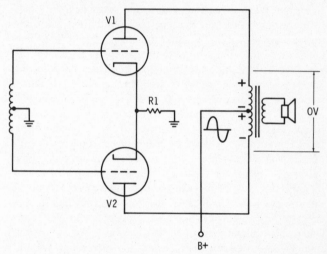

Fig. 2-9. Hum cancellation in a push-pull output transformer.

4. Audio hum voltages fed in from the power supply on the centertap of the power transformer also cancel in the windings of the transformer, see Fig. 2-9.

Note. At the time when the hum voltage on the power supply is positive, the polarity of the voltages which it induces across the two halves of the primary winding are out of phase with each other. The net voltage across the primary due to the hum is zero.

The design considerations and service considerations for a push-pull stage are essentially the same as for a single-ended amplifier. There are some special considerations, however. Since no audio voltage appears across the common cathode resistor, or the power supply, bypassing the cathode has no effect on the low-frequency response, and power supply filtering is not critical from a motorboating standpoint.

If good hum cancellation and minimum distortion are to be obtained, the two plate currents must be balanced. A balance control, usually located in the cathode of the output stage, is provided on some amplifiers. It is adjusted usually for minimum hum at the speakers with no signal voltage applied, and the input grid to the amplifier terminated.

3. Class B and Class AB Power Amplifiers

When a push-pull amplifier is used, it is not necessary that each tube pass both the positive and negative halves of the cycle. In fact, it is possible to bias the two output stages so that one tube passes the positive half cycle, and the other passes the negative half cycle. These two voltages will add in the secondary, restoring the full sine wave in the secondary.

Class B Amplifier

The class B amplifier is a push-pull amplifier where the tubes are biased so that one tube passes the negative half cycle, and the other tube passes the positive half cycle. See Fig. 2-10.

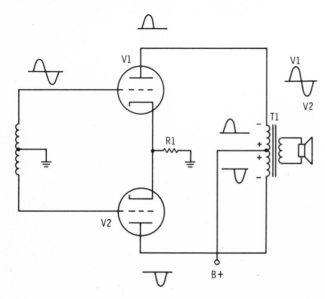

Fig. 2-10. Push-pull class B power amplifier.

When no signal is applied, the plate currents of V1 and V2 will be zero. The grids of the class B amplifier, as in the case of the class A push-pull amplifier, are fed with equal signals 180° out of phase. When the grid of V1 is swinging positive, the plate is swinging negative, causing a minus–plus drop across the top half of T1 only. At the same time, the grid of V2 is being driven negative. Since the tube is already biased to cutoff, no plate current flows in V2. The current through the top half of the transformer induces a positive-going voltage in the secondary of T1 as shown. When the audio signal is reversed in polarity, V1 is cut off, and V2 conducts for one-half of the cycle, causing a negative–positive drop across the lower half of T1. Note that the voltage drop caused by V2 is 180° out of phase with that produced by V1. Therefore, the voltage

induced into the secondary will be 180° out of phase with the voltage that was induced by V1 one-half cycle earlier. V1 produces the top half of the sine wave; when the polarity of the drive signal reverses, V2 produces the bottom half of the sine wave.

Class AB Amplifier

The class AB amplifier is a push-pull amplifier where the tube is biased somewhere between class A and class B. The operating principle is the same as the class B amplifier. The advantages of the class AB and B amplifiers are the higher outputs and high efficiencies that are found in class A amplifiers. All the principles of operation that apply to class A amplifiers apply to the class B and AB amplifiers.

The regulation of the power supply is very important in a class AB and B amplifiers because the output tubes draw varying currents as the signal varies, causing a pulsing load on the power supply. If the power supply does not have good regulation, distortion and poor low-frequency response can occur. Also, the balance of the amplifiers, and the bias on the amplifiers of the class B stage are very critical, and should be adjusted very carefully for best performance.

Crossover Distortion

Crossover distortion occurs at very low volume levels on class B amplifiers only. It is caused by improper bias. If the waveform of an amplifier with crossover distortion is observed on an oscilloscope, it will appear as the waveform shown in Fig. 2-11. To observe this waveform, the volume must be adjusted to a very low level.

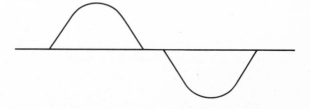

Fig. 2-11. Output waveform of a class B amplifier with crossover distortion.

As the volume is increased, the distortion will disappear. To prevent crossover distortion, the bias should be adjusted at a very low volume level for a sine wave response, or minimum distortion. Crossover distortion is caused by too much bias. One tube goes into cutoff before the other conducts. When the bias is correct, one tube cuts off at the same instant the other starts to conduct.

4. Phase Inverters

It is necessary to provide two identical audio driving signals to the push-pull power amplifier, ranging from 30 to 40 volts (for an amplifier with a high negative feedback) to 4 to 10 volts (for amplifiers with a low negative feedback). The driving voltage varies considerably from tube to tube, and design to design.

Practically all consumer products use phase inverters to provide the driving signals for push-pull output stages. Figure 2-12 is a simplified schematic of a simple phase inverter circuit. R1 and R2 are equal-value resistors. The signal voltage across them will be the same since the same current flows in the plate circuit of the tube as in the

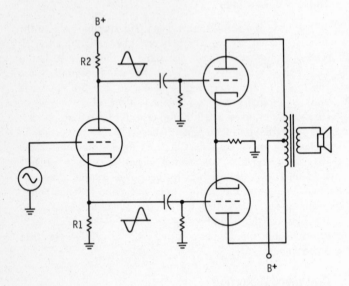

Fig. 2-12. Simplified version of a phase inverter.

cathode. However, the signal in the plate will be 180° out of phase with the signal on the grid. The signal on the cathode will be in phase with the driving voltage. This condition is true in any vacuum-tube resistance-coupled amplifier. Thus, the voltages in the plate of the cathode are 180° out of phase with each other.

Another commonly used power amplifier is shown in Fig. 2-13. This power amplifier is commonly used in medium- and low-power audio systems. The amplifier is a two-channel stereo amplifier using three output transformers in the plate circuit of a right- and left-channel power amplifier tube. T1 and T3 are right- and left-channel output transformers, and the bass frequencies from both channels appear across T2. A single transformer can be used to combine the bass frequencies from each channel since bass frequencies do not carry stereo information.

This system, therefore, produces three separate outputs using two amplifier tubes, a right- and a left-channel stereo output, and a combined right and left bass output. Separa-

tion of the treble and midfrequencies from the bass frequencies is accomplished in the plate circuit of the amplifiers. The bass transformer, T2, has a much higher primary inductance than the right- and left-channel output transformer primaries, T1 and T3. Capacitor C across T2 also offers a very low impedance to the mid- and treble frequencies. They, therefore, do not appear across the primary of T2. The left- and right-channel amplifiers then operate as single-ended outputs for right- and left-channel stereo information. The stereo information appears across the primary of T1 and T3, but does not appear across T2 because of the bypass capacitor, C. T2 acts as a push-pull bass channel. To prevent the cancellation of the bass frequencies in the output transformer, T2, it is necessary to drive the amplifier with two signals 180° out of phase. Since

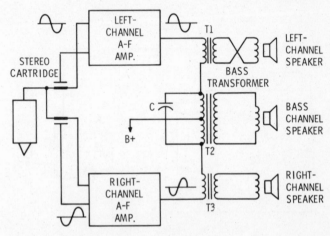

Fig. 2-13. Power amplifier used in medium- and low-power audio systems.

this reverses the stereo information in the left and right channels, the speaker phase is reversed on one of the channels to correct this.

When servicing this amplifier, always make certain that the speakers are phased properly. If both speakers are phased in the same manner, poor channel separation will result. Also, some loss in midfrequency response will be noted. If the two input signals are not 180° out of phase, the bass frequencies will cancel, resulting in extremely poor bass performance. The reversal of the drive signals is commonly obtained by reversing one of the connections on either the right or the left stereo cartridge. It is, therefore, not uncommon to find that the drive signals may be reversed, especially if the cartridge has been changed.

3 – The Preamplifier, Audio Service Methods, and Solid-State Amplifiers

1. The Preamplifier

Purposes

The purposes of the preamplifier are to provide:

1. Sufficient driving voltage to drive the power amplifier to full output.

2. Customer controls to control the loudness and tone of the audio system.

3. Input switches to connect various instruments to the input of the audio system, such as the record changer, the tape recorder, and the AM-FM tuner.

4. Input circuitry to match these various instruments to the audio system, and frequency equalization, such that the device feeding the amplifier will present a flat frequency response to the audio system.

Circuits

The preamplifiers in common use today vary in complexity from the circuit of Fig. 3-1 (which consists of a stereo cartridge input, a loudness control, and a single

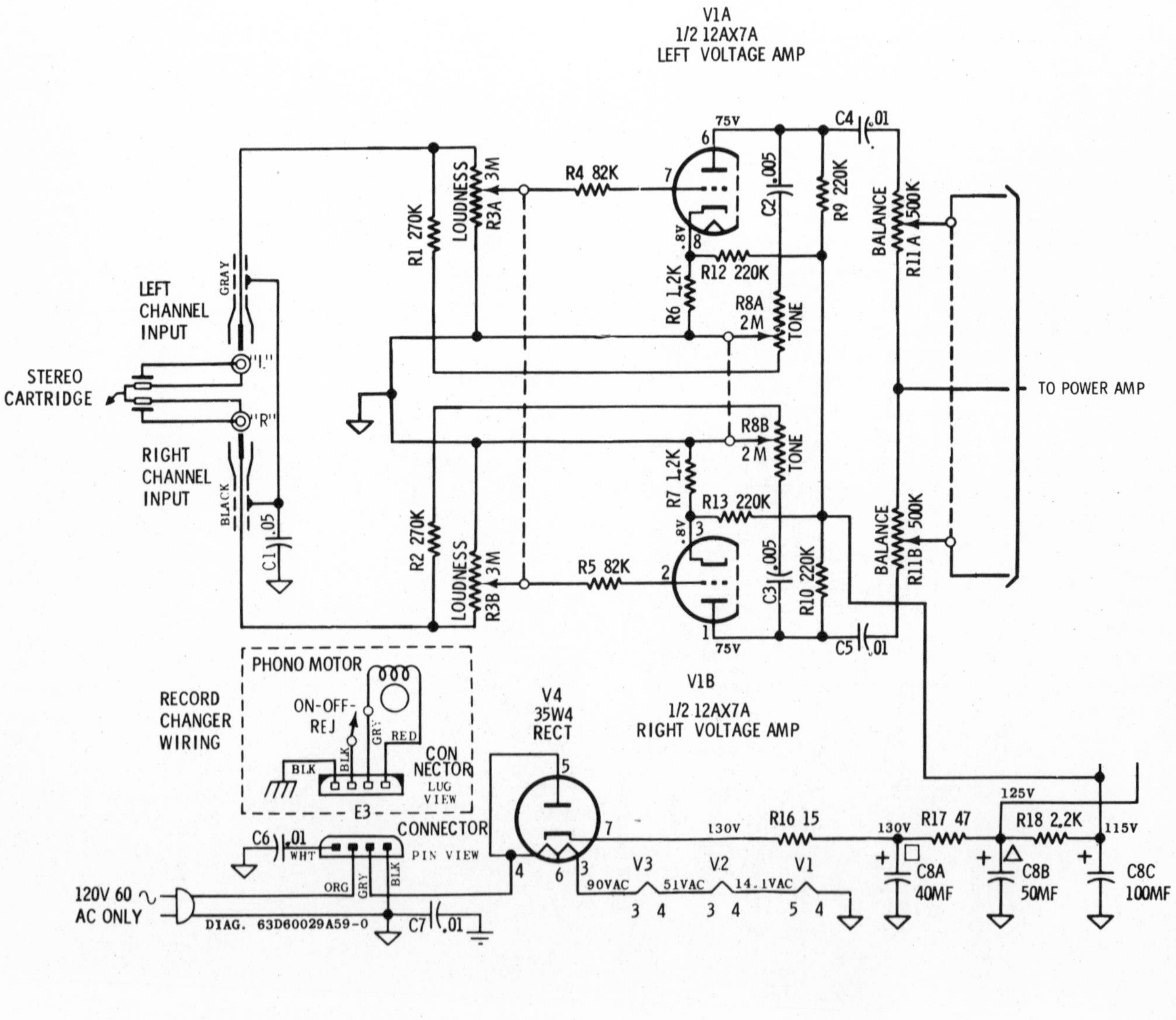

Fig. 3-1. Schematic of a simple preamplifier consisting of a single voltage amplifier, and loudness and tone controls.

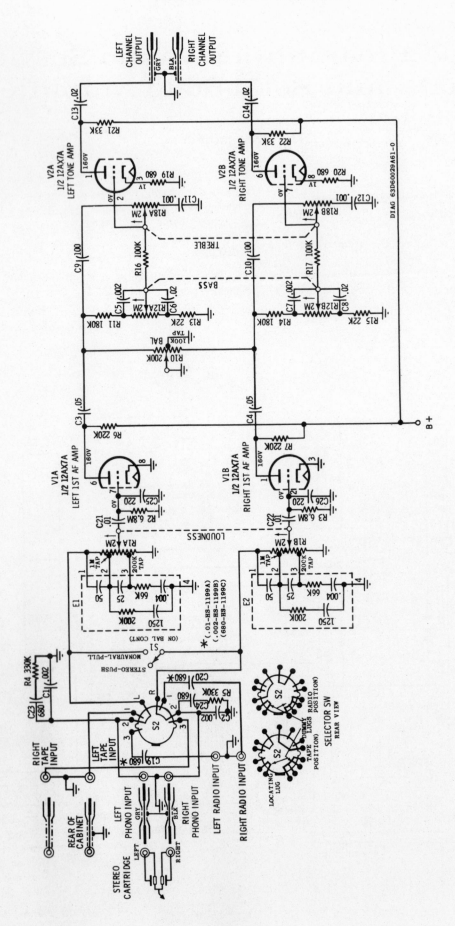

Fig. 3-2. Schematic of a typical preamplifier with input switching for a record changer, stereo tape recorder, radio, and stereo FM.

right- and left-channel voltage amplifier to drive the power amplifier) to the circuit of Fig. 3-2 (which provides input switching for an AM radio, a stereo FM input, a tape recorder input, and a phonograph input). The preamplifier of Fig. 3-2 also includes loudness and separate treble and bass tone controls, and two voltage amplifiers for driving the power amplifier. This preamplifier includes most of the basic circuitry found in most preamplifiers in use today.

The function switch, S2, selects the desired input, such as radio, phonograph, or tape recorder, and also switches in frequency compensation networks, when necessary, so that each device presents a flat frequency response to the input amplifiers, V1A and V1B. There are two sections to switch S2; the top section switches the left-channel input, and the bottom section switches the right-channel input.

The wiper on the switch sections is connected to the grids of the input amplifiers, V1A and V1B. As the switch is rotated, it contacts each of the contactors, 1, 2, and 3, in sequence. The switch is shown in the phono position. Note that there is a connection between terminal R, which is connected to the input to the right-channel amplifier, V1A, and the right phonograph input jack. On the bottom half of S2, there is a connection from the L terminal, which is connected to the left-channel input amplifier, V2, to the left phonograph input jack. These terminals are labeled 2.

Also, from terminals No. 2 to ground on both the top and bottom sections of S2 are two frequency-equalizing networks, consisting of R4, C1, and C23 in the right channel, and R5, C2, and C24 in the left channel. These networks terminate the cartridge in the proper impedance, and adjust the frequency response of the record and the cartridge to provide a flat response to the amplifier.

In the tape position, the connections on the top half of S2 are from the L terminal to terminal No. 1. On the bottom half of S2, the connection is from the R terminal to terminal No. 3. Terminals Nos. 1 and 3 are connected to the right and left tape input jacks. No frequency compensation network is provided in the tape position, since tape recorders have their own preamplifier and equalizing networks, and present a flat frequency response to the amplifier.

In the radio position, the connections from the top of S2 are from L to terminal No. 3. In the bottom half of S2, the connection is from terminal R to terminal No. 1. These two terminals are connected through two 680-pf blocking capacitors to the right and left radio inputs. Since the radio provides a flat audio response, no equalization is necessary in these channels. The audio signals at this point are extremely low, sometimes of the order of 0.1 to 0.5 volts. This is the point of maximum gain in the audio system. It is very important, therefore, that stray a-c fields be kept away from this area of the amplifier. The dress of any leads in the area should not be disturbed. As a general rule, all leads carrying a-c current should be dressed away from the input circuitry, and down as near the chassis pan as possible.

Dirt on the switch contactors of S2 can also cause hum and noise in the system.

The value of R4 has a considerable influence on the fre-

quency response of the stereo cartridge. Any of the components which are replaced in the equalizer networks on the phono input should be replaced with like values.

Another common problem in the low-level stages is noise, usually of an intermittent nature, caused by resistors with poor contacts between the wire and the carbon body of the resistor.

Microphonism is also an important service consideration. It can cause feedback, or howl, in severe cases. The speaker may vibrate the microphonic tube on high-volume bass notes at an audio rate causing feedback and oscillations.

Switch S1 is a stereo-monaural switch. In the monaural position, the switch simply connects the right and left channels together, producing a monaural signal in the output of the two amplifiers.

Loudness Control

The loudness control consists of E1 and R1A. E1 contains the equalizing capacitors and resistors, and R1A and R1B are ganged 2-meg audio potentiometers. A loudness control is a frequency compensated volume control. The frequency response of the ear varies with sound intensity. At high volume levels, the ear has an essentially flat response, see Fig. 3-3, while at medium volume levels there is a pronounced roll-off, both above and below 1000

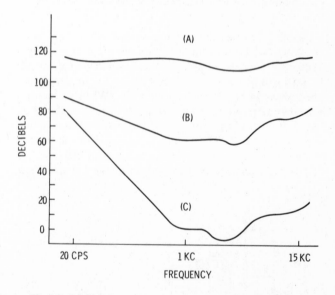

Fig. 3-3. Relative frequency response of the ear at (A) high, (B) medium, and (C) low sound levels.

cycles. At low volume levels, greater attenuation of bass and treble response occurs. As the volume is reduced, it requires more and more bass boost and treble boost to present a flat frequency response to the average ear.

If a loudness control is not used when the volume control is tuned to a low level, the program material sounds thin. The bass and high frequencies are lacking. To enjoy a stereo amplifier at a low level, the volume control is sometimes compensated to boost the high and low frequencies at low volume settings; such a control is called a loudness control.

Figure 3-4 shows a circuit of a loudness control. Figure 3-4C is the equivalent circuit of the control with the volume set to maximum. Figure 3-4B shows the frequency response of the ear at this loudness level which is essentially flat, and Figure 3-4D shows the frequency response of the control under these conditions.

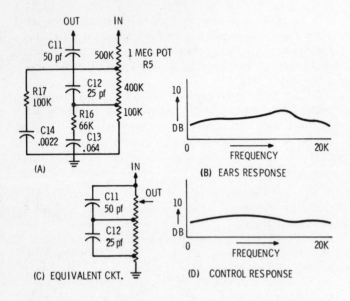

Fig. 3-4. Loudness compensation at high volume levels.

Figure 3-5 shows the conditions when the volume control is set to the midpoint. At this level, the bass and high-frequency response of the ear are beginning to drop off. To compensate for this, the response of the loudness control boosts the bass notes and the highs. When the control is in the midposition, it appears to the signal as shown in Fig. 3-5C. R5 is the top half of the potentiometer which is shunted by C11. The frequency response of the control in this position is shown in Fig. 3-5B. The reactance of C12 is high, and the bottom portion of the potentiometer

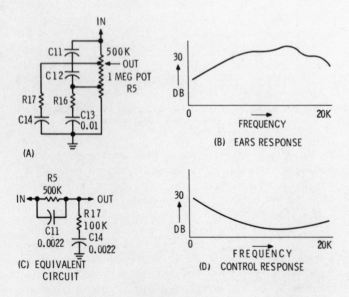

Fig. 3-5. Loudness compensation at medium volume levels.

is in series with R16 and C13. They, therefore, appear as open circuits. At very low frequencies, the reactance of C11 is very high, and appears as an open circuit. The impedance of R17 and C12 is also high, and appears as an open circuit. To the low frequencies, therefore, the control appears as a 500,000-ohm resistor in series with the signal. At midfrequencies, the reactance of C11 is still high, and it appears as an open circuit, but the impedance of R17 and C14 becomes lower as the frequency is increased, decreasing the middle frequencies. At the extreme-high frequencies, the reactance of C11 starts to become less and finally shorts out the 500,000-ohm portion of the control.

Figure 3-6 shows the conditions when the control is at the low end. Since the output at this position is lower, the

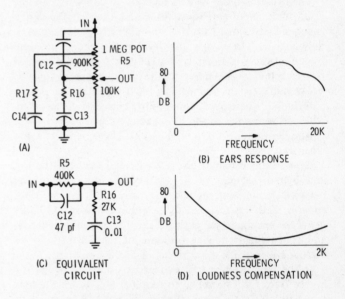

Fig. 3-6. Loudness compensation at low volume levels.

ear response to the bass and highs is attenuated further. It is desirable, therefore, to boost the bass notes especially to a greater degree than at the midposition of the control. The bass response of the ear at this volume setting is shown in Fig. 3-6B. The frequency response of the control is shown in Fig. 3-6D. The circuit of the loudness control in this position is shown in Figure 3-6C. Since the arm of the control is about 900,000 ohms below the center-tap, R17 and C14 are out of the circuit. They are replaced by R16, which has a lower resistance value, and C13, which has a higher capacitance value. They offer a considerably greater amount of attenuation at the middle frequencies. Essentially, this circuit looks to the audio signal as the 900,000-ohm portion of the control shunted by C12. At the very low frequencies, the reactance of C12 is high, and the impedance of R16 and C13 is high. At the middle frequencies, however, the reactance of R16 and C13 becomes lower and lower as the frequency is increased, attenuating the middle frequencies. At the extreme-high frequencies, the reactance of C12 shorts out the 900,000-ohm portion of the control, increasing the highs.

The effect of the loudness control, therefore, is to widen

the frequency response of the system at very low listening levels. At high listening levels, the control is uncompensated because the ears response at these higher audio levels is essentially flat, and does not require frequency compensation. The loudness controls in a stereo system are usually mounted on the same shaft so that R1A and R1B are increased or decreased simultaneously by adjusting the loudness control.

The loudness compensated signal is fed from the loudness control to the grids of two voltage amplifiers, V2A and V2B. These are conventional resistance coupled amplifiers. Their plate load resistors are R6 and R7. See Fig. 3-2.

The right- and left-channel stereo signals are then coupled to either end of a centertapped control which is called the balance control. The arm of the balance control is returned to ground. It is the purpose of this control to compensate for any unequal gain in the right and left channel. It is adjusted to produce equal outputs in the right and the left channels. The control is adjusted either on a monaural signal, or on a stereo signal with the stereo-monaural switch placed in the monaural position. It is preferable to set the balance control on stereo program information with the switch in the monaural position. When the adjustment is made in this manner, it not only compensates for any unequal gain in the stereo amplifier system, but also will compensate for any unequal output in the stereo cartridge, stereo tape, or FM receiver connected to the preamplifier. When the arm of the balance control is adjusted to the end of the control connected to C3, part of the signal in the left channel is shunted to ground through the small resistance of the potentiometer, making the right channel louder than the left. Conversely, when the potentiometer arm is moved toward the end of R10, connected to C4, then part of the signal in the right

channel is shunted to ground through the small resistance of the control.

From the balance control, the signal is fed to the bass and treble controls. Both the bass and treble controls are identical in both the right and left channels. The bass control in the left channel consists of R11, R12A, C5, C6, and R13. R12A is a two-meg potentiometer. Shunted across this control through a 100-pf capacitor, C9, is the treble control. It consists of R18A, and C11 to ground. The left-channel bass and treble controls ganged with the right-channel controls, and the tone compensation is automatically introduced into each channel as the control is rotated. R16 is an isolation resistor to prevent interaction between the treble and bass controls. The reactance of C9 to bass frequencies is extremely high, therefore, only the high frequencies appear across R18. When the control is at the full clockwise position, or at the high voltage end of R18A, the treble gain will be maximum. Conversely, when it is at the low end of R18A, the treble gain will be minimum. Only the bass frequencies appear across R12A and B. The highs are bypassed around the control by capacitors C5, C6, C7, C8. When the arm of R12A and R12B are at the high end of the resistance, the bass response of the system is maximum. When the arm of R12A and R12B are at the low end of the resistance, the bass response is minimum. With these separate bass and treble controls, it is possible to obtain approximately 10 db of bass and treble cut and boost, and there is little interaction between the bass and treble controls. The output of the bass and treble controls feed two voltage amplifiers, V2A and V2B, whose output in turn feeds the right and left power amplifier. The entire audio system consists of the preamplifier just described, and the power amplifier feeding a speaker system.

2. Servicing the Audio Amplifier

To properly service the audio system, the following test equipment is recommended:

1. Audio oscillator.
2. A-c vacuum-tube voltmeter.
3. Five-in. oscilloscope.
4. D-c vacuum-tube voltmeter.
5. Distortion analyzer.
6. Intermodulation distortion meter (optional).
7. Power output meter (optional).
8. Test records for testing turntable, and cartridge performance.
9. Stroboscope.
10. Stylus pressure gauge.

Audio Oscillator

The audio oscillator should be a sine wave generator. The frequency range should be 20 cycles to 100 kc. The output voltage of the generator should be reasonably flat across the entire frequency range. The output voltage should be approximately 2 volts maximum. The distortion at the output of the generator at maximum output should be on the order of 1% or less.

A-C VTVM

The a-c vacuum-tube voltmeter should have a range of approximately 0.03 to 300 volts, and the accuracy should be constant from 20 cycles to about 100 kc. The instrument should be well shielded to prevent stray pick-up, which can cause erronous readings on the extreme low voltage scales. The input impedance of the instrument should be as high as possible, so that it does not load the circuits being measured, causing errors in readings.

Oscilloscope

The oscilloscope should be a 5-in. scope with good brightness and good focus at high brightness levels. The trace should be clearly visible, and sharply focused with normal room lighting. The frequency response of the scope should be at least 20 cps to 200 kc, and the transit response should be good. The vertical sensitivity should be as high as possible, and the sync stability should be good.

Distortion Analyzer

The distortion analyzer may not be as familiar to you

as the other instruments previously listed. When a sine wave is not distorted, it contains energy of only one single frequency. When its shape is altered from that of a sine wave in any manner, harmonics appear. The combined amplitudes of the harmonics generated are in direct proportion to the distortion.

The distortion analyzer contains a very sharp filter. The output signal of the amplifier under test is fed into the distortion analyzer, see Fig. 3-7. The sharply tuned filter

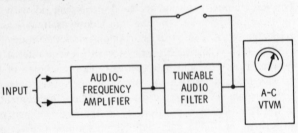

Fig. 3-7. Block diagram of a distortion analyzer.

is adjusted to trap the fundamental frequency, and a very sensitive a-c vacuum-tube voltmeter measures the harmonics that remain. The meter is calibrated in percentage distortion, and the distortion, therefore, may be read directly.

Intermodulation Meter

An optional piece of test equipment used for measuring the performance of audio oscillators is the intermodulation distortion meter. Intermodulation distortion is caused by the mixing of two frequencies in an audio amplifier. It is caused by subtle nonlinearities in the system. Intermodulation measurements are simply more sensitive measurements of harmonics distortion. When these subtle nonlinearities occur, they can cause modulation of the higher audio frequencies by the lower audio frequencies. A block diagram of an intermodulation analyzer is shown in Fig. 3-8A. A high-frequency signal from an audio oscillator is

fed through the amplifier under test, and the output of the amplifier feeds the input to the intermodulation meter. At the same time, a low-frequency signal from the intermodulation meter is also fed to the input of the amplifier under test. If the amplifier introduces intermodulation distortion, the low-frequency signal will appear as a modulation on the high-frequency signal, see Fig. 3-8B. When these two signals enter the intermodulation analyzer, they are first fed through a highpass filter, and the low-frequency signal is removed. This leaves only the high-frequency signal, and if intermodulation is present, it will be modulated by the low-frequency signal. The high-frequency signal is then passed through a conventional AM detector, and the low-frequency modulation is removed. The rectified signal is then passed through a lowpass filter which removes any remaining high-frequency carrier information, and a very sensitive meter, which is calibrated in percentage, reads the percentage modulation of the high signal by the low signal. A high-performance high-fidelity amplifier will measure something of the order 1 to 2% intermodulation distortion. The lower the figure, the better the amplifier. The high frequencies in an audio amplifier having high intermodulation distortion will not sound clean and distinct.

Test Records and Stylus Pressure Gauge

Test records are another valuable tool in servicing of high-fidelity amplifiers. There are many test signals available on test records such as frequency response, channel separation, stereo balance, quiet grooves for turntable rumble, tests for wow, and stroboscopes for measuring the speed of the turntable, and many others.

Another valuable aid in audio servicing is a stylus pressure gauge. The gauge is very important for good sound reproduction and minimum record and stylus wear.

Locating Malfunctions

The service procedure for locating malfunctions in the audio system is the same as those used in servicing all

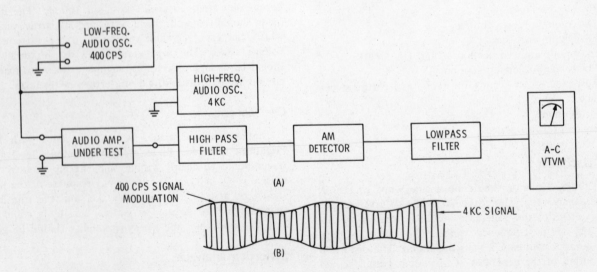

Fig. 3-8. (A) Block diagram of an intermodulation distortion analyzer; and (B) 4-kc signal modulated by 400-cps signal.

electronic equipment. First, isolate the malfunction to a stage, and then locate the defective components in that stage by voltage and resistance measurements.

The most often used method of locating a defective stage is the use of signal injection. A signal from an audio oscillator of approximately 1 kc should be used for troubleshooting the audio system. One kc is the approximate center of the audio band, and this frequency is unaffected by the setting of the tone controls and other frequency compensation networks.

Isolating Malfunctioning or Inoperative Stages

Figure 3-9 is a block diagram of a typical audio amplifier and preamplifier, consisting of three voltage amplifier stages in the right and left channels driving two power

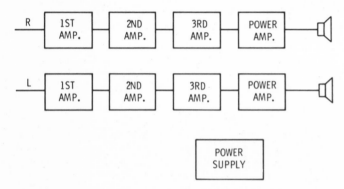

Fig. 3-9. Block diagram of a stereo amplifier and power supply.

amplifiers, one for the right channel and one for the left channel. The outputs of the power amplifiers are connected to their individual speaker systems.

When the audio system is completely dead or inoperative, this is a good indication that the power supply is not operating, since it is the only circuit common to both amplifiers. In this case, the first step should be to check the power supply by visually inspecting the fuses, then measuring the output of the rectifier and filter sections for the presence of B+ voltage at points 1, 2, 3, and 4 in Fig. 3-10.

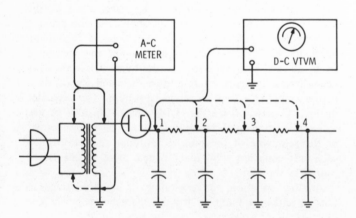

Fig. 3-10. D-c voltage checks on a power supply. No voltage present at points 1, 2, 3, and 4 indicates a defective rectifier or a defective transformer.

The voltage should be highest at point 1, and should be progressively lower at points 2, 3, and 4. In some power supplies, the series resistance may be a choke instead of a resistor. In either case, the procedure is the same.

If one of the amplifiers is operating, this is an indication that the power supply is functioning, but that one of the stages in one of the channels is not functioning, or that the speaker system in that channel is not functioning. When multiple speakers are used, as is the usual case, the probability of all speakers not functioning, or being defective simultaneously is rather remote. In systems having single speakers at the output of each channel, the speaker can be easily checked by placing a d-c ohmmeter on the lowest scale across the terminals of the speaker. If the speaker is operating, a click should be heard in the output when the ohmmeter is connected and disconnected. If the speaker is functioning, this is an indication that one or more of the amplifier stages is not operating. To locate the inoperative stage, the signal injection method should be used, see Fig. 3-11.

The first step in the signal injection method is to set the amplifier frequency to 1000 cycles, approximately, set the audio signal generator output to maximum, and inject

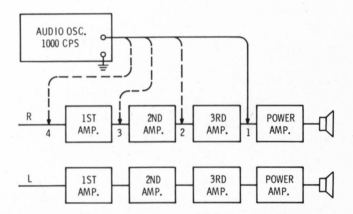

Fig. 3-11. Signal injection method of isolating a malfunction to a single stage.

a signal into the grid of the power amplifier. If the power amplifier stage is operating, an output should be heard in the speaker. If the signal is present, the audio oscillator should be moved to the grid of the preceding stages, points 2, 3, and 4, until very low or no output is heard. If no output is heard at point 3, the output is very low, and the malfunctioning stage is the second voltage amplifier, for example. A voltage and resistance check in that stage will reveal the defective component.

In many cases, the amplifier may not be completely dead but may exhibit hum, severe distortion, motorboating, or high-frequency regeneration. If one of the above symptoms appears in both amplifiers, this is an indication that the power supply is probably the source of the malfunction. If only one of the amplifiers, either right or left channel, is involved then the malfunction most probably is in one or more of the amplifier stages.

Hum

Hum describes a low-frequency tone, generally 60 or 120 cycles in the output of the amplifier. Hum may be present when no signal is applied, or it may be present only with signal. The most common sources of hum are lack of filtering of the B+ supply, heater-to-cathode leakage in one of the amplifier stages, 60-cycle hum induced into the grid of one of the low-level amplifier stages caused by the dressing of leads carrying a-c voltages near the grid, or the output tubes' plate currents not being balanced in push-pull amplifiers.

If hum is present in both channels, the power supply filter system should be checked. A 100-μf, 600-volt electrolytic capacitor with two test leads, one connected to the negative terminal, and one to the positive terminal, is a good test instrument for checking power supplies, see Fig. 3-12.

The first step in checking the power supply filter should be to bridge the test capacitor across the filter capacitors in the power supply. If the hum disappears, or is reduced substantially when it is bridged across one of the filter sections, this is an indication that the filter is probably defective, and should be disconnected and measured. This test will usually only indicate open or low-value capacitors. If the capacitor has high leakage, or a high power factor,

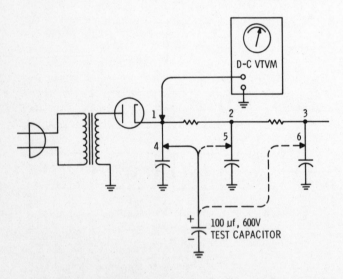

Fig. 3-12. Checking for open or leaky filters.

the bridging will usually not eliminate the hum. Indications of a leaky capacitor in a power supply are the presence of electrolyte leaking out of the capacitor, evidence of overheating of the series resistors in the power supply filter, and/or low voltage out of the power supply.

A good fast method of checking for leaky capacitors is to disconnect the positive terminal of the suspected capacitor, and substitute the test capacitor in its place momentarily. If the hum disappears, it indicates that the capacitor has high leakage or a high power factor. A capacitor of the same value should be substituted. If this eliminates the hum, the capacitor should be replaced.

If the hum is in one channel only, this is a definite indi-

cation that the power supply filtering is most likely adequate, and that the malfunction is in one of the amplifier stages. In this case, the recommended procedure is to first try and isolate the hum to a specific stage or section of the system. If the preamplifier is on a separate chassis, and plugs into the power amplifier, it should be disconnected from the power amplifier, and the input to the power amplifier shorted. If the hum is still present, then it is originating in the power amplifier chassis. If it is eliminated, it indicates that it is in the preamplifier chassis.

Another method that can be used to isolate the hum to a general area of the amplifier system is to turn the volume control to minimum. If the hum disappears, it is originating ahead of the control; if that is not the case; it is in a stage after the control, or from the B+ supply.

To locate the specific stage once the hum has been isolated to certain sections, the grid of each stage in each section may be shorted to ground starting at the first stage, see Fig. 3-13. If, when the grid of an amplifier stage is

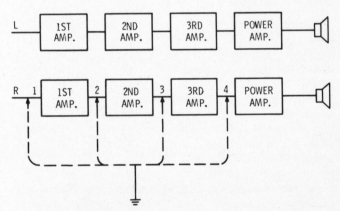

Fig. 3-13. Isolating hum to a specific stage by shorting the grids to ground.

grounded, hum disappears in the speaker, this indicates that the hum is originating in the preceding stage. Once the hum is isolated to a specific stage, the most probable cause is heater-to-cathode leakage in the amplifier tube. A substitution of tubes will determine quickly if this is the source.

If the hum is originating in a low-level stage of the amplifier, the power supply circuit should be checked for the presence of extra filtering in the form of decoupling filters to the low-level stages. Because of the high gain from the low-level stages of the amplifier, it is sometimes necessary to add extra filtering to the first and second stage of the amplifier system to reduce the hum. The capacitor in this RC network, see Fig. 3-14, may be open or of low value. The bridging of a test capacitor across the condenser, or the removing of the positive terminal and substitution of a test capacitor, will quickly determine if this is the source of the hum.

Another common source of hum in low-level stages is the capacitive coupling of the a-c filament or power line voltages into the grids of one or more of the amplifier stages. Leads carrying filament voltage or a-c line current should be dressed well away from the grids of all of the

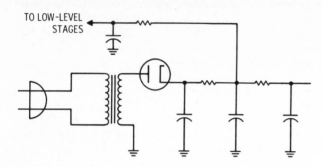

Fig. 3-14. Extra filtering is sometimes used for low-level stages to prevent hum.

low-level amplifier stages.

Open grounds in shielded cables can also cause hum, especially if the open ground is in the grid of the first amplifier stage in the system.

Severe Distortion

As in the case of hum, if severe distortion is present in both channels, it indicates that the low-voltage power supply is malfunctioning. The most probable cause of severe distortion originating from the power supply would be a low output voltage due to a defective rectifier tube or due to a faulty component in the filter network of the power supply. If only one of the amplifiers is effected, the first step should be to isolate the distortion to a single stage. There are two methods that may be used to accomplish this, see Fig. 3-15. An audio oscillator may be fed into the grid of the output stage first, and the output monitored on a speaker. If the distortion is heard with the oscillator connected to the output stage only, then this stage would be the source of the distortion. If distortion is

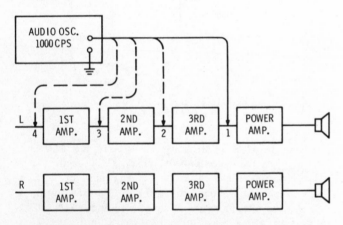

Fig. 3-15. Method of isolating distortion using a speaker as an indicator.

not present, it is an indication that the distortion is ahead of the output amplifier. The output of the signal generator should then be moved back to the grid of the preceding stages, points 2, 3, and 4. If the distortion is heard when the generator is connected to the grid of the second voltage amplifier stage, point 3, it is an indication that the distortion is originating in the second voltage amplifier, for

example. The output of the generator should be reduced as it is moved back toward the input of the amplifier to prevent overloading.

Another method of checking for distortion is shown in Fig. 3-16. In this method, the signal from the generator is fed to the input of the defective channel, and an oscillo-

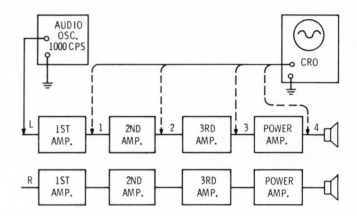

Fig. 3-16. Method of isolating distortion using a scope as an indicator.

scope is used to observe the signal at various points in the system. The scope should be first connected across the generator output to observe the signal waveform coming from the generator. The scope should then be moved to the output of the first amplifier stage. If no distortion is present in the first amplifier, the waveform should look identical to that of the output of the generator except for an increase in amplitude. If no distortion appears at point 1, the scope should be moved to points 2, 3, and 4. If the waveshape looks different from the output of the signal generator at point 3, it indicates that the distortion is originating in the third amplifier stage, for example.

Once a defective stage is located, the most probable causes of distortion, see Figure 3-17, after the tubes have been eliminated are:

1. Leakage in the coupling capacitor, resulting in a positive voltage in a control grid of the amplifier, which in turn causes positive-peak clipping.

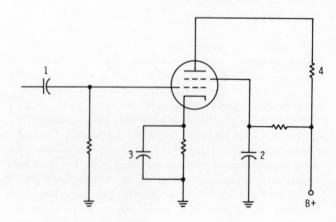

Fig. 3-17. Most probable causes of distortion in a stage.

2. Leakage in the screen capacitor, causing a low screen voltage, and positive peak clipping.

3. Shorted cathode bypass capacitor, causing a loss of bias.

4. An increase in the value of the plate load resistor, possibly due to overheating.

If the value of the plate resistor shows signs of overheating and the value is high, this is an indication that the amplifier tube has shorted momentarily from plate to suppressor or control grid at one time. The tube should also be replaced as normal procedure. Although a resistance-coupled amplifier is shown here, the same general procedures with the exception of the plate load resistor apply to the power output stage as well.

Motorboating

Motorboating is a very low-frequency oscillation appearing in the output of the amplifier. The oscillation may sometimes be as low as two or three cycles per minute, or it may be up to 10 to 20 cycles per second. Motorboating is most often caused by an open or low-value filter capacitor in the power supply. This may be checked by using the same procedure as outlined in testing the power supply filters. If the amplifier has negative feedback, there are other sources which may cause motorboating, see Fig. 3-18. If the value of the coupling capacitor in the stages within the feedback loop is low in value, this can cause motor-

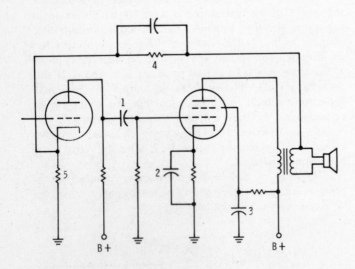

Fig. 3-18. Most probable causes of motorboating in a stage with negative feedback.

boating. This can be checked by bridging a capacitor of equal value across the coupling capacitors in the system. If the value of the cathode bypass capacitor is low, this can cause motorboating. This can also be checked by bridging a capacitor of the same value as the bypass across the suspected capacitor. If the value of the screen bypass is low, then this can also cause motorboating. Again, the bridging of a capacitor of equal value across the suspected capacitor can be used to check this source. A change in

the value of the feedback resistor can also cause motorboating.

High-Frequency Oscillation

High-frequency oscillation in an audio amplifier usually causes either an audible high-pitched squeal in the background, or severe distortion. In some cases, the oscillation may be out of the audible range. If the oscillation is severe, the power amplifier tube may overheat.

If the amplifier exhibits severe distortion, and does not respond to normal service procedures, this indicates that high-frequency oscillation may be present. The quickest method to check for high-frequency oscillation is to look at the output of the amplifier with an oscilloscope with no signal input. If the amplifier is regenerating at high frequencies, the oscillation will be seen on the scope.

High-frequency oscillations are most common in stages with negative feedback. The most probable causes, see Fig. 3-19, are a change in the value of R1 or C1 in the

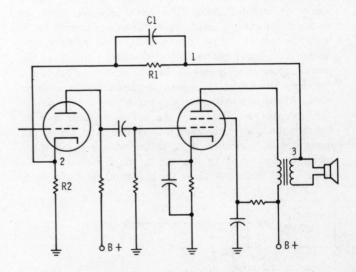

Fig. 3-19. Most probable causes of high-frequency regeneration in amplifiers with negative feedback.

feedback network, or a change in value of R2. A change in value of these components changes the feedback. A change in C1 changes the frequency and phase of the feedback at certain frequencies. If the output transformer is changed in the high-fidelity amplifier, and an exact replacement is not used, it is possible to introduce high-frequency regeneration.

High-frequency regeneration is most likely to occur after the amplifier has been on for some time, and is more likely to occur at high line voltages. If an amplifier is serviced for regeneration, it should be allowed to run for several hours in a confined area where air circulation is restricted at high line voltages before it is returned to the customer. If it does not regenerate under these conditions, the probabilities are that it will operate satisfactorily.

3. *Performance Measurements*

The service procedures discussed are designed to isolate the amplifier malfunction to a stage, and to locate the defective component causing the malfunction. There are other types of performance deficiencies in hi-fi amplifiers which are not as definite as the symptoms described above. The customer may comment that the amplifier does not sound good, or does not sound like it once did, or that on certain records the amplifier does not operate properly while on others it is OK. These malfunctions are the most difficult to analyze. Many hours of valuable time can be wasted in trying to locate these obscure difficulties if the proper equipment and techniques are not used.

The measurements on an audio system should not be performed until the normal service procedures have been completed, and it is operating near normal. In general, there are four measurements which will predict very accurately the degree of performance that can be expected from an audio amplifier system. They are (1) the frequency response of the system, (2) the power output of the system, (3) the harmonics distortion of the system, and (4) the hum.

Frequency Response

The frequency response of the system should be flat for all frequencies within the audible range. To measure the response, various frequencies of equal voltages are fed to the input of the amplifier under test, and the output voltage at each frequency is recorded. The frequency response requirements for the audio amplifier are not very specific. There is considerable variation in the frequency response of the amplifiers because there is a considerable variation in the tastes and requirements of the listener. The highest quality audio system may have a frequency response of approximately ± 3 db from 20 cps to at least 20 kc from a nominal response. The average hi-fi system has a response ± 3 db from approximately 80 cycles to about 15 kc from a nominal response.

A test set-up for measuring frequency response is shown in Fig. 3-20. The loudness control on the amplifier under test should be set for maximum gain. The tone controls should be set for flat response. The audio-signal generator should be fed into the tape or tuner input to the preamplifier, or another input which does not contain frequency-compensation networks such as those commonly found in phono inputs.

The signal generator should first be set to 1000 cycles, and the output adjusted to the desired output level which is usually normal listening level. The a-c VTVM should be connected to a double-pole double-throw switch. In one position, the switch connects the VTVM to the output of the oscillator feeding the amplifier, and in the other position, it connects the VTVM to the output of the amplifier under test. The output of the amplifier should be terminated in a resistance equal to the impedance of the speaker. The meter switch should be rotated to the output position, and switched to the proper scale, and the output of the audio oscillator adjusted slightly until the meter reads zero db on the db scale. The switch should then be rotated to the oscillator position, and the output of the audio oscillator read and recorded. This establishes a reference at 1000 cycles for both the input and the output of the

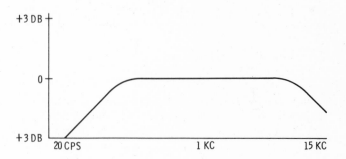

Fig. 3-21. Typical frequency response of a hi-fi amplifier.

amplifier. The same procedure should be followed for the following frequencies at a minimum 30 cycles, 50 cycles, 100 cycles, 400 cycles, 1 kc, 5 kc, 7 kc, 10 kc, 12 kc, 13 kc, 14 kc, and 15 kc.

As the frequency is changed, the meter switch should be rotated to the output of the generator, and the output of the generator should be adjusted so that it reads exactly the same as it did at 1000 cycles. Then the switch should be rotated to the output position, and the output read in decibels and recorded. More frequencies than above may be used if desired. The response is usually plotted at both the low- and high-frequency ends until the response is 6 db down from that of 1000 cycles.

This same technique can be used to check the action of tone controls also by adjusting the bass and treble controls first to full boost position, and then to the full cut position, and plotting the response using the same procedure as described. A good quality amplifier may have as much as 10 db bass and treble boost and cut. In Fig. 3-21, a plot of the response of a typical high-fidelity amplifier is shown.

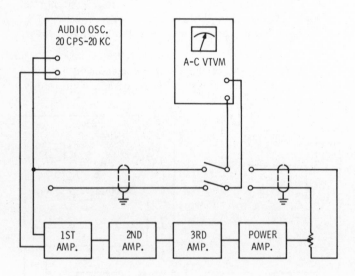

Fig. 3-20. A set-up for measuring frequency response of an audio amplifier.

Power Output

Power output, as the name implies, is a measurement of the rms output power generated by the amplifier system. The power output of high-fidelity amplifiers may vary from 1½ to 150 watts depending on the type of power amplifier stages, and the number of amplifier stages used in the system. The power output ratings of an amplifier is usually rated at 1000 cycles. Table 3-1 lists the power output for packaged audio equipment for home use. There are two levels of power output in which we are interested, the maximum power output and the power output at 10% distortion. Figure 3-22 is a block diagram showing a method of checking maximum power output.

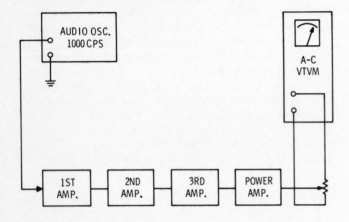

Fig. 3-22. A set-up for measuring maximum power output.

The amplifier is adjusted for flat response, and maximum loudness with the balance control in the midposition. The output of the amplifier is terminated in an impedance equal to the speaker impedance, and the power output meter, or an a-c VTVM is connected across the load resistance. The audio oscillator is set at 1000 cycles, and the output of the oscillator is increased for a maximum reading on the power output meter or the a-c VTVM. If a power output meter is used, the termination resistance is in the output meter, and the power output may be read directly from the meter. If an a-c VTVM is used, an external load must be used to terminate the amplifier, and the power output is determined by the formula: power output $= E^2/R$, where E is the meter reading, and R is the output impedance of the amplifier. This measurement indicates the maximum power output capabilities regardless of the distortion present.

On the average amplifier using a ceramic cartridge, the voltage required at the input to the first stage to produce maximum power output should be on the order of 0.2 to 0.75 volts. This figure will depend on the amplifier.

A more meaningful power output measurement is the power output generated at 10% distortion. This measurement defines the maximum useable power output of the system. Ten percent distortion is considered to be the maximum distortion that the average listener will tolerate. Figure 3-23 shows a set-up for measuring power output at 10% distortion. The set-up is the same as in Fig. 3-22, with the exception that the distortion analyzer is added to

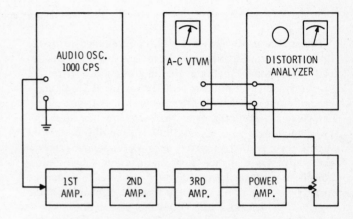

Fig. 3-23. A set-up for measuring power output at 10% distortion.

the system. The procedure here is to set the loudness control to maximum, the tone controls to flat, and the balance controls to the center position. Feed in an audio signal from the audio oscillator, and increase the output at 1000 cycles until the distortion analyzer reads 10% distortion. Then read the power output of the amplifier on the a-c VTVM, or the power output meter which is connected across the input of this distortion analyzer. The procedure for measuring distortion is outlined below. The 10% distortion, as a rule of thumb, should be from ½ to ⅔ of the maximum output of the amplifier. The closer the 10% distortion output is to the maximum output, the better the amplifier.

Harmonic Distortion

Harmonic distortion is a measure of the percentage distortion which is introduced to a sine wave fed through the audio amplifier system. It is used to define the "trueness," or fidelity of the system.

Higher quality high-fidelity amplifiers will measure distortion percentages on the order of 1 to 2% at normal listening levels, with the average at approximately 3%. The lower the percentage distortion, the better the quality of the amplifier.

A block diagram of the set-up for measuring harmonic distortion is shown in Fig. 3-24. As described previously,

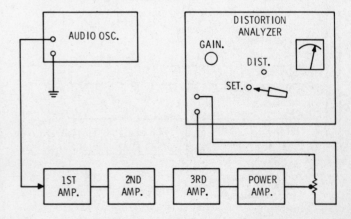

Fig. 3-24. A set-up for measuring harmonic distortion.

Table 3-1. EIA Power Output Ratings of Packaged Audio Equipment For Home Use

1. STANDARD TEST CONDITIONS

Standard test conditions shall be maintained for all tests except as otherwise specified:

1.1 Power Line Voltage: The amplifier shall be tested on 117 volts, rms.

1.2 Power Line Frequency: It shall be within ± 2% of the power line frequency for which the amplifier is rated.

1.3 Power Line Voltage Waveform: It shall be sinusoidal with less than 5% harmonic content.

1.4 Operating Temperature:
1.4.1 Precondition by operating at ⅓ power output for at least one hour in an ambient temperature not less than 20° C., and in still air, and in normal operating position.

1.5 Vacuum-Tube or Solid-State Device Characteristics:
1.5.1 Where the performance of the amplifier is significantly affected by one or more tubes or solid-state characteristics, tests shall be made using selected tubes or solid-state devices in which these critical characteristics are within ± 10% of their significant published characteristics.

1.6 Signal Input:
1.6.1 A low-impedance signal generator of not more than 600 ohms internal impedance shall be used. The signal-input connection shall be made to the phonograph input.
1.6.2 Waveform shall be sinusoidal, with the rms value of all components, other than the fundamental less than 20% of the rated harmonic distortion of the amplifier to be tested, at the level of measurement.
1.6.3 Standard Test Frequencies for Power Output: A standard test frequency of 1000 cycles shall be used to measure power output, except in divided frequency amplifiers which shall use a frequency of one octave below the lowest nominal crossover frequency for the low-frequency amplifier, a frequency midway arithmetically between the nominal crossover frequencies for an i-f amplifier, and a frequency one octave above the highest nominal crossover frequency for the high-frequency amplifier. In divided frequency amplifiers, tests may be made at frequencies different from those above provided the new frequencies are indicated by the manufacturer.

1.7 Load:
1.7.1 Amplifiers rated to supply signal power to one or more loudspeakers shall be terminated in a resistance load, with not more than 10% reactive components at any frequency up to 5 times the highest test frequency, capable of continuously dissipating the full output of the amplifier while maintaining its resistance at the rated value of ± 1%.
1.7.2 The nominal value of load impedance used shall be that specified by the manufacturer, or if such a specification is not available, the optimum load for the amplifier under test.

1.8 Shields, Covers, and Bottom Plates: Shields, covers, and bottom plates, if normally supplied, shall be in place and fastened.

1.9 Connection of Line Cord:
1.9.1 The line cord shall be connected for minimum hum at maximum gain setting, and shall not be changed for any other test. One side of the power source to the amplifier shall be grounded.

1.10 Controls: Loudness (or volume) control shall be set for maximum gain, and tone controls shall be set for as near flat electrical output as possible. If any other position of the loudness (or volume) control is more favorable, it may be used.

2. TESTS AND RATINGS

2.1 Output:
2.1.1 Purpose: To measure and express the capability of an amplifier to supply signal energy to its load.
2.1.2 Definition of Terms:
2.1.2.1 Music Power Output shall mean the single frequency power obtained at 5% total harmonic distortion or less, when measured immediately after the sudden application of a signal and during a time interval so short that supply voltages within the amplifier have not changed from their no-signal values. Unless otherwise specified, MPO shall be measured at 5% distortion. Music power output shall be expressed in terms of watts as defined by the formula: $P = E^2/R$, where P = music power output, E = rms voltage across the load, and R = resistance of the load in ohms.
2.1.2.2 If more than one amplifier is used to selectively cover the audio-frequency range, the power shall be expressed by individual amplifier power ratings to indicate the music power output of each range as measured at the frequencies shown in 1.6.3. The sum of the power outputs may be used provided that frequency division (bass-midrange treble) is indicated.
When multiple channel amplifier sets (such as in stereo systems) are used, the power outputs of each channel may be added arithmetically.
2.1.2.3 Supply Voltages: Supply voltages are bypassed plate and screen voltages for tube amplifiers, and bypassed supply voltages of solid-state device amplifiers.
2.1.3 Test Procedure:
2.1.3.1 Measurement of Music Power Output:
2.1.3.1.1 Operate amplifier under standard test conditions with no signal applied and note supply voltages.
2.1.3.1.2 Adjust input frequency to value specified for the test.
2.1.3.1.3 Adjust signal input level to the maximum value for which the total harmonic distortion percentage is the same as that specified in 2.1.2.1, maintaining supply voltages at the same value as they were under no-signal conditions.
2.1.3.1.4 Measure the rms voltage across the load.
2.1.3.1.5 Compute the music power output by the formula of 2.1.2.1.
2.1.3.1.6 Accuracy of the overall measurements of the music power output shall be within 10%.

the distortion analyzer is an amplifier which has a very sharply tuned filter which filters out the fundamental of the oscillator, and measures the percentage of harmonics generated by the amplifier. If there is no distortion in the system, there will be no harmonics, and the percentage distortion will be zero. The distortion analyzer includes a very sensitive a-c VTVM which measures the harmonic voltage after the fundamental has been nulled out. It also measures any noise or hum in the system. Distortion is usually measured at normal listening levels of the order of one to two watts. It may be measured at any level desired, however.

The procedure is to feed a signal from an audio oscillator at the desired level and frequency into the amplifier under test, and terminate the output of the amplifier in a resistance equal to the value of the impedance of the speaker. A distortion analyzer is connected across the load resistor. The meter switch on the analyzer should be set to the

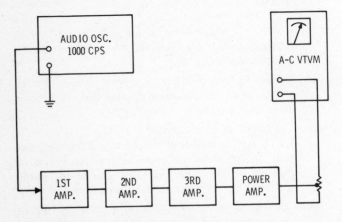

Fig. 3-25. A set-up for measuring hum and noise.

100% position, the function switch rotated to the set position, and the input level on the distortion analyzer adjusted so that the meter reads 100%. The function switch on the analyzer should then be switched to the distortion position. This switches in the filter. The frequency dial on the distortion analyzer should be rotated to the same frequency to which the generator is set, and should be adjusted carefully for a null or dip in the meter on the distortion analyzer. There is usually a phasing control on a distortion analyzer. This should be rotated for a minimum reading. The meter switch should then be rotated progressively to a lower and lower scale, and the adjustment of the frequency and the phasing on the analyzer rechecked for a minimum reading. Once the lowest meter reading has been reached, the percentage distortion can be read directly from the meter.

Measurements should be taken at several frequencies throughout the range of 30 cps to 15 kc. The most probable causes of distortion are tubes; improper bias; wrong-value plate load resistors; unbalance in the input signal on push-pull amplifiers; unbalance in the plate currents in the output tubes on push-pull amplifiers; low B+ voltages; and, since hum and noise are measured, noisy resistors in the low-level stages, and poor filtering in the power supply can also contribute to high distortion measurements. It is

a good practice to look at the waveform at the output of the distortion analyzer when high distortion is measured with an oscilloscope to determine the waveform of the voltage being measured by the meter. This will indicate whether or not it is plain harmonic distortion, or whether it is random noise or hum.

Hum

Hum measurement is the measurement of the ratio of the maximum output power to the hum power developed with no input signal. The ratio is usually expressed in decibels. A good amplifier will measure a ratio of the order of 60 db; the minimum tolerable is about 30 db. Figure 3-25 is a test set-up for measuring hum. The amplifier tone controls should be set to the flat position, the balance control to the center position, and the loudness control to maximum. The output of the generator should be increased for maximum voltage output, and the reading recorded.

The generator should then be turned OFF, and the output of the amplifier read. The hum and noise is expressed by: $db = 20 \log (E1/E2)$, where E1 is the signal voltage for maximum output, and E2 is the voltage with no signal. If the meter has a db scale, the output may be read directly in db.

Intermodulation

Intermodulation measurements are simply a more sensitive method of measuring harmonic distortion. As a general rule, if the harmonic distortion is very low, the intermodulation distortion will also be very low. It is normally not necessary to measure intermodulation distortion on an amplifier in normal routine servicing. This is usually a measurement which is performed in the design of the amplifier. However, we will outline the method of measuring intermodulation distortion briefly; see Fig. 3-26. Two frequencies, one low and one high, are fed into the amplifier under test. Normal practice is for the separation between frequencies to be a minimum of ten times.

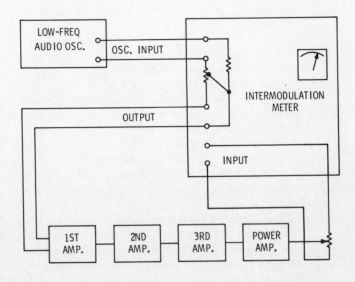

Fig. 3-26. A set-up for measuring intermodulation distortion.

The output of the amplifier under test is then fed into the distortion analyzer. If intermodulation distortion is present in the amplifier, the low-frequency signal will amplitude modulate the high-frequency signal. The distortion analyzer simply demodulates the high-frequency signal which it looks at as a carrier, and measures the percentage of modulation caused by the low-frequency signal. This is read directly on the instrument. Frequencies commonly used are 400 cycles and 4000 cycles. Typical readings of intermodulation distortion on a good quality amplifier are on the order of 1 to 2%. The symptom on an amplifier having severe intermodulation distortion is that the high frequencies although they are not distorted do not sound clear, crisp, and distinct.

4. Solid-State Amplifiers

Introduction

Transistors have been used extensively in many types of electronic equipment for a number of years. Their use has been confined primarily to specialized equipment for the armed forces, and to small radios for the consumer. Initially, the cost of transistors precluded their use in consumer products to a large degree. As manufacturing techniques became more sophisticated, costs declined to the point where transistor prices became comparable to tube prices. As a result solid-state equipment can be produced to compete with the tube versions.

Transistors have a number of characteristics which make

The circuitry of a solid-state stereo amplifier and pre-amplifier is examined in the following paragraphs. Since the two channels are identical, only one will be discussed.

Preamplifier

The preamplifier, see Fig. 3-27, contains a "bootstrap" input stage followed by a high-gain amplifier. Two negative feedback paths are provided for shaping the overall frequency response, and to equalize audio amplitudes between functions. One feedback path is used when the instrument is operated in the phono position, and the second path is switched into the circuit for all other functions.

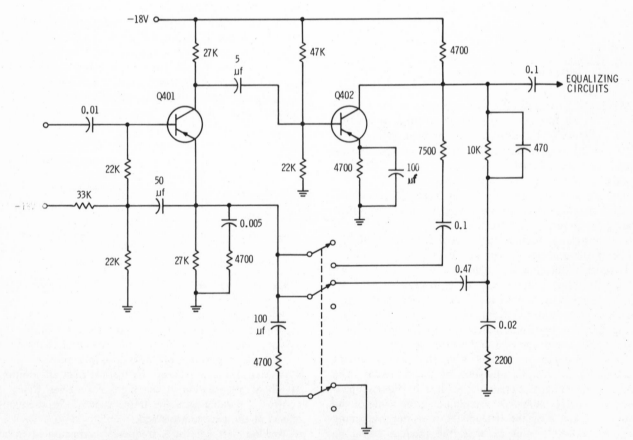

Fig. 3-27. Transistor preamplifier stage with a "bootstrap" input followed by a high-gain amplifier.

them suitable for consumer products. Among them are small physical size, low heat dissipation, stability, and long life expectancy. These features, coupled with good circuit design, result in a dependable, high-quality instrument.

The tuner and phono cartridge have high-impedance outputs, and must be terminated by a high impedance. The correct match is provided by the bootstrap circuit of the input stage. The 50-μf bootstrap capacitor increases the input impedance by coupling the signal developed across the emitter resistor to the junction of the base-biasing resistors.

To understand how the input impedance is raised by the bootstrap capacitor, consider what takes place when the capacitor is out of the circuit, see Fig. 3-28A. With a 1-volt signal applied to the base, the signal voltage will divide across the two 22K resistors. Since they are equal resistances, half of the signal voltage will appear at their junction point. Ignoring the transistor impedance for the moment, the total impedance would be the sum of the two resistors, or 44K. By Ohm's Law, current through upper resistor is: $I = E/R = 0.5/22K = 23\mu a$.

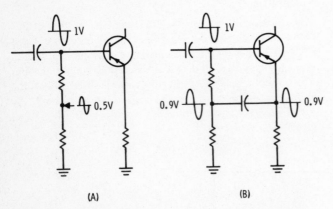

Fig. 3-28. Effect of the bootstrap capacitor of Fig. 3-27: (A) without the capacitor, and (B) with the capacitor.

When the bootstrap capacitor is placed in the circuit, see Fig. 3-28B, the 0.9-v signal on the emitter is coupled to the junction of the resistors. It now appears that only 0.1 v is being dropped across the upper 22K resistor. Using Ohm's Law to calculate the current through the upper resistor: $I = E/R = 0.1/22K = 4.5\mu a$.

The signal from the emitter has reduced the current through the upper resistor to 1/5 of its previous value. Stating it another way, the effective impedance of the upper resistor has been increased by 5 times, to 110K, by reducing the current through it.

In practice, the effective input impedance is considerably higher than the example just given. Instead of 90% of the input impedance appearing at the junction of the resistors, the value will run from 95% to 98%. This would cause the effective input impedance to be from 2 to 5 times higher than calculated in this example.

This impedance is parallel with the emitter circuit through the base-emitter junction of the transistor. The effect of an unbypassed emitter resistor on input impedance can be approximated by multiplying the value of the emitter resistance by the Beta of the transistor. Assuming Beta to be 100 in this example, the product would be $100 \times 27,000 = 2.7$ megohms. This value in parallel with up to 0.5 megohms impedance of the base circuit provides a combined input impedance of about 0.4 megohms.

With 1 volt applied to the input of the bootstrap stage, about 0.05 volts of signal appears in the collector circuit. Gain was sacrificed to get an impedance match on the

input. The collector signal couples through the 5-μf capacitor to the low-impedance input of Q402. The collector and emitter resistors are relatively low value, 4700 ohms. The emitter resistor is bypassed by a 100-μf capacitor to provide a low-impedance path for the signal currents. The 0.05-volt signal on the base is amplified to 4.5 volts at the collector. This level is high enough to be applied to the tone-compensating circuits with their associated losses.

The desired control of the audio-frequency range can be achieved by passing the audio signal through filter networks composed of resistors and capacitors. Adding the RC components to the circuit cannot increase the amplitude of any of the audio frequencies; they can only take away. Two basic RC networks are used to achieve equalization.

The circuit used to attenuate high frequencies is shown in Fig. 3-29A. A resistor and capacitor are arranged in series and inserted across the high-impedance load. The reactance of the capacitor decreases with increasing frequency, providing a controlled amount of high-frequency roll-off. The low frequencies are unaffected by this circuit due to the high reactance of the capacitor to low frequencies.

Figure 3-29B shows the arrangement used to attenuate the low frequencies. The capacitor has a low impedance to the high frequencies. These frequencies will choose the path of least resistance, and couple through the capacitor to the load resistance, virtually unattenuated. The reactance of the capacitor is high for the low frequencies, and the value of the resistor, in series with the load resistor, determines the attenuation. If the filter resistor value equalled the load resistance, the low-frequency audio voltage would divide equally across them. As the filter resistor is lowered in value, more of the lows develop across the load.

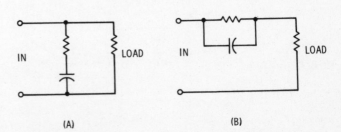

Fig. 3-29. Frequency attenuation circuits: (A) high frequency, and (B) low frequency.

Switches are used as treble and bass controls, see Fig. 3-30, so that preset attenuation may be connected into the circuit. Each position of these switches provides about 4 db attenuation. The timbre control provides an additional 10 db of attentuation at the high frequencies. Since the control is parallel with the treble switch, the attenuating effects of the two controls add.

The loudness control is frequency compensated to correct for the loudness characteristics of the human ear. The ear is most sensitive to frequencies in the 3000-to-5000-cycle range. Above and below this range, the loudness sensitivity of the ear falls off rapidly, i.e., the highs and lows must have a greater intensity to appear as loud as the middle frequencies.

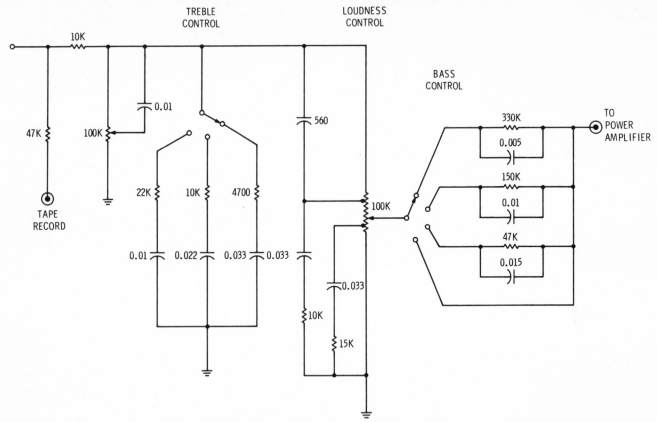

Fig. 3-30. Switches used for bass and treble controls.

The ear response to low frequencies falls off faster than for the highs. As the volume is reduced, the lows seem to be attenuated more than the middle and high frequencies. The compensated control is used to overcome this effect by providing additional treble attenuation. As a result, the ear hears a smooth attenuation of all the audio frequencies.

Power Amplifier

After passing through the tone-compensating circuit, the signal is fed to the input of the power amplifier. Six transistors are used for each channel. The amplifier provides a total of 100 watts music power output, 50 watts per channel.

Dual heat sinks are provided in the output stage for heat dissipation. The output signal is directly coupled to the speaker, and feedback networks are used to improve frequency response, and to reduce distortion.

Input Stage

The input stage, see Fig. 3-31, is connected in a bootstrap common-collector circuit to form a high impedance to the input signal. The operation of this circuit was described during the discussion of the preamp.

The emitter resistor is the same value as the collector resistor. Since the two are in series through Q1, the voltage drop across the two resistors will be the same. The voltage drop across the emitter resistor forms the bias for Q2.

Low-value resistors are used in the driver stage because we are interested in power gain. On signal peaks, a large current will flow through the power transistor. The audio signal is coupled to the output stage through a transformer. The d-c current through the primary winding is limited by a series and parallel resistor. This is done to prevent the transformer core from becoming saturated at high signal levels, and causing a loss of low-frequency response.

An unbypassed 10-ohm resistor is connected in the emitter. Negative feedback voltage from the speaker is introduced at this point to improve overall frequency response, and to reduce distortion. The feedback applied to the emitter is controlled by the balance control. Reducing the feedback voltage increases the gain of the driver. When the control is adjusted to reduce the feedback to the driver in channel 1, more feedback is applied to the channel 2 driver. The gain of the two channels may be made equal by adjusting the balance control. Additional negative feedback for the high frequencies is introduced into the collector circuit by a 0.01 capacitor connected to the speaker. This further improves the overall frequency response of the amplifier.

Output Transistors

The output transistors are connected in a single-ended, series-arranged push-pull circuit, see Fig. 3-32. Two power supply voltages of opposite polarity are required: a +36 volts for one half of the output stage and a negative −36 volts for the other half.

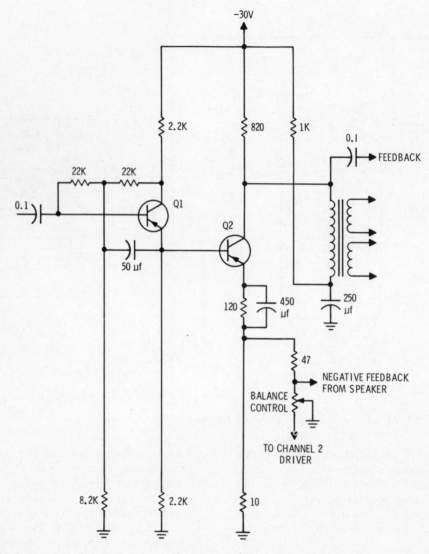

Fig. 3-31. Transistor input stage.

Assume that a positive audio peak is present at the top of the primary of the driver transformer. The two secondary windings are connected in such a manner that a negative voltage is applied to the base of Q4, and a positive voltage is applied to the base of Q6. In a p-n-p transistor, a positive signal on the base will reverse bias it, causing it to cut off. Since Q5 is in series with Q6, both transistors will be cut off, and no current will flow in this half of the amplifier.

Q4, in the other half of the circuit, has a negative voltage applied to the base which gives it a forward bias. Q4 will conduct more heavily, causing the voltage at its collector to become more positive. Since the collector is connected directly to the emitter of Q3, Q3 becomes forward-biased, and conducts more heavily also. Electrons travel from the negative supply voltage, through Q3 and Q4 *down* through the speaker coil, minus to plus, to ground. As a result, a large negative voltage is developed across the speaker.

Now assume the audio peak across the driver primary

is negative. Q4 will now have a positive peak on its base which cuts it off. Q6 is forward-biased by the negative-going signal voltage on its base, and will conduct more heavily. With more current flowing, the collector of Q6 becomes more positive which forward-biases Q5. Electrons now flow from ground, through the speaker coil, minus to plus, through Q5 and Q6 to the positive supply voltage. In this manner, both halves of the audio signal are reproduced across the speaker voice coil.

Correct bias voltages are obtained by 4 low-value resistors connected between the supply voltage and the speaker. About 60 ma of current through these resistors assure good bias regulation under varying load conditions.

The transistors are not completely cut off under no-signal conditions. An idling current of about 45 ma flows through each leg of the amplifier. Since both these d-c currents flow through the speaker, but in opposite directions, the two currents cancel, and no voltage is developed across the speaker. This assumes that the two legs are perfectly balanced for dc. In actual practice, this perfect d-c

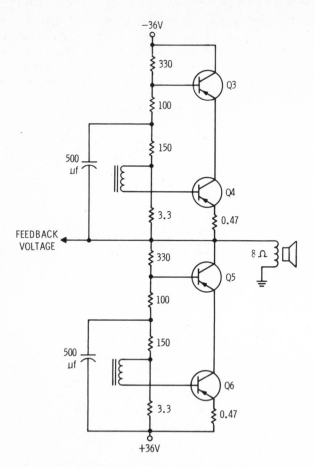

Fig. 3-32. Transistor single-ended, series arranged push-pull output circuit.

ing, collector-to-emitter breakdown voltage, frequency response, and saturation current. In the S.E.S.A.P.P. circuit, half the transistors operate common-base with much less stringent requirements placed upon them. Replacement with matched pairs is only required for the common-emitter stages.

Power Supply

The power supply provides both positive and negative voltages for the power amplifier and a negative voltage for the tuner. Four diodes form two separate full-wave rectifier circuits, see Fig. 3-33. The polarity of the diodes are

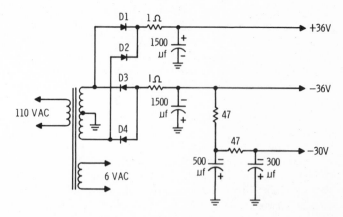

Fig. 3-33. Power supply for a transistor amplifier.

connected to obtain the proper d-c polarity. 1500-μf capacitors filter the output voltage. The negative supply bus has an additional filter network to provide a lower voltage for the input and driver stages in the power amplifier.

When the power is first turned ON, there is a large surge of current through the 1500-μf capacitors. To prevent damage to the diodes, a 1-ohm, 5-watt resistor is inserted in series to limit the surge current to a safe value.

Current Regulator

The −36-volt bus connects to the input of the current regulator on the tuner chassis, see Fig. 3-34. Variations in input voltage are corrected by the regulator to produce a constant −23 v for the tuner stages. A 1000-ohm resistor

balance is not always achieved, nor even desirable. It is more important to have an a-c balance under signal conditions. This type of balance insures that both halves of the audio signal will be amplified by the same amount.

Measuring the d-c voltage at the speaker gives a useful indication that the balance is reasonably close. With signal applied at low level and gradually increasing the drive, the d-c voltage across the speaker will be seen to change. This voltage may be either positive or negative, or even change from one to the other at different driving levels. If the two legs are reasonably balanced, the d-c voltage at the speaker should not vary more than a volt or so either side of zero from a minimum to maximum power output.

Current through each leg of the amplifier changes from zero when cut off by a positive-going signal on the base to about 1¼ amps when driven to 50 watts output. The combined current of both legs is 2.5 amps. By Ohm's Law: $P = I^2R = (2.5)^2 \times 8 = 50$ watts power output.

Any 120-cycle hum voltage coming from the power supply will cancel in the output circuit. Since one power supply produces a negative d-c voltage, and the other a positive voltage, any hum voltage on one supply bus will be 180 degrees out of phase with the hum voltage on the other supply bus. The two currents cancel, and no hum voltage appears across the voice coil.

Transistors operating in the common-emitter configuration must meet rather severe requirements of Beta match-

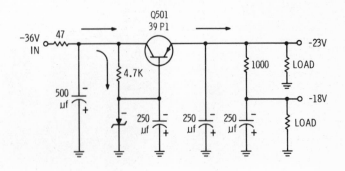

Fig. 3-34. Current regulator for the transistor power supply.

drops the output voltage to 18 v to operate the preamp stages.

Notice how the bias is developed for the base. Normally, a voltage divider made up of two resistors would be used. In this case, a Zener diode has been substituted for the lower resistor. The voltage across the Zener remains constant even though the current through it may be changing. As a result a constant voltage is applied to the base of the regulator. The characteristic curve of a diode shows what is taking place, see Fig. 3-35.

When forward bias is applied, the current increases as voltage is increased. This is the way diodes are operated as detectors, rectifiers, etc. A different characteristic is observed when the bias voltage is reversed. A very small current flows in the reverse direction through the diode. As the voltage becomes more negative, the current remains constant. If the voltage continues to increase in the negative direction, a point is reached where current begins to increase greatly (AB). This is known as "breakdown," and the portion of the curve that shows this transition is called the Zener knee. The diode is operated along the AB portion of the curve. For a small change in voltage around the operating point, a relatively large change in current takes place.

When the supply voltage increases because of line voltage variations, a larger voltage is applied to the diode. Current through the diode increases, causing a larger voltage drop across the series resistor. As a result, the voltage across the diode remains constant within a fraction of a volt.

It may be easier to visualize the operation of the diode by thinking of it as a variable resistor. As voltage increases across the diode, its resistance decreases, and the voltage is prevented from rising further. Conversely, if the voltage decreases, the resistance of the diode increases which prevents the voltage from decreasing further. The Zener used in this circuit has a nominal operating voltage of −23 volts, and this voltage is applied to the base of the regulator.

In Fig. 3-34, electrons move from the −26-v bus to the collector, out of the emitter, and down through the load, minus to plus. On the schematic, a resistor is shown as a load to simplify the explanation of the regulator actions. As current passes through the load, a negative voltage is developed. Now assume that the −36 v has increased to −38 v. A larger current is caused to flow, and a larger negative voltage is dropped across the load. The emitter of the regulator must be positive with respect to the base. The base voltage has remained constant at about −23 v by the action of the Zener. The increased negative voltage across the load reduces the forward bias on the regulator. Therefore, the current through the regulator is reduced. The current through the load is also reduced. With less current flowing, the voltage drop across the load is reduced to its original value.

Now assume that the power supply voltage changes in

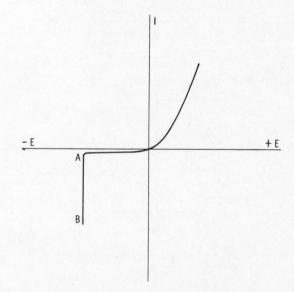

Fig. 3-35. Characteristic curve of a diode.

the opposite direction by dropping to −34 v. Less current will flow through the load, and the voltage drop becomes less negative than it was before. This results in an increased forward bias on the regulator. More current will flow with a corresponding increase in voltage across the load. In this manner, variations in supply voltage are corrected to produce a constant voltage at the output of the regulator.

4 – Servicing AM-FM Tuners

1. AM-FM Tuners

Most FM tuners in use today are combination AM and FM tuners. At least part of the i-f system usually functions as both a 455-kc amplifier for AM, and a 10.7-mc amplifier for FM. The dual-function stage normally is the last i-f amplifier. A separate r-f amplifier is normally used for FM. The AM receiver, in most cases, does not have an r-f amplifier. In the instances where an r-f amplifier is included on AM, the r-f amplifier is separate. The audio system is also normally common to both AM and FM.

Block Diagram

A block diagram of a representative FM and AM tuner equipped for receiving stereo FM is shown in Fig. 4-1. The AM section of the receiver consists of a separate converter which converts the incoming AM signal to 455 kc. The last i-f stage has two tuned circuits in its plate, one at 455 kc and one at 10.7 mc. It, therefore, functions as both a

10.7-mc limiter if on FM, and a straight 455-kc amplifier on AM. The 455-kc output of the last i-f stage feeds an AM detector which demodulates the carrier. The output of the AM detector feeds both the left and right stereo amplifiers which are connected together, providing a monaural output.

In the FM function, the FM signal is coupled to a separate r-f amplifier stage which tunes from 88 to 108 mc. The output of the r-f amplifier feeds an FM mixer which converts the signal to 10.7 mc. This stage is sometimes a converter containing an oscillator, or it may be a mixer fed by a separate oscillator.

The FM if usually consists of three stages, the last stage serving as a limiter which limits, or clips all AM noise, and passes only the FM signal. The 10.7-mc output of the limiter feeds the FM detector. In most cases, this circuit is a ratio detector. In some cases, a discriminator is used. The basic operation of the two circuits is very similar. The

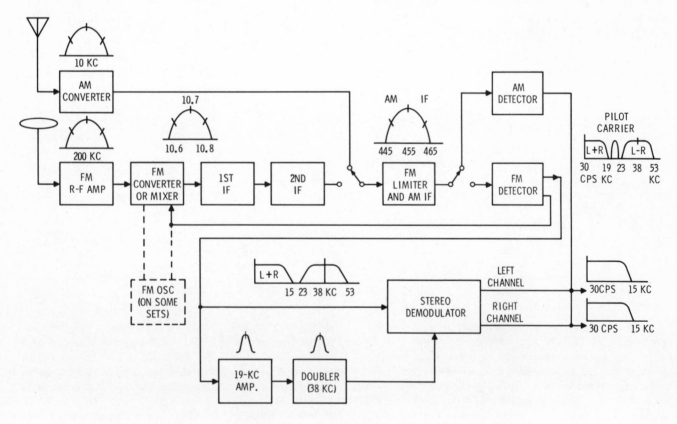

Fig. 4-1. Simplified block diagram of an AM-FM stereo tuner.

37

main difference is that the ratio detector functions as a limiter as well as an FM demodulator. The output of the FM detector feeds the audio system directly on a monaural FM receiver, and feeds the stereo FM decoder if the receiver is equipped for stereo. The output of the FM stereo decoder feeds the separate left and right stereo audio amplifiers.

The typical frequency response of the FM tuner is shown in Fig. 4-1. The response of the tuner is normally a peaked response with the center frequency of the incoming carrier at the peak of the curve. The bandwidth of the tuner at the 3-db points is normally on the order of 200 kc, which passes all of the sidebands of the monaural and the stereo FM signal without frequency response distortion.

The bandpass of the i-f amplifier is also a peaked response, normally centered at about 10.7 mc with a bandwidth at the 6-db points, or 50% gain points of approximately 200 kc.

The output of the FM detector on a monaural receiver is flat from 30 cycles to 15 kc, normally. On the FM stereo receiver, there is no deemphasis network in the output of the FM detector. The response of the detector

The R-F Amplifier

Figure 4-2 is a circuit diagram of a typical r-f amplifier stage used in commercial FM receivers. This circuit is called an *autodyne* circuit. The balanced FM antenna is fed to the centertapped primary of T101, which couples the FM signal into the grid of the 12DT8 r-f amplifier, V101A. This stage is a neutralized triode amplifier. C104 is the neutralizing capacitor. L101A and C109 form a series-tuned circuit which is tuned to the incoming carrier. The resonant rise in voltage is taken off C109, and applied to the centertap of the oscillator tank in the grid of V101B. The oscillator tank consists of L101B and L101C in series, tuned to 10.7 mc above the incoming carrier by C110, C111, C112, C115, and the capacitance of CR101, the AFC diode. The r-f signal is fed in at the center of the oscillator transformer because the oscillator voltage is zero at this point. Therefore, a minimum of oscillator voltage is fed back through the capacitance of the r-f amplifier to the antenna, minimizing oscillator radiation. T102A in the plate of the 12TD8 is tuned to 10.7 mc, and this signal is coupled into the grid of the first i-f amplifier, V7.

Another common type of FM tuner and mixer is shown

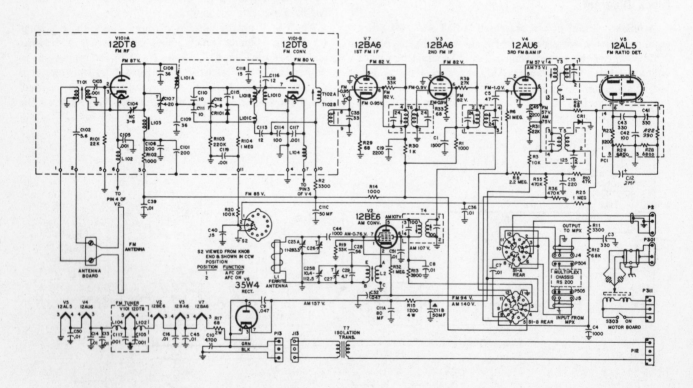

Fig. 4-2. Schematic of an FM receiver.

on these receivers is relatively flat from 30 cycles to approximately 53 kc. The operation of the stereo FM decoder, the servicing procedures recommended, and the alignment procedure is outlined in detail in Chapter 5. We will concern ourselves with the FM portion of the receiver since the AM portion is rather straightforward, and the servicing techniques are familiar to most service technicians.

in Fig. 4-3. In this circuit, the r-f amplifier is a pentode, V1A. The output signal of the r-f amplifier is fed to a triode mixer. A separate oscillator, V2A, is also fed to the grid of the mixer. The oscillator runs at 10.7 mc above the incoming carrier. The plate load of V1B is tuned to 10.7 mc.

The i-f amplifier consists of three stages, V7, V3, and V4. V4 functions as a limiter on FM, and as an i-f ampli-

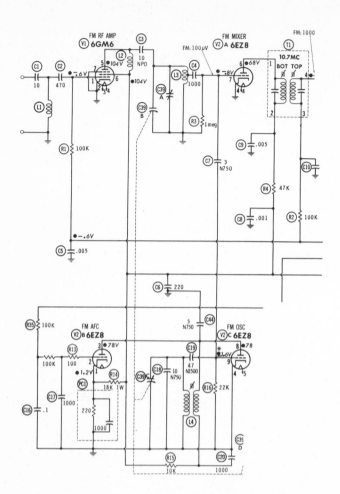

Fig. 4-3. Schematic of an FM tuner with a pentode r-f amplifier and a separate oscillator and mixer tube.

fier on AM. The plate circuit of V4 has two transformers. T3 is a ratio detector transformer which feeds the FM demodulator, and is tuned to 10.7 mc. T5 is tuned to 455 kc, and acts as the plate load when the stage is being used as an AM i-f amplifier. CR1 is a diode detector for AM signals.

Receivers having discriminators as FM detectors usually have 2 limiter stages because the discriminator does not offer limiting action. The majority of receivers employ the ratio detector. A schematic of a discriminator is shown in Fig. 4-4.

The rf or mixer on an FM receiver is very similar to that of an AM receiver, with the exception of the frequencies involved, and requires few special techniques or considerations in servicing. There are special considerations in the design of the receiver, however, because of the frequencies involved.

The limiter, the FM detector, and automatic frequency control, however, are somewhat different than circuits found in AM receivers, and require special considerations and techniques in servicing and measuring.

The Limiter

The purpose of the limiter stage is to remove all amplitude modulation due to noise, or static which may appear on the FM signal. Noise or static in the FM band, for the most part, causes only AM modulation, and produces little FM modulation. If the AM modulation is removed, the noise can be removed without affecting the program material. In an AM receiver, the program material is amplitude modulation. It is not possible, therefore, to remove the noise without affecting the program material.

The limiter stage usually does not employ fixed bias, see Fig. 4-5. The plate and screen voltages are low. Any signal

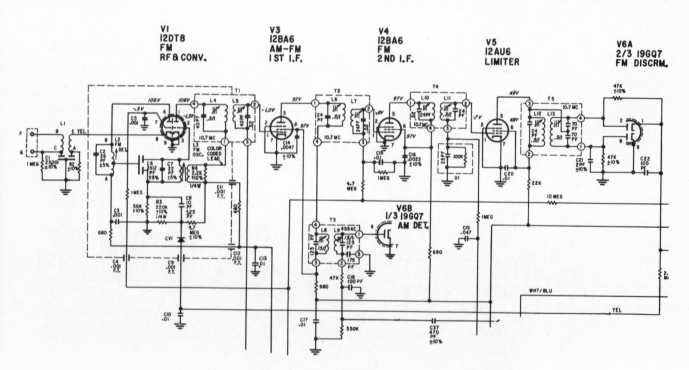

Fig. 4-4. Schematic of an FM receiver with a discriminator FM detector.

present on the grid of the limiter will cause grid current to flow due to the positive peaks of the carrier driving the grid into conduction. This causes clipping of the positive peaks of the carrier. Since the plate and screen voltages are low, the tube is very easy to drive into cutoff and saturation. A signal of the order of 1 to 2 volts will usually drive the limiter into saturation and cutoff.

On extremely weak signals, below the limiting threshold and near the sensitivity limits of the receiver, the limiter functions essentially as a straight amplifier, and the amplitude variations in the form of noise will be contained in the output of the FM detector connected to it. Figure 4-6 shows the conditions present when the limiter is receiving

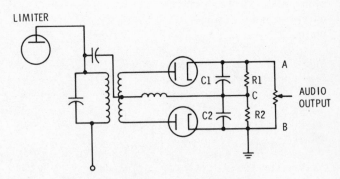

Fig. 4-5. Discriminator FM detector.

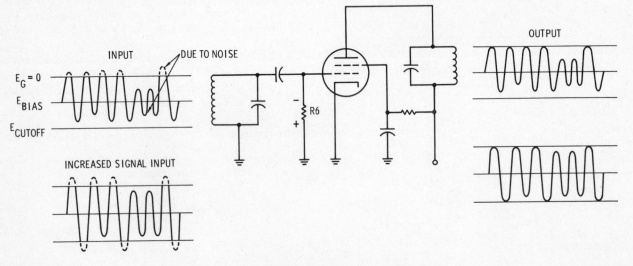

Fig. 4-6. Signal condition in the limiter on very weak signals.

a very weak signal below the limiting threshold. This signal would be present on the average FM receiver at signal inputs from 10 to 30 microvolts. The positive high-amplitude escursions of the carrier due to noise, cause a slight grid current to flow through R6, which is the grid-leak resistor. This causes a negative-positive drop across the resistor, and puts a small bias on the tube. The signal axis is superimposed on this bias voltage. The positive low-amplitude escursions of the carrier do not cause the grid to draw sufficient current through R6 to cause limiting

on any but the highest, positive amplitude peaks of the signal. The bias is not great enough to cause the tube to be cut off on the negative peaks. Under these conditions, noise modulation appears in the output of the limiter.

If the signal is increased slightly, the increased signal amplitude swings the grid of the limiter more positive, causing more grid current to flow, and increasing the bias. This shifts the axis of the input signal towards cutoff. On the positive peaks, all except the deepest modulation points cause the limiter to draw current on the negative half

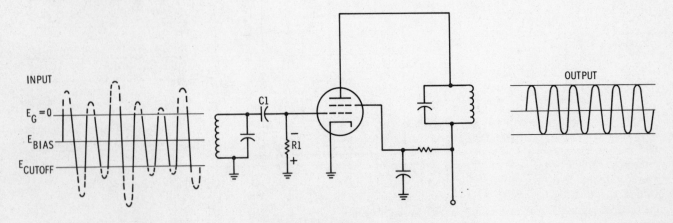

Fig. 4-7. Limiter with the input signal strong enough for full limiting.

cycles, driving the limiter to cutoff. Under these conditions, all of the noise except the highest amplitude noise is removed.

If the signal is increased slightly above this level, see Fig. 4-7, then even the lowest amplitude portions of the carrier drives the tube into cutoff at grid current. At this signal level and all signal levels above it, the output of the limiter on both the positive and negative cycles will be clipped at a constant level, removing all noise from the signal.

The value of R1 and C1 in the grid of the limiter is important for good limiting operation. When R1 and C1 are small, they load the stage driving the limiter, and the sensitivity of the receiver suffers. If R1 and C1 are extremely large, they have a tendency to charge up on high-impulse noises, such as ignition noise. When R1 is large, the capacitor cannot discharge when the noise pulse is removed. This causes a hole to appear in the carrier following the noise burst. The hole in the carrier appears as a "plop" in the speaker. Normal time constants, with R1 (in ohms) and C1 (in farads) in the limiter grid, are on the order of 1.25 to 5 microseconds. Care should be taken to replace R1 and C1 with like values for best limiter performance.

There is normally no AGC on FM receivers. It is desirable to supply as much signal as possible at all times to the grid of the limiter to eliminate any noise which might be present in the carrier in the form of amplitude modulation.

FM Detectors

By far the largest percentage of FM receivers use a ratio detector for demodulating the FM signal. A partial schematic of a ratio detector is shown in Fig. 4-8. When a 10.7-mc i-f signal is coupled to the ratio detector, the

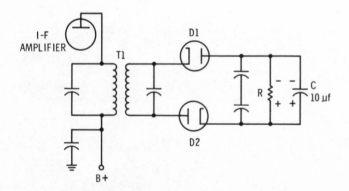

Fig. 4-8. Partial schematic of a ratio detector showing the noise limiting circuit.

secondary diodes, D1 and D2, conduct equally. The rectified carrier flows through D1 and R, charging C, and returns to the secondary of T1 through diode D2. If the average amplitude of the carrier is increased gradually, the voltage across R will increase in proportion. However, if the carrier amplitude is increased or decreased instantaneously, such as which might occur from the noise caus-

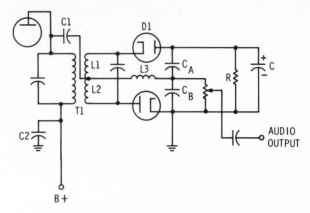

Fig. 4-9. The ratio detector.

ing AM modulation of the carrier, the charge on capacitor C across R will tend to hold the voltage across R constant, smoothing out the amplitude modulation on the carrier. The ratio detector is, therefore, a noise limiter as well as an FM detector.

The circuit shown in Fig. 4-8 will not demodulate the FM carrier. To demodulate the carrier, we must add C1 and L3 to the circuit, see Fig. 4-9. The addition of these parts makes the detector frequency selective, converting changes in frequency due to the frequency modulation to audio signals. The secondary of T1 is centertapped; therefore, the signal fed to the cathode and plate of D1 and D2 is 180 degrees out of phase. This voltage can be represented by two lines, or vectors, whose lengths indicate the strength of the voltage, and whose directions represent the relative phases of the voltages with respect to the center-tap. See Fig. 4-10.

The voltages on the top half of the secondary and the bottom half of the secondary (with respect to the center-tap) are 180 degrees out of phase, opposing each other, and are equal. Because it is centertapped, the voltage on the top half of the secondary, E_{L1}, is applied to D1; the voltage across the bottom half of the winding, E_{L2}, is applied to D2. C1, L3, and C_B are effectively connected across the primary of T1. C1, C_2, and C_B have very low reactances at the i-f frequencies, and appear as short cir-

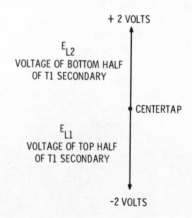

Fig. 4-10. Vector representation of the voltages in the top and bottom halves of the secondary of T1 in Fig. 4-9.

cuits. The voltage which appears across L3 is, therefore, the primary voltage, since L3 effectively is connected directly across the primary. This voltage is equal to the primary voltage in phase and amplitude.

At resonance, the tank circuit (L1 and C1) appears as a resistance. The current of the tank circuit will, therefore, be in phase with the induced voltage. (The induced voltage is at all times 180° out of phase with the primary voltage.) Because of the action of the coil, the voltage across the secondary will lead the tank circuit current by 90°. Hence, the voltage across the secondary will lead the induced voltage by 90°, or lag the primary voltage by 90°.

As explained previously, the secondary voltage can be divided into E_{L1} and E_{L2}. The voltage across D1 is the vector sum of E_{L1} and E_{L3}. The voltage across D2 is the vector sum of E_{L2} and E_{L3}. (C_A and C_B have negligible reactances at these frequencies.) We can represent this graphically as shown in Fig. 4-11.

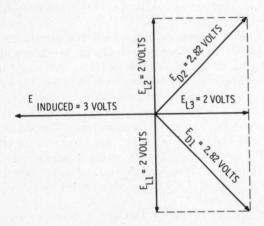

Fig. 4-11. Vector representation of the voltages across diodes D1 and D2 when the i-f signal frequency is at 10.7 mc.

The voltage across C_B represents the condition when the input signal from the primary of T1 is exactly at the center frequency of the if. This voltage is eliminated by a d-c blocking capacitor placed in series with the arm of the volume control.

Above resonance, the series tank circuit will act as an inductor (considering the tank as a series circuit, not as a parallel circuit). The current will, therefore, lag the induced voltage by some angle, depending on the relative values of the inductance and the effective R. For a high-Q circuit, which is the case, R will be be small. If we suppose that the tank circuit current lags the induced voltage by some angle (X), the secondary voltage will still lead the current by 90°, and, therefore, the secondary voltage will lead the induced voltage by the complement of X. For example, if the series tank circuit lags the induced voltage by 30° (X = 30°), the secondary voltage will lead the induced voltage by 60° (90° − 30°). Because of the centertap, the secondary voltage is divided into E_{L1} and E_{L2} as shown in Fig. 4-12. The voltages across D1 and D2 are again the vector sums of E_{L3} and E_{L1}, and E_{L3} and E_{L2}, respectively (found by the parallelogram

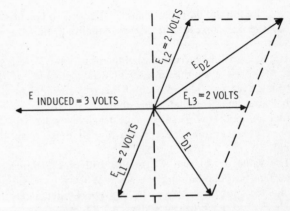

Fig. 4-12. Vector representation of the voltages across diodes D1 and D2 when the i-f signal frequency is above 10.7 mc.

method). As shown, the voltage across D2, E_{D2}, is greater than E_{D1}, and the voltage across C_B will, therefore, be greater than that at resonance.

Below resonance, similar events occur, but the series tank circuit current will be capacitive, and will lead the induced voltage by some angle (X). The secondary voltage will lead this current by 90° so that the secondary voltage leads the induced voltage by 90° plus the angle (90° + X), and lags E_{L3} by the supplement of 90° plus the angle [180° −(90° + X)]. For example, if the current leads the induced voltage by 30°, the secondary voltage leads the induced voltage by 90° + 30°, or 120°, and lags E_{L3} by 180° −(90° + 30°), or 60°.

As shown in Fig. 4-13, the voltages across D1 and D2 are the vector sums of E_{L3} and E_{L1}, and E_{L3} and E_{L2}, respectively. Now E_{D2} is less than that at resonance so that the voltage cross C_B will be less. The blocking capacitor takes care of the d-c component, and yields the original modulation. As the frequency goes above and below resonance, the output will be an a-c voltage.

E_{L3} does not change in phase or amplitude with frequency because it is part of a low-Q circuit.

A variation of this circuit commonly seen in modern receivers is shown in Fig. 4-14. The operation of this circuit is identical to the one described in Fig. 4-9. It is merely rearranged. R is divided into two resistors, and

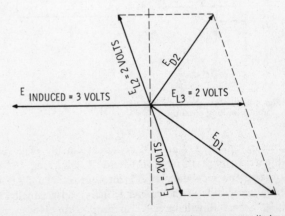

Fig. 4-13. Vector representation of the voltages across diodes D1 and D2 when the i-f signal frequency is below 10.7 mc.

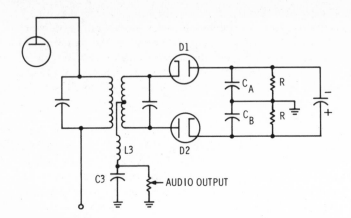

Fig. 4-14. A variation of the ratio detector circuit.

the center of the two is grounded. C_A and C_B are also centertapped and grounded. L3 is electrically connected to the centertap of C_A and C_B as in Fig. 4-9, through capacitor C3. The audio output voltage is taken off across C3. When the incoming carrier is exactly 10.7 mc, the currents through D1 and D2, as described, are equal. Their currents flow in opposite directions through L3. The voltage across L3 and C3 under these conditions, therefore, is zero. When the carrier swings above 10.7 mc, the current through D2 increases and the current through D1 decreases. D1 is connected in such a manner as to cause the high side of C3 to go in one direction. At frequencies below 10.7 mc, D1 conducts more than D2. This diode is connected in such a manner as to cause the voltage at the high side of C3 to swing in the opposite direction. We, therefore, recover the original modulation across C3.

The Discriminator

The basic principles of operation of a discriminator are the same as that of the ratio detector except that the discriminator does not function as a limiter. It is, therefore, usually preceded by two stages of limiting to assure good AM rejection. The audio output signal is taken across the entire output of the detector, points A and B of Fig. 4-15, rather than across half of the output detector as is the case in the ratio detector. When a signal of 10.7 mc is fed

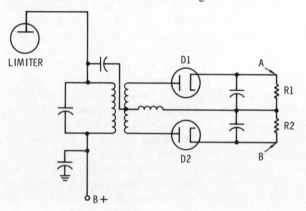

Fig. 4-15. Discriminator FM detector.

into the discriminator of Fig. 4-15, both diodes draw equal currents and create equal voltage drops across R1 and R2. The voltages across R1 and R2, however, oppose each other. Therefore, under these conditions, the voltage measurement from A to B is zero. When the frequency of the incoming signal is above 10.7 mc, D2's conduction is greater than that of D1. Let us suppose that at 10.7 mc the voltage across R1 is +4 volts, and the voltage across R2 is −4 volts. Under these conditions, the voltage across A and B is zero. As we raise the frequency of the incoming carrier above and below 10.7 mc, we find that the voltages across R1 and R2 are no longer equal, and a difference voltage appears across terminals A and B. If we raise the carrier frequency above 10.7 mc, D2 conducts more than D1. Let us suppose that the voltage across R2 decreases to −6 volts. The voltage across R1, since D1 does not conduct as heavily, will decrease. Let us suppose that it decreases to +2 volts. The voltage across the two resistors (terminals A and B) will be the sum of these two voltages which is −4 volts. If the carrier frequency is moved below 10.7 mc by the same amount, then D1 will conduct heavier than D2. The voltage across R1, therefore, will be +6 volts, and that across R2 will be −2 volts. The sum of these two voltages is +4 volts. Thus, as the frequency of the carrier deviates with modulation, the audio signal will appear across terminals A and B. If we place a voltmeter across either R1 or R2 separately, we find that as we increase the strength of the signal into the receiver, the voltage across either R1 or R2 will increase proportionately.

Note. Placing the voltmeter across A and B will not demonstrate this point since the output will be zero regardless of the input.

Automatic Frequency Control

The purpose of the automatic frequency control is to lock the oscillator frequency at 10.7 mc above the incoming carrier so that the center frequency of the if will be exactly at 10.7 mc. Automatic frequency control has two advantages:

1. It makes the receiver easier to tune.
2. It minimizes oscillator drift.

When the oscillator is set at exactly 10.7 mc above the incoming carrier signal, the d-c voltage at the output of the ratio detector or discriminator should be zero volts. If the oscillator frequency is changed slightly, the voltage at the output of the discriminator or ratio detector will swing either positive or negative according to the direction that the oscillator frequency is moved. This change in d-c voltage at the output of the detector may be used as an indication of an oscillator frequency change. The d-c voltage may be used to cause a reactance change in the oscillator tank, bringing it back on frequency.

There are two common methods of changing the reactance across the oscillator to keep it locked to the proper frequency. In one method, a varicap or a silicon junction diode, which is reverse-biased and placed across a portion of the oscillator tank, serves as a variable capacitor. When a junction diode is reverse-biased, it appears as a capacitor.

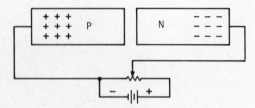

Fig. 4-16. Junction diode with high reverse bias and low capacitance.

If the voltage is changed slightly, the capacitance changes. When a diode is reverse-biased, see Fig. 4-16, the carriers, which are positive in the p-type material and negative in the n-type material, are drawn away from the junction. If the reverse bias is high, the carriers are drawn further away from the junction. The positive and negative carriers act as though they were plates of a capacitor. When they are far apart, the capacitance is low. When they are close, the capacitance is high. As the reverse bias is reduced, the carriers move closer to the junction, increasing the capacitance of the diode. As the bias is increased, the carriers move farther apart, decreasing the capacitance. See Fig. 4-17.

If a fixed d-c bias is applied to such a junction-type diode which reverse-biases it, and the output of the detec-

tor is also connected across the diode as the d-c voltage at the output of the FM detector swings plus and minus due to the oscillator frequency changes, the bias will add to and subtract from the reverse bias already placed on the diode, and therefore, change its capacitance. If the diode is a part of the tuned circuit of the oscillator, the change in voltage across it will cause a capacitance change and shift the oscillator frequency. When the oscillator frequency tries to change, it will produce either a positive or a negative voltage, according to the direction which the oscillator frequency changes. The voltage, in turn, will be coupled back to the diode, and will change the capacitance of the varicap, returning the oscillator to its original frequency.

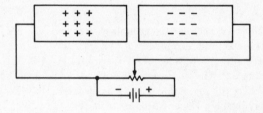

Fig. 4-17. Junction diode with low reverse bias and high capacitance.

2. Servicing the FM Receiver

Test Equipment

Test equipment required to service the FM receiver are
1. AM signal generator.
2. FM signal generator (optional).
3. D-c VTVM.
4. Oscilloscope.

AM Signal Generator

The AM signal generator frequency range should be from 550 to 1600 kc, 88 to 108 mc, and 10.7 mc. The output of the generator should be sufficient to drive a signal from the plate of the limiter to the output of the detector. The attenuator on the AM signal generator, and the spray and leakage from the cabinet should be such that the output signal may be attenuated below the limiter threshold or until noise is heard when the signal is fed into the input terminals of the receiver.

FM Signal Generator

FM signal generators should have a frequency range of 88 to 108 mc, and 10.7 mc. The output requirements are the same as those for the FM generator. The attenuation characteristics as to stray rf from the cabinet is the same as the requirements for the AM signal generator.

D-C VTVM

The d-c VTVM should be a standard one with a high input resistance to prevent loading and a low input capaci-

tance. The range on the meter should be a minimum of 1 volt full scale on the lowest range and 1000 volts on the highest range.

Oscilloscope

The frequency response of the scope should be flat from 30 cps to 200 kc, minimum. The input impedance should be high, and the sensitivity should be high.

General Service Procedure

The general service procedure for isolating the malfunction in an FM receiver to a specific stage is the same as for all electronic equipment. The first step is to isolate the malfunction to a single stage, and then by resistance and voltage measurements to determine the defective component. Figure 4-18 is a simplified block diagram of an FM tuner. We will not include or discuss the multiplex section of the receiver here since it is discussed in detail in Chapter 5. If, when the receiver is turned ON, it does not operate on either AM or FM, then the malfunction is either in the power supply or the limiter stage. A voltage and resistance check in the power supply will determine whether or not it is operating satisfactorily. If the power supply operates satisfactorily, then the malfunction is most likely in the limiter stage. Other common malfunctions in FM receivers which may not necessarily cause them to be inoperative are regeneration, poor AM rejection or noise rejection, and distortion on weak signals.

If the receiver operates on FM, but not on AM, it is

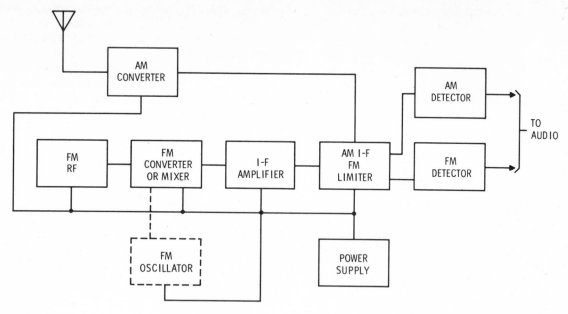

Fig. 4-18. Simplified block diagram of an AM-FM tuner.

an indication that the r-f amplifier, mixer, the first, second, and third if's, the limiter and FM detector are operating satisfactorily, and the malfunction is either in the AM detector, or in the AM converter. Since the FM section of the receiver operates satisfactorily, then the limiter stage is functioning. Therefore, if an AM signal at the i-f frequency is fed into the grid of the limiter and no output is heard at the output of the detector, then the detector is defective. If an output is heard at the detector, then this is an indication that the AM converter is not functioning. This means that either the oscillator is not functioning, or that the stage is not amplifying. If the 455-kc signal is moved to the grid of the AM converter and an output is heard in the detector, but when an r-f signal of 550 to 1600 kc is fed into the converter no output is heard, this is an indication that the oscillator is not functioning. If no output is obtained at 455 kc, then this is an indication that the converter is not functioning as an amplifier.

If the receiver operates on AM, but not on FM, then the malfunctioning stage can either be the FM detector, the limiter, one of the two i-f stages, the mixer, the oscillator, or the r-f amplifier. The first step in this case is to isolate the malfunction to one of the stages. The signal injection method is recommended. There are two types of signals that may be used. One is an FM generator, and the other is an unmodulated r-f carrier signal at either the center of the i-f frequency, or at the r-f frequency. The only difference between the two is the signal indicator used at the output of the detector. If an FM signal generator is used, the output may be heard in the speaker or at the output of the detector. If an unmodulated r-f carrier is used, then no output may be heard, and a d-c vacuum-tube voltmeter connected to either the grid or the limiter or the output of the FM detector must be used as an indicator.

We will describe the procedure for isolating malfunctions to a single stage using an unmodulated r-f carrier.

Checking the FM Detector

To check the FM detector, see Fig. 4-19, the d-c VTVM should first be placed across C1, in position No. 1. An r-f signal generator tuned to 10.7 mc should be coupled to the plate of the limiter. The output of the signal generator should be increased until a d-c voltage reading is obtained on the meter. If a reading is obtained on the meter, it is an indication that the ratio detector primary and secondary are probably functioning normally. For the

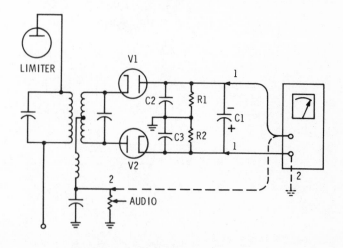

Fig. 4-19. Checking the FM detector.

next step, the leads should be moved to the position No. 2, and the meter should be set to zero at center scale. The frequency of the generator should be rocked above and below 10.7 mc, approximately 75 kc.

If the detector secondary is operating properly, the meter should swing plus and minus as the frequency is varied above and below 10.7 kc. If no d-c voltage is obtained with the leads in position No. 1, or across the filter capacitor of the ratio detector, it could indicate an open winding in the secondary of the ratio detector transformer, T1. Diode rectifiers, V1 or V2, may be open; R1 or R2 may be open; or C1 may be shorted. If, when the meter is in position No. 2 and the frequency of the oscillator is rocked, the meter does not swing positive or negative, or it swings only in one direction, this is an indication that the secondary of the transformer is not tuned to 10.7 mc, that R1 and R2 are not of equal values, that the forward impedances of the diodes are not the same, or that there is leakage in C1 or C3.

If the FM detector is functioning properly, the signal generator should be moved to the grid of the limiter, and the meter should be connected across the output of the ratio detector. The frequency of the generator should be set to 10.7 mc, and the output of the generator increased until a d-c reading is obtained on the meter. If no reading is obtained, this is an indication that there is a malfunction in the limiter stage.

If a discriminator is used in the receiver being tested, the first step in checking the detector should be to place the VTVM as shown in Fig. 4-20 across No. 1. The signal generator is fed into the plate of the limiter stage at 10.7 mc. The output of the generator should be gradually increased until a d-c reading is obtained on the VTVM. If a reading is obtained, this is an indication that the stage is probably functioning. The next step should be to place the VTVM leads as shown in position No. 2. Then the output of the signal generator should be varied approximately 75 kc above and below 10.7 mc. If the discriminator is operating normally, the voltage should swing plus or minus as described above in the service procedure for ratio detectors.

If the limiter is operating satisfactorily, the VTVM should be moved to the grid of the limiter shown in Fig. 4-21. It should be placed on the negative scale, and on approximately the 10-volt range. The signal generator should be placed first on the grid of the second i-f stage. The frequency should be adjusted to 10.7 mc, and the output of the generator should be increased until a negative reading is obtained on the VTVM. If a negative reading is

obtained, this is an indication that the second i-f stage is probably functioning properly. The signal generator should then be moved to the input of the first i-f amplifier. The output of the signal generator should have to be reduced considerably to obtain the same voltage reading as obtained in position No. 1, since the gain of the amplifier should be greater at this point.

If the signal is obtained at position No. 2, then this is

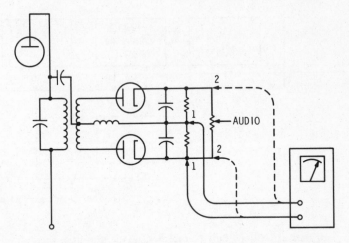

Fig. 4-20. Checking the discriminator.

an indication that the i-f amplifier is functioning properly. The next step should be to change the frequency of the generator to some convenient frequency in the FM band between 88 and 108 mc, and tune the receiver to that frequency. The output of the generator should then be moved to the grid of the mixer tube, point No. 3. If an output is obtained, this is an indication that the oscillator is functioning properly, and that the mixer is functioning properly. If no output is obtained at the r-f frequency, but an output is obtained at 10.7 mc, then this is an indication that the oscillator is not functioning. The signal generator should then be placed on a convenient r-f frequency, and moved to the input of the r-f amplifier. If no signal is obtained, this is an indication that the r-f stage is not functioning.

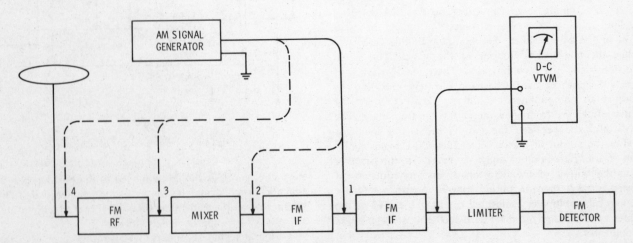

Fig. 4-21. Checking the i-f and r-f sections with an unmodulated carrier.

Regeneration

Regeneration is a rather common malfunction in FM receivers. It is normally caused by the coupling of harmonics of the if from the limiter and ratio detector to the input of the tuner or i-f amplifier stages. Any type of detector or limiter, since it severely distorts the incoming signal, radiates harmonics of the if. Harmonics as high as the 10th to the 15th are common.

In an FM receiver, the frequencies involved are high. The wiring harness of the set, therefore, becomes a very efficient radiator at these frequencies. Lead dress, the dressing of components in the if and detector, and shielding around the detector are very important considerations. The most common symptoms of a set having regeneration is motorboating at certain spots in the band, dead spots in certain parts of the band, or, in less severe cases, it may cause distortion. The distortion may be intermittent, and may be present on some stations but not on others. Distortion due to regeneration will usually be more severe on the weaker stations. Another common symptom of regeneration is an apparent loss of sensitivity.

The first step in servicing a receiver which exhibits any of these symptoms is to check the lead dress around the limiter and second detector to make certain it has not been disturbed. All components in this area should be dressed down as near to the chassis pan as possible, and should have short leads. The B+ leads, the AFC leads, and the filament leads are common to all circuits in the receiver, and are, therefore, good conductors and radiators of i-f harmonics back into the low-level stages. These leads are usually heavily bypassed with small disc-type capacitors.

If one of these capacitors is open it can cause regeneration. A good device for checking for open bypass capacitors is an insulated alignment tool with a small 0.001 disc-type capacitor taped to the end of the tool. This capacitor should be bridged across each of the bypass capacitors from the B+ lead and filament busses and AFC buss. If a capacitor is defective when it is bridged, the regeneration symptoms should disappear. If the capacitor is held in the hand and bridged across the bypass capacitors, a false indication may be obtained because the bypassed r-f energy may be radiated by the hand back into the lower-level stages. If one side of the antenna inadvertently becomes grounded on a receiver designed for balanced antenna input, this can cause severe regeneration.

When the probable source of regeneration has been located and remedied, the receiver should always be checked on the lowest signal available to make certain that the regeneration does not reappear at lower signal levels. A receiver which exhibits regeneration should also be operated for a minimum of one hour before servicing since the probabilities of regeneration are greater after the receiver is hot. Line voltage also has an effect on regeneration. The higher the line voltage, the more likely the receiver is to regenerate. Therefore, when checking a receiver for regeneration, the line voltage should be adjusted at least 10% over the normal rating of the receiver.

Poor AM Rejection or Noisy Reception

The most common cause of poor AM rejection in an FM receiver is low sensitivity, and the most probable cause of low sensitivity, other than defective vacuum tubes, regeneration, or defective components, is alignment. The first step in servicing a receiver where the complaint is poor AM rejection should be a complete alignment of the receiver. If your signal generator has a calibrated output voltage, the sensitivity of the receiver should be checked after alignment is performed. The sensitivity of the average FM receiver will be on the order of 2 to 20 microvolts.

Distortion On Weak Signals

Distortion on weak signals is usually caused by regeneration. On strong signals, the i-f amplifier and the limiter draw heavy grid current. This loads the tuned circuits in the if and reduces the gain, and therefore, reduces the probability of regeneration or feedback. As the signal input to the receiver is reduced and less grid current is drawn, the gain of the if and limiter increases. It is possible, therefore, for a receiver which has a tendency to regenerate to operate normally on strong signals, but to regenerate on weak signals.

Usually the first symptoms of a subtle regeneration of this type is distortion in the output. When an i-f stage is on the verge of oscillation, the bandpass of the system narrows considerably. This clips off the upper and lower sidebands of the FM signal, causing distortion in the output. The service procedure for such a receiver should be the same as that of a receiver exhibiting regeneration, however, the input signal when the checks are made should be at a level low enough to cause the distortion to appear. One symptom of regeneration at a low signal is that the zero set on the FM detector shifts at low signal levels. If regeneration is suspected, connect a signal generator set to 10.7 mc at high output and adjust the FM detector secondary for zero volts. If the zero setting shifts rapidly as the signal is reduced into noise, this indicates regeneration.

Oscillator Drift

Because of the frequency involved, oscillator drift is more common on FM receivers than on AM. In the average receiver, there will be some oscillator drift during the first 30 minutes of operation. The drift sometimes may cause some slight distortion, requiring retuning during the first 30 minutes of operation. Oscillator drift is normally a function of temperature. The first step in checking for excessive oscillator drift should be to turn the receiver ON, and tune it in properly by placing a VTVM across the output of the FM detector and tuning the oscillator until the VTVM reads zero volts. The receiver should then be allowed to operate under these conditions for a minimum of one hour. The direction which the voltage changes in the VTVM should be noted.

The receiver should then be turned OFF for a minimum of two hours. Then, it should be turned back ON without retuning. If each time this procedure is followed the voltage change is in the same direction, this is an indication that the drift is caused by a temperature-sensitive component.

The next step should be to take a soldering iron, and hold it near each of the components in the oscillator, watching for the oscillator drift in the same direction as during the normal warm-up meter indication.

Temperature-compensated capacitors are sometimes used in oscillator circuits to prevent oscillator drift. Of course, this heat test should not be used on temperature-compensated capacitors as they will always cause the oscillator to drift if they are heated. If none of the components cause the drift when heated except the temperature compensating capacitor, then this is an indication that the temperature compensation in the capacitor is probably not correct and should be replaced with an identical capacitor.

If there is no pattern to the drift as indicated in the initial checks using the VTVM as an indicator, this is an indication that there is an intermittent or defective component. Since there are only a few components involved in the oscillator, the capacitors should be substituted one at a time, and the drift check repeated until the results are satisfactory. The oscillator coil can also cause drift; however, this is usually unlikely in FM receivers.

3. Aligning the FM Tuners

There are two general methods for aligning FM tuners. One is the single-frequency method, and the other is the use of an FM sweep generator. We will first outline the method using the single frequency generator since this is the most common method in use. Then we will discuss the various methods of using the FM sweep generator for alignment. The procedures outlined here are general. In all cases, the specific service manual for the receiver being aligned should be consulted for detailed instructions.

Single-Frequency Method

In the single-frequency alignment method, a signal generator with an unmodulated r-f carrier output at the frequencies of the i-f and the r-f should be used. The first step is to align the i-f tuned circuits to 10.7 mc. To accomplish this, the signal generator with an unmodulated carrier is tuned to 10.7 mc. The output of the generator may be coupled to the grid of the mixer through a 0.01 blocking capacitor, or the output may be connected to the antenna input terminals on the receiver.

When the generator is connected to the antenna terminals of the receiver, it will require more signal to produce an output. The first step in the alignment is to align all of the tuned circuits with the exception of the secondary of the FM detector to 10.7 mc. In the ratio detector, the voltage across the filter capacitor at the output of the detector indicates the strength of the carrier. As the carrier voltage increases, the voltage across the capacitor will increase.

As discussed previously in the discriminator, the voltage across one of the resistors in the output, see Fig. 4-22B, indicates the strength of the signal reaching the detector. As an indicator, therefore, the VTVM should be connected as shown in Fig. 4-22A or B, depending on whether or not the receiver has a ratio detector or a discriminator.

The meter should be rotated to the lowest scale, and the output of the signal generator should be increased for suitable deflection on the meter. Throughout the entire alignment procedure, the meter should be kept on as low a range as possible, and the signal generator output should be kept as low as possible. In all cases, there should be considerable noise in the background at the output of the receiver. The tuned circuits in the plates of the limiter

and i-f and mixer tubes should be tuned for a maximum indication on the VTVM, starting with the primary circuit of the discriminator and proceeding to the plate of the tuned circuit in the mixer, in sequence. The procedure should always be repeated for best accuracy.

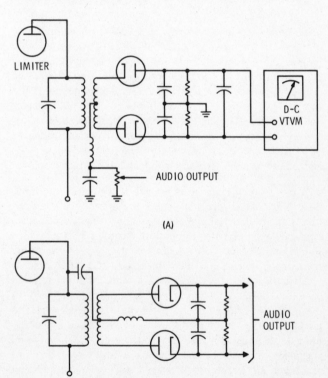

Fig. 4-22. (A) Connections for peaking i-f and r-f amplifiers on receivers having ratio detectors. (B) Connections for peaking r-f and i-f amplifiers on receivers having discriminators.

The next step is to tune the ratio detector secondary to 10.7 mc. This is accomplished by connecting the VTVM as shown in Fig. 4-22. Figure 4-22A shows the connections necessary for the ratio detector, and Fig. 4-22B shows the connections for a discriminator. The output of the signal generator should be increased to maximum. The VTVM should be zeroed at center scale, and placed on a low scale.

As the secondary of the mixer is rotated, the meter will swing positive and negative, and will pass through zero on either side of the positive and negative swings. The secondary should be adjusted until the meter reads exactly zero. This peaks all the tuned circuits in the if, including the secondary of the mixer to 10.7 mc. The next step in alignment is to align the r-f amplifier.

In aligning the r-f amplifier, it is necessary to set the oscillator range so that it tunes throughout the entire FM band, and to track the oscillator to the r-f tuning throughout the entire band. This is accomplished by placing the VTVM, as shown in Fig. 4-22A or B. The next step is to tune the oscillator either against the high-end or low-end stop, and to set the frequency generator to either 88 or 108 mc, according to which end of the dial is used, and adjust the oscillator trimmer with the AFC system disabled for a maximum indication on the meter. Some receivers may have adjustments for both the low end and high end. In these cases, this procedure should be repeated for both low and high end.

The next step is to track the r-f tuned circuits to the oscillator circuits. This is usually done by tuning the receiver to the middle of the FM band, approximately 98 mc, setting the generator to 98 mc, and adjusting the r-f trimmer for a maximum indication on the meter as shown in Fig. 4-22. For all r-f adjustments, it is extremely im-

ment. The generator with a sine wave modulation, however, is much simpler to use. When the sawtooth is used, it is necessary to provide accurate markers at 10.7 mc and at 200 kc above and below 10.7 mc to do a good

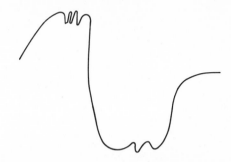

Fig. 4-23. Distortion present when the sweep width is wide and the disc secondary is set properly.

alignment job. With generators having sine wave FM modulation, the output of the detector can be observed on an oscilloscope directly.

The procedure for alignment using a sine wave FM signal generator is to connect an oscilloscope across the output of the detector. Connect the signal generator to the FM antenna input or the i-f input, whichever is more

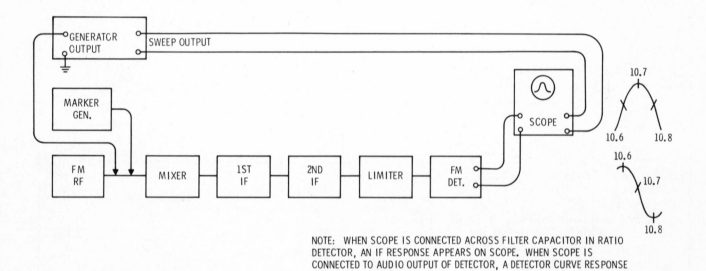

Fig. 4-24. Set-up for FM i-f alignment using sawtooth modulation.

portant that the input signal be kept as low as possible, and the meter be kept on as low a scale as possible.

FM Signal Generator Method

There are two types of FM signal generators normally used for alignment: one has sine wave modulation, and one has sawtooth modulation.

The generator with sawtooth modulations is recommended for use when an oscilloscope is used for align-

convenient. Set the center frequency to 10.7 mc, and increase the modulation on the FM signal generator to a frequency swing of approximately ±75 kc. Reduce the output of the signal generator as low as possible, and increase the sensitivity of the oscilloscope so that the output of the receiver is well into the noise. Peak all of the tuned circuits in the if, starting with the tuned circuit in the plate of the limiter stage, and proceeding back towards the mixer.

The frequency of the generator should then be changed

ALIGNMENT PROCEDURE

AM ALIGNMENT

The function switch should be set to the AM position. AM loop must be connected. Use 1000 cycle modulation. As circuits are peaked, reduce output of signal generator so as not to exceed 1.4V AC (.25 watt) on output meter; this will prevent overloading. Either speakers or an 8 ohm load must be connected to output transformers. (Power-amp chassis must be used.)

STEP	GENERATOR FREQUENCY, CONNECTION AND TUNER SETTING	INDICATOR	ADJUST	ADJUST FOR AND/OR REMARKS
IF ALIGNMENT				
1.	Generator set for 455Kc - connect to AM converter V-5) grid and chassis thru .1mf - gang fully open. Low side of generator to chassis.	Output meter - connect across speaker terminals.	Top and bottom cores of T-7 and T-8.	Adjust for maximum reading. Repeat adjustment at least once.
RF ALIGNMENT				
2.	Radiation loop* generator set for 1620Kc - gang fully open.	"	Oscillator trim of C-53.	Adjust for maximum reading.
3.	Radiation loop* generator set for 532Kc - gang fully closed.	"	Oscillator core L-9.	**Adjust for maximum reading. Repeat Steps 2 and 3 until no further change occurs.**
4.	Radiation loop* generator set for 1400Kc - gang tuned to 1400Kc.	"	Antenna trim C-53.	Adjust for maximum reading.

*Connect generator across 5" diameter, 5-turn loop and couple inductively to receiver AM loop. Keep radiation loop approximately 24" from receiver AM loop.

FM ALIGNMENT

Function switch should be in the FM position. Use an unmodulated CW signal for alignment. As circuits are peaked, reduce output of signal generator so as not to exceed -2 volts DC on VTVM; this prevents overloading. Either speakers or an 8 ohm load must be connected to output transformers. Defeat AFC.

STEP	GENERATOR FREQUENCY, CONNECTION AND TUNER SETTING	INDICATOR	ADJUST	ADJUST FOR AND/OR REMARKS
IF ALIGNMENT				
1.	Generator set for 10.7Mc - connect to grid of 6AU6 - 1st FM IF amplifier - V-2 thru .005. Tuner to high end frequency end mechanical stop.	DC-VTVM - connect to negative end of C-29 and chassis, 1 meg in series with probe.	Bottom core of T-6, top and bottom cores of T-4 & T-5	Adjust for maximum negative voltage reading.
2.	"	VTVM - connect to junction of R-14 - C-33 and chassis. **Negative lead to chassis.**	Top core of T-6	Adjust for zero reading on VTVM. A positive and negative reading will be obtained on either side of correct setting. Re-peak bottom core of T-6.
RF ALIGNMENT				
3.	Generator set for 98Mc - connect to FM antenna terminals through proper equipment terminations - tuner tuned to generator frequency.	VTVM - connect to negative end of C-29 and chassis.	T-2 - 1st IF FM transformer.	Adjust for maximum negative voltage reading.
4.	Generator set for 108.5Mc - tuner to high end mechanical stop.	"	Oscillator trim, C-14	Adjust for maximum negative voltage reading.

Fig. 4-25. Typical alignment procedure for an FM receiver. (Sheet 1 of 4.)

STEP	GENERATOR FREQUENCY, CONNECTION AND TUNER SETTING	INDICATOR	ADJUST	ADJUST FOR AND/OR REMARKS
5.	Generator set for 87.5Mc - tuner to low end mechanical stop.	VTVM - connect to negative end of C-29 and chassis.	T-3	Adjust for maximum negative voltage reading. Repeat Steps 4 and 5 at least once; Step 4 should be last adjustment made.
6.	Generator set for 98Mc - tuner tuned to generator frequency.	"	C4B, L-1, C-4A and T-1.	Adjust for maximum negative voltage reading.

NOTE: Some versions of these tuners may not have some of the adjustments as listed here.

FM MULTIPLEX CIRCUIT ALIGNMENT

Two alignment procedures are presented; one procedure used Motorola Stereo-FM Aligner, Model TU-1681 (Part No. 1P60024A10); the other uses a FM-Stereo station signal. The preferred alignment is that using the Stereo-FM Aligner.

FM MULTIPLEX ALIGNMENT USING MOTOROLA STEREO — FM ALIGNER

Tuner function switch should be in the FM position. Set tuning control to high end mechanical stop; fully clockwise.

STEP	ALIGNER CONNECTION	INDICATOR	ADJUST	ADJUST FOR AND/OR REMARKS
67Kc TRAP ALIGNMENT				
1.	Generator set to SCA (67Kc) - connect to junction of L-4 - L-5 and ground to chassis; generator output to maximum.	VTVM - connect to junction of E-6 & terminal #1 of E-12 thru 100K resistor and chassis.	L-5 (top core)	Adjust for minimum reading on VTVM; use 5 volt range.
2.	Connect generator to junction of L-4 - C-39 and ground to chassis.	"	L-4 (bottom core)	Adjust for minimum reading on VTVM. If VTVM indication is too low to use short L-5 and then make adjustment. Remove short from L-5.
19Kc PILOT AMPLIFIER ALIGNMENT				
3.	Generator set to PILOT (19Kc) - connect to base of V-6 thru 22K and chassis; output about 1/4 turn from full counter-clockwise.	VTVM - connect to base of V-7 and chassis. Use 5 volt range.	L-2	Adjust for maximum reading on VTVM. NOTE: Reduce output of generator so meter reading does not exceed 3 volts.
38Kc DOUBLER ALIGNMENT				
4.	Generator set to PILOT (19Kc) - connect to base of V-6 thru 22K and chassis; output about 1/4 turn from full counter-clockwise.	VTVM - connect to junction of E-6 & terminal #1 of E-12 thru 100K resistor and chassis.	Top and bottom of T-9.	Adjust for maximum reading on VTVM. NOTE: Reduce output of generator so meter reading does not exceed 3 volts.
ADJUSTMENT OF FM-STEREO INDICATOR LAMP				
5.	Generator set to PILOT (19Kc) - connect to base of V-6 thru 22K and chassis; generator output at maximum.	Stereo indicator lamp.	L-7	Adjust L-7 until lamp fires and both lamp electrodes have an even glow. Readjust generator output so that lamp fires with a minimum signal input.

Fig. 4-25. Typical alignment procedure for an FM receiver. (Sheet 2 of 4.)

STEP	ALIGNER CONNECTION	INDICATOR	ADJUST	ADJUST FOR AND/OR REMARKS
SEPARATION ALIGNMENT				
6.	Generator set to COMP (19 and 38Kc) - connect to base of V-6 thru .5mf capacitor and chassis.	VTVM - connect to junction of E-6 & terminal #1 of E-12 thru 100K resistor and chassis.	L-2	Connect a jumper from output of generator to center tap of T-9 secondary. Adjust for maximum reading on VTVM. NOTE: Use 5 volt range on VTVM, adjust generator output to give a meter reading of approximately 3.5 volts.

ALTERNATE METHOD OF FM MULTIPLEX ALIGNMENT USING AN FM – STEREO STATION

NOTE: The 67Kc Storecast traps cannot be aligned using an air signal. An alignment generator must be used for trap alignment.

19Kc Pilot Alignment and 38Kc Doubler Alignment

With radio tuned to a good FM-Stereo broadcast and output connected to stereo amplifier system, proceed as follows:

1. Move positive lead of VTVM to junction of E-6 and terminal #1 of E-12 thru 100K resistor and adjust L-2 and top and bottom core of T-9 for maximum meter reading. Repeat adjustment until no further increase.

FM-STEREO LAMP & SEPARATOR ALIGNMENT

2. With radio tuned to a good FM-Stereo broadcast as above, adjust L-7 until FM Stereo lamp fires with an even glow on both lamp electrodes.

3. With VTVM connected as in Step #1 to monitor the voltage, adjust L-2 for maximum separation in left and right channels. (Use listening test for this purpose.) This point will be near maximum VTVM reading.

NOTE: A good time to perform this adjustment is when an FM-Stereo station is broadcasting on one channel only; adjust L-2 for minimum output from unused channel.

FM GENERATOR TERMINATION DETAIL

ALIGNMENT POINTS LOCATION

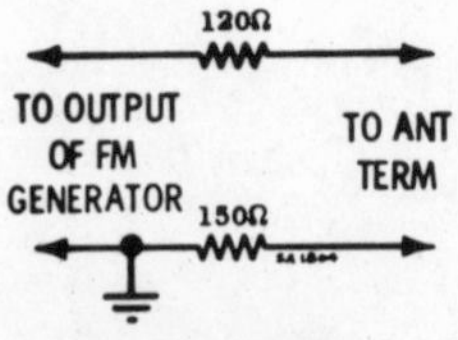

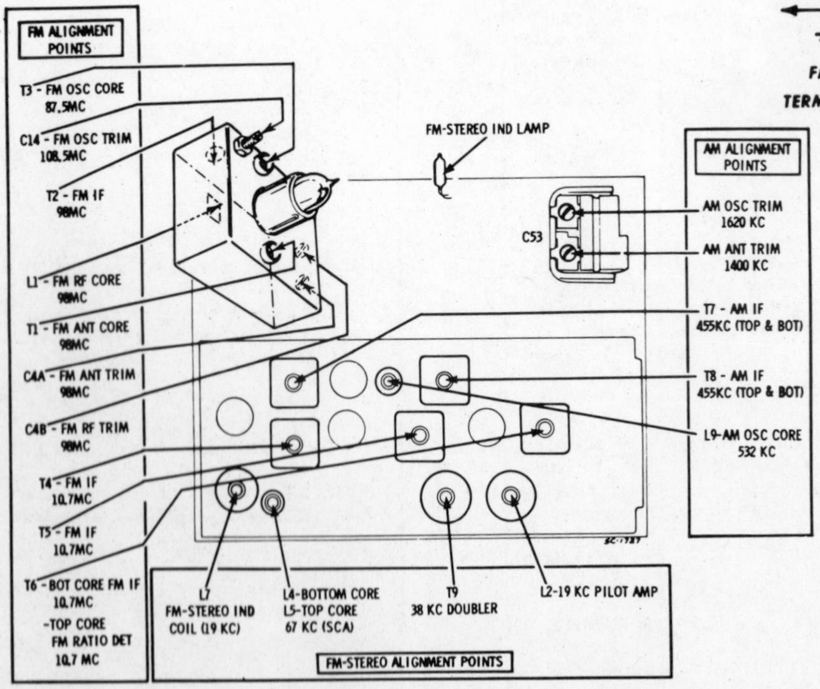

Fig. 4-25. Typical alignment procedure for an FM receiver. (Sheet 3 of 4.)

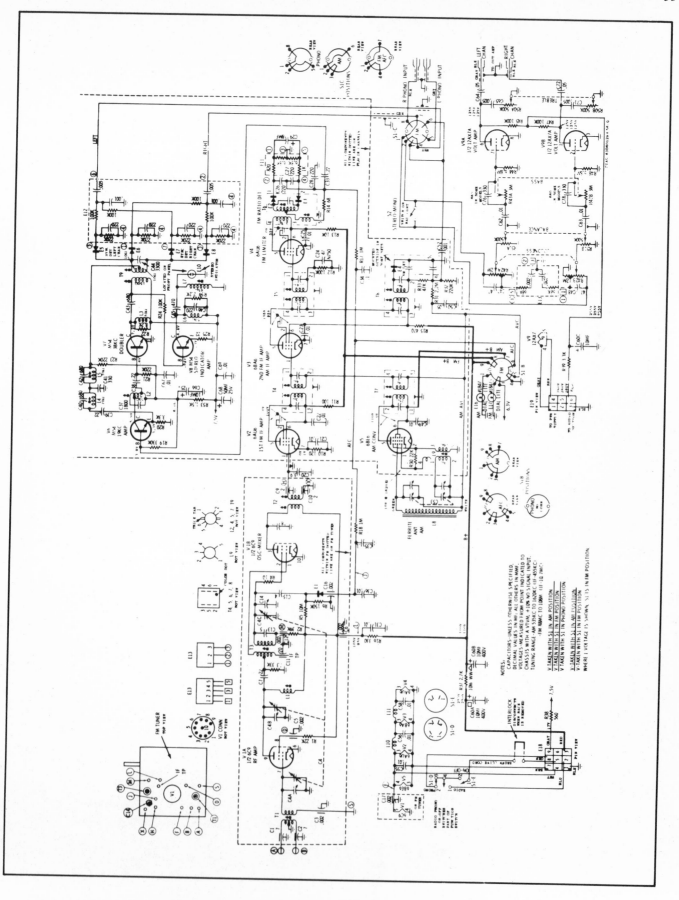

Fig. 4-25. Typical alignment procedure for an FM receiver. (Sheet 4 of 4.)

to either the high or low end of the FM band to set the oscillator range, and the oscillator trimmer peaked for a maximum indication on the meter. Signal generator frequencies should then be changed to the tracking frequency, which is approximately 98 mc, and while still keeping the input signal as low as possible, adjust the r-f trimmer capacitors for maximum output. The output of the signal generator should then be increased until full limiting action, or no noise, is present in the output. The frequency deviation should be increased until distortion starts to appear in the sine wave, see Fig. 4-23.

The VTVM should then be moved as shown in Fig. 4-22, and the secondary of the ratio detector should be adjusted for minimum distortion or for equal distortion on both the positive and negative peaks of the sine wave. This point should occur when the meter reads zero volts on center scale. The zero indication on the meter is usually more accurate than the distortion indication.

Figure 4-24 shows the set-up for using a FM signal generator with a sawtooth modulation. In this set-up, the same sawtooth which causes the FM modulation is fed to the horizontal plates of the oscilloscope. The output of the generator is fed through the receiver under test, and to the vertical input of the oscilloscope.

Figure 4-25 is a typical alignment chart and schematic of an FM receiver, outlining the complete alignment procedure.

5 – The FM Stereo System

1. Introduction

Basically, the FM stereo system consists of the following. Audio information from both the left and right channels is added, and modulates the FM transmitter directly. This signal is called "Left + Right," or L + R. It is, for all practical purposes, a monaural or a monophonic signal. A 38-kc subcarrier is modulated with a left—right (L—R) signal. This voltage is the *difference* between the signal in the left channel, and the signal in the right channel. It modulates a 38-kc balanced modulator, and produces sidebands that extend from 23 kc to 53 kc, depending on the modulating frequency. The carrier is suppressed. These sidebands contain the stereo information. This L—R subcarrier signal also modulates the FM transmitter.

To recover the modulation on the subcarrier in the receiver, it is necessary to reinsert the 38-kc carrier at the stereo receiver in phase and frequency sync with the subcarrier oscillator at the transmitter. It is, therefore, necessary to send along a reference signal. This is accomplished by also modulating the transmitter about 10% with a 19-kc pilot carrier for synchronizing purposes. The input to a FM transmitter transmitting stereo, therefore, consists of a 30-cps to 15-kc left + right signal, a subcarrier consisting of 23-kc to 53-kc sidebands representing the stereo information, and a low-level 19-kc sine wave for synchronizing the 38-kc oscillator used for demodulating the stereo subcarrier at the receiver.

A standard FM receiver receives and reproduces only the left + right, or the monaural, signal. A stereophonic receiver has additional circuits which separate and amplify the 23-kc to 53-kc subcarrier. Sidebands reinsert the synchronized 38-kc carrier, demodulate the subcarrier signal, add the L + R and L — R signals, and produce left and right stereo signals.

2. Modulation Review

Before we examine the exact method of operation of the FM stereo system, let us first review briefly some of the pertinent facts relating to modulation systems. Refer to Fig. 5-1.

Frequency Modulation

Frequency modulation is a system where the carrier amplitude remains constant, but the carrier frequency changes in step with the modulating voltage. See Fig. 5-1A. The FM receiver detector changes these frequency changes to amplitude changes, corresponding to the original modulation voltages.

If an FM transmitter is modulated by a 15-kc signal, the frequency of the transmitter will change about a resting frequency in a manner corresponding to the instantaneous amplitude of the modulating sine wave. When the modulating voltage is at zero volts, the frequency of the transmitter will be unchanged. When the modulating voltage is at its positive peak, the frequency of the transmitter will be at its highest frequency; when the voltage is at its negative peak, the frequency will be at its lowest frequency.

In the FM broadcast band, the maximum change in frequency of the carrier, due to the modulating voltage is ± 75 kc, or a total swing of 150 kc. However, investigation will show that the bandwidth requirement for a receiver or transmitter which transmits a 15-kc signal that causes a frequency swing of ± 75 kc is actually 240 kc. Eight sets of sidebands will appear above and below the carrier frequency due to the modulation. These sidebands are spaced 15 kc apart. They diminish gradually in amplitude as they are removed further above and below the carrier frequency.

In receiving this signal, the receiver must pass all of the significant sidebands if the original modulation voltage is to be recovered without distortion. There are two factors in FM that determine the bandwidth requirement: the amplitude of the modulation, and its frequency. The maximum bandwidth is a condition where a 15-kc modulating signal swings the carrier frequency 75 kc. The theoretical bandwidth requirement for a FM receiver or transmitter, under these conditions, is 2 (because there are two sets of sidebands) × 8 (since there are eight significant sets) × 15 kc (which is the spacing between the sets of sidebands). This equals 240 kc.

If the amplitude of this 15-kc sine wave were reduced by ½, causing a frequency swing of only 37.5 kc, the bandwidth requirement will only be 2 × 4 × 15 kc, or 120 kc. If a lower modulating frequency is used to modulate the carrier 75 kc, then the bandwidth requirement is also reduced, because the separation between the sidebands is reduced.

The amplitude of the modulating voltage determines the frequency swing. The frequency of the modulation determines how rapidly the frequency changes in a given time

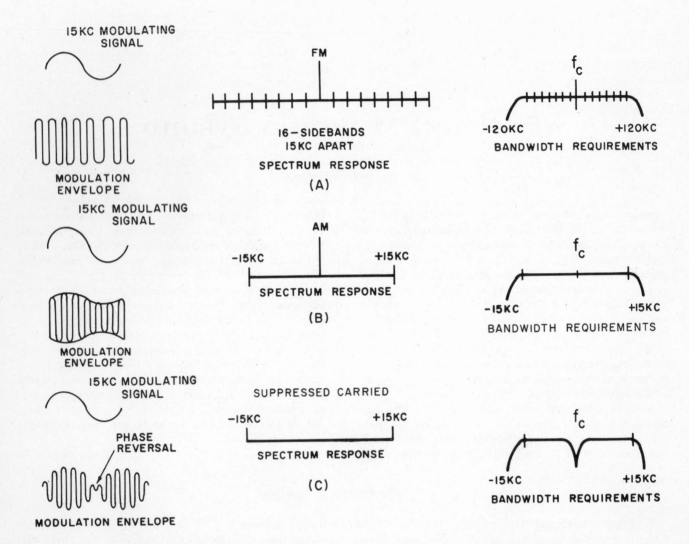

Fig. 5-1. Modulation methods: (A) FM, (B) AM, and (C) suppressed carrier. (Courtesy of Motorola)

period. The theoretical bandwidth requirement for a standard FM station, with a maximum frequency swing of 75 kc and a maximum modulating frequency of 15 kc, is 240 kc. In actual practice, it is 200 kc because 15-kc notes seldom have sufficient power to modulate the transmitter over 50%. It is, therefore, found in practice that a 200-kc bandwidth is sufficient for the transmission of 30 to 15-kc information in the FM broadcast band.

Amplitude Modulation

Amplitude modulation is a system of modulating a carrier in which the frequency of the carrier remains constant, but the amplitude is varied in step with the modulating voltage. See Fig. 5-1B. The AM receiver detector rectifies the carrier voltage, and produces a low-frequency voltage which corresponds to the amplitude changes in the carrier caused by the original modulating signal. If an AM carrier is modulated with a 15-kc sine wave, the amplitude of the carrier at the output of the transmitter will vary in proportion to the instantaneous amplitude of the modulating voltage. When the sine wave is at zero, the amplitude of

the carrier is at its average value. When the modulating voltage is at its positive peak, the amplitude of the carrier is at its highest value. When the modulating wave is at its negative peak, the carrier amplitude is at its minimum value.

In AM modulation, unlike FM, a single 15-kc modulating signal causes only one set of sidebands to appear: one is 15-kc above the carrier, and one is 15 kc below the carrier.

All of these sidebands must be passed on by the AM receiver to faithfully reproduce the original modulating voltage at the detector. The bandwidth requirement for an AM receiver broadcasting a 15-kc signal, therefore, is 2×15, or 30 kc. If the amplitude of the modulating voltage is reduced 50%, then the bandwidth requirement does not change as it does in FM, but still remains at 2×15, or 30 kc. If the frequency of the modulating signal is reduced, to say 1000 cycles, then the bandwidth requirement is decreased. This 1-kc modulating voltage would produce a set of sidebands—one which is 1 kc above, and one, which is 1 kc below the carrier frequency, or a total bandwidth of 2 kc.

For a system which is designed to pass a maximum frequency of 15 kc, therefore, the bandwidth requirement is 2 × 15 kc, or 30 kc. The amplitude of the modulating voltage determines the degree of amplitude change the carrier undergoes. The frequency of the modulating voltage determines how rapidly the amplitude changes. It should be noted that the carrier only serves as a reference; it does not carry any intelligence. All of the intelligence, or the modulating voltage information, is contained in the sidebands.

Suppressed Carrier Modulation

Since all of the intelligence, or the information pertaining to the modulating voltage on an AM signal is contained in the sidebands, it is possible to remove the carrier in the transmission, and transmit only the sideband signals. See Fig. 5-1C. This affords several advantages:

1. The carrier requires considerable power. In fact, the power in the carrier is the greatest percentage of the total

The control grids are fed with a 38-kc oscillator which is the carrier. Since the secondary of T2 is centertapped, the signals fed to the grids of V1 and V2 are 180° out of phase. Thus, when the grid of V1 is swinging positive, trying to increase the 38-kc current through R1, the grid of V2 is swinging negative by the same amount, decreasing the current through R1 by an equal amount. There is, therefore, no change across R1 due to the 38-kc carrier signal, and this signal (38 kc) does not appear in the output.

When an audio signal is applied to the screen grids of V1 and V2, 180° out of phase, however, an output appears across R1. Investigation shows that this output is 38 kc sidebands, which represent the modulating signal. To see how this occurs, let us take an instance when the audio signal is swinging positive on the screen grid of V1. As the audio signal swings positive, it amplitude modulates the carrier on the control grid. A modulation envelope appears in the plate of V1, containing the 38-kc carrier and sideband frequencies, as is the case for all amplitude modula-

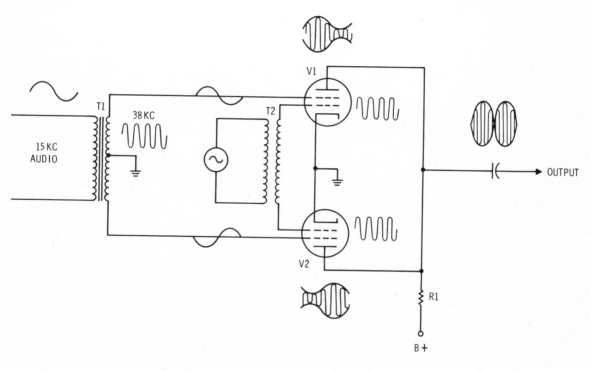

Fig. 5-2. Balanced modulator circuit. (Courtesy of Motorola)

power being transmitted, and its only useful purpose is as a reference.

2. When two carriers are mixed in a common amplifying system, they sometimes produce heterodynes. If one carrier is removed, the effect is virtually eliminated.

3. Since only 50% of the power is contained in the sidebands, and this is all intelligence, it is possible to transmit, with a given transmitter, twice as much signal voltage than is possible when the carrier is included.

To generate sidebands and remove the carrier, a circuit called a balanced modulator is generally used, see Fig. 5-2. In this balanced modulator, the plates of two tetrode tubes are tied together, and fed to a common load resistor, R1.

tion systems. At the same time, the screen grid of V2 is going negative, modulating the carrier on the control grid. This produces the amplitude modulated envelope at the plate of V2 which is 180° out of phase with the envelope at the plate of V1. Note that even the carriers are 180° out of phase, and the sidebands in V1 and V2 plates are in phase. Thus, the sideband voltages add and appear across the plate load resistor, R1; the carrier is suppressed or cancelled.

The characteristics of this type of modulation, so far as bandwidth requirements, is exactly the same as the conventional amplitude-modulated signal. The only difference is that the carrier is not present; in order to recover the

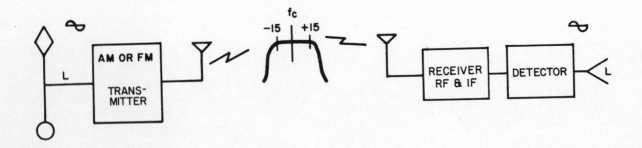

15 KC MIKE
INPUTS

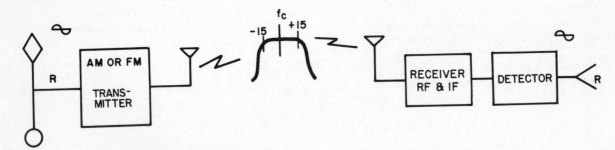

Fig. 5-3. A method of transmitting and receiving stereo using two transmitters and two receivers. (Courtesy of Motorola)

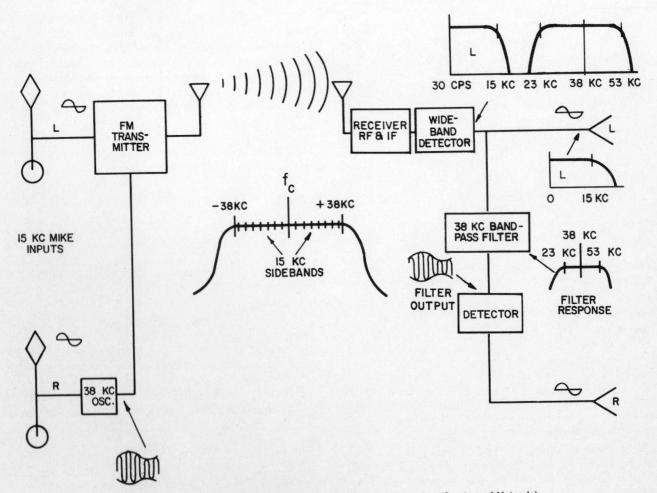

15 KC MIKE
INPUTS

Fig. 5-4. A method of transmitting and receiving stereo using multiplex. (Courtesy of Motorola)

original modulating voltage at the receiver, it is necessary to reinsert a 38-kc carrier in the exact phase as the 38-kc signal, which was used to drive the balanced modulator at the transmitter. This reestablishes a reference, making it possible to change the sidebands to a conventional amplitude modulated envelope. If this envelope is rectified by a conventional AM detector, the original audio signal can be recovered.

3. The System

Broadcasting FM Stereo

Let's investigate some of the possible methods of broadcasting a stereo signal, and their relative advantages and disadvantages.

Two Channels. Perhaps the simplest system is one which uses two transmitters and two receivers that operate on a different frequency, and have equal frequency response, or bandwidth. These transmitters could be both AM, both FM, or both suppressed carrier, or any combination of the three types. See Fig. 5-3.

The left-channel signal modulates one transmitter, and the right-channel signal modulates the other. One receiver is tuned to one of the transmitters, and the other receiver to the other transmitter. This system will produce excellent stereo, but it has some disadvantages. It is not compatible, i.e., if the listener has only one standard receiver, he receives only one-half of the program information—either the right channel or the left channel, depending on which transmitter signal is received. To receive the entire program he must have two complete receivers—one tuned to each of the broadcast stations. This system also requires the use of two broadcast channels. This reduces the number of stations that could operate in a single band by 50%. Also, two complete sets of broadcast equipment and receivers are necessary, making the system rather expensive.

One-Channel Multiplex, Noncompatible. We could eliminate the need for two complete broadcast channels, two transmitters and two receivers if the left- and right-channel signals could be impressed on the same carrier frequency without interfering with each other. Figure 5-4 is a block diagram of such a system.

The left-channel information modulates the transmitter directly; the right-channel information first amplitude modulates a supersonic tone, and this tone, in turn, modulates the FM transmitter. The right-channel tone generator could just as well be frequency modulated or amplitude modulated with suppressed carrier. For purposes of explanation, we will assume that it is a conventional amplitude-modulated oscillator with a frequency of 38 kc.

Let us assume that both channels are receiving the same signal, and that the signal is a 15-kc sine wave. The output of the transmitter would consist of sets of sidebands on either side of the carrier, spaced 15 kc apart, representing the left-channel information. The right-channel information would appear as sets of sidebands on either side of the carrier, spaced 38 kc apart. At the output of the FM detector in a receiver, the transmitter signal would be converted to the original voltages which were used to modulate the transmitter. We would recover, directly, the 15-kc sine wave representing the left-channel input voltage, and, in addition, a 38-kc carrier and a set of sidebands 15 kc

above, or 53 kc, and 15 kc below, or 23 kc. The carrier and sidebands would not be heard in the left-channel speaker because they are out of audible range.

To recover the right-channel information from the 38-kc tone, we sample the output of the wideband FM detector, and pass it through a bandpass filter, which passes only frequencies from 23 to 53 kc, and rejects the low-frequency left-channel signal. We then detect the signal with a conventional AM detector, and recover the original right-channel voltage at the output. This is passed to a separate right-channel speaker.

This system will also produce excellent stereo and, because of the use of the 38-kc signal "multiplexed" on the main carrier to transmit the right channel information, it requires only one transmitter and one receiver. However, this system is still not compatible. If the listener has only a standard monophonic receiver, he will receive only the left-channel signal. If all FM stations converted to stereo broadcasting using this method, then all of the standard FM receivers would be obsolete unless an adapter was attached.

Neither of the two systems described would be desirable for transmitting stereo. In the first system, two transmitters and two receivers were required to broadcast stereo, and the system was not compatible. In the second system, one transmitter and one receiver was eliminated by using multiplex transmission, but the system still was not compatible.

One-Channel Multiplex, Compatible. The ideal system is one which uses one transmitter and one receiver. The listener who has a conventional receiver receives the broadcast in monaural, and the listener who has a stereo receiver receives the same program in stereo. Let's first consider what is necessary to transmit stereo programs so that the listener who has a monophonic receiver receives both the left and right channel, or a monaural signal. See Fig. 5-5.

If we combine the output voltage from the left and right channels in an adder, and modulate an FM transmitter with this signal, the person receiving the program on a monaural receiver receives the sum of the left and right channels which represents all of the program information.

To provide the stereo listener with the proper information to receive the broadcast in stereo, it would be necessary to transmit the stereo information separately on a multiplex subcarrier as in Fig. 5-4, and to recover the two signals separately in a receiver and recombine them with the monaural signal to produce separate left- and right-channel signals.

In any stereo system, when a sound originates directly in front of and midway between two microphones, the voltages at the output of these microphones will be equal in amplitude. Under this condition, there is no stereo information present in the system. We find that if under

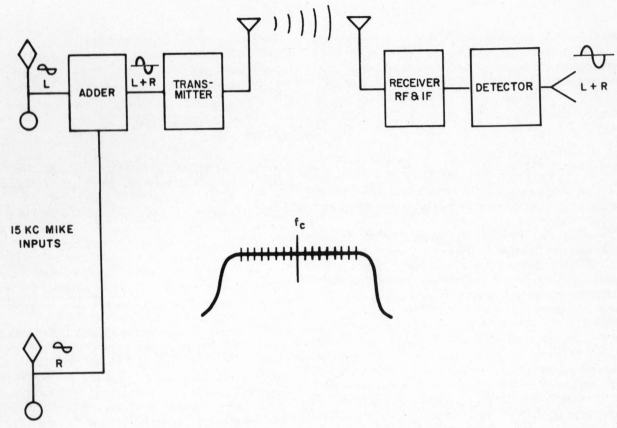

Fig. 5-5. Transmission and reception of a monaural signal. (Courtesy of Motorola)

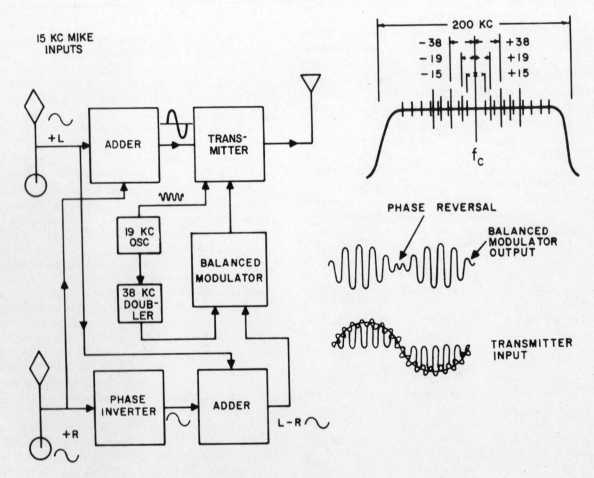

Fig. 5-6. A method of transmitting stereo using one transmitter. (Courtesy of Motorola)

these conditions we subtract the voltage in the left channel from the voltage in the right channel, the difference is zero, indicating that there is no stereo information present. We also find that if we subtract the left-channel voltage from the right-channel voltage when only the left channel is receiving a signal that the difference is a voltage equal to the left signal, and of the same phase. When the right channel only is receiving a signal, the difference between the two signals is a signal equal to the right-channel signal, but 180° out of phase with the voltages obtained when a left-channel signal only was being received. In other words, when there is no stereo present, such as when the signal voltages in both the left and the right channels are equal, L−R equals 0. When a voltage is present only in the left channel, then L−R equals 1 unit in the same phase as L. When there is an output voltage in the right channel only, L−R equals 1 unit 180° out of phase with L.

We can conclude from this that if we subtract the left-channel signal from the right-channel signal, the difference voltage tells us which microphone or channel is receiving the most input voltage (by its phase), and how much more voltage it is receiving than the other (by the amplitude). Therefore, if we continuously combine L and −R, and use the difference voltage to modulate a multiplex subcarrier, we can transmit stereo information to any listener who has a receiver capable of demodulating the L−R subcarrier channel, and recombining it with the L + R signal. Such a transmission system is shown in Fig. 5-6.

First note that to obtain the L + R signal, or the monophonic signal, we apply the outputs of the left and right channels to an adder. The output of this adder is used to modulate the FM transmitter directly. To obtain the stereo information (L−R modulating voltage), we feed the output of the left microphone to the input of the L−R adder, and invert the right channel signal 180° and feed this to the L−R adder. The output of this adder is a voltage which is the difference between the left and the right channels.

The L−R voltage is fed to the control grids of a balanced modulator. The suppressor grids of the balanced modulator is fed with a 38-kc oscillator voltage. The output of the balanced modulator is a set of double sidebands, generated from the 38-kc carrier. The carrier is suppressed or removed. The modulating voltages fed to the L−R channel is 30 cycles to 15 kc as it is in the L + R channel. When the L−R channel is modulated with a 15-kc note, two sidebands appear at the output of the balanced modulator: one is 15 kc above 38, or 53 kc, and one is 15 kc below 38, or 23 kc. This, therefore, is the maximum bandwidth requirement in the L−R channel.

Since this is a suppressed carrier signal, it is necessary to insert a 38-kc carrier at the receiver detector of the same frequency and phase as the 38-kc signal used in the balanced modulator at the transmitter to recover the L−R signal. To accomplish this, the 38-kc oscillator signal at the transmitter is derived from the second harmonic of a 19-kc oscillator. A sample of the 19-kc oscillator also modulates the FM transmitter at a very low level. This 19-kc signal serves as a frequency and phase reference to lock the 38-kc oscillator in the receiver for demodulating the L−R signal. Therefore, the FM transmitter transmitting stereo FM is modulated by three signals:

1. The L+R signal modulates the transmitter directly with frequencies of 30 to 15 kc.

2. The L−R signal, containing frequencies from 30 to 15 kc, modulates a 38-kc balanced modulator. The output of this modulator is sideband information from 23 to 53 kc, representing the L−R voltage.

3. A 19-kc oscillator signal, called the "Pilot Carrier," also modulates the transmitter at a very low level.

The output of the transmitter consists of a conventional frequency-modulated signal with sets of sidebands corresponding to the L+R signal, spaced the modulating frequency apart, and sets of sidebands representing the pilot carrier 19 kc apart, and sets of sidebands spaced 38 kc apart, representing the L−R stereo information. All of this information can be transmitted in a standard 200-kc FM channel without interference or crosstalk between the three sets of information.

When this signal is fed to a wideband FM detector, we recover separately all of the original signals used to modulate the transmitter at the output of the detector. See Fig. 5-7.

The 30 to 15-kc L+R signal, the 19-kc pilot carrier, and the 23- to 53-kc sidebands, representing the L−R signal will be demodulated. If the receiver receiving this signal is a standard receiver, then it will only pass L−R or monaural signal.

Figure 5-8 shows a block diagram of a receiver which will receive this signal in stereo. The output of the detector of this receiver is the same as in Fig. 5-7. To recover the L+R modulating voltage, we pass it through a lowpass filter. This filter passes only the L+R signal of 30 to 15 kc. Next, we use a very sharply tuned high-Q circuit, tuned to 19 kc, and take off the pilot carrier, amplify and feed it directly to a 19-kc amplifier. We then double this frequency in a frequency doubler to 38 kc for a reference carrier, and feed this to a balanced demodulator. We also pass the output of the detector through a bandpass filter which passes frequencies from 23 to 53 kc. These 23- to 53-kc sidebands are fed to the balanced demodulator where they are combined with the 38-kc reference carrier.

The original 30 to 15-kc signal voltages that were fed to the L-R balanced demodulator at the transmitter are recovered at the output of the balanced demodulator. We recover two phases of this signal—one which is the original signal and called +(L−R), and one which is 180° out of phase and called −(L−R).

The +(L−R) signal is fed to the left-channel adder, and is combined in the adder with L+R. When these two voltages are added, right-channel signals always cancel since they are 180° out of phase, leaving left-signal voltages at the output. The −(L−R) signal is fed to the right-channel adder. When this voltage is combined with L+R in the adder, the left-signal voltage always cancels, leaving right-signal voltages only. Thus, the right speaker responds to signals from the right-channel input at the transmitter only.

To better understand how this system operates, let us trace the waveforms at various points in the transmitter and the receiver for first, the condition where the signal is monophonic or the voltage in the right and left channel are equal. Then, when only the left channel is receiving a

DETECTOR BANDPASS

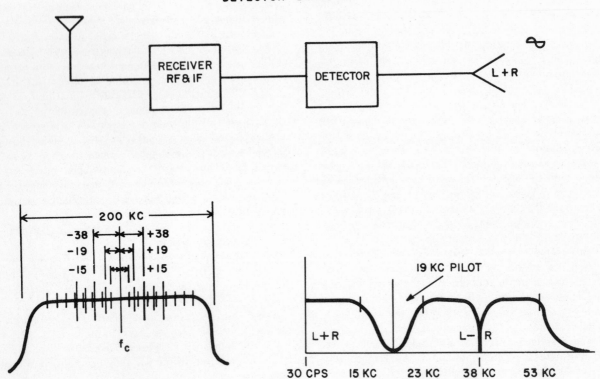

Fig. 5-7. Reception of the stereo signal with one receiver. (Courtesy of Motorola)

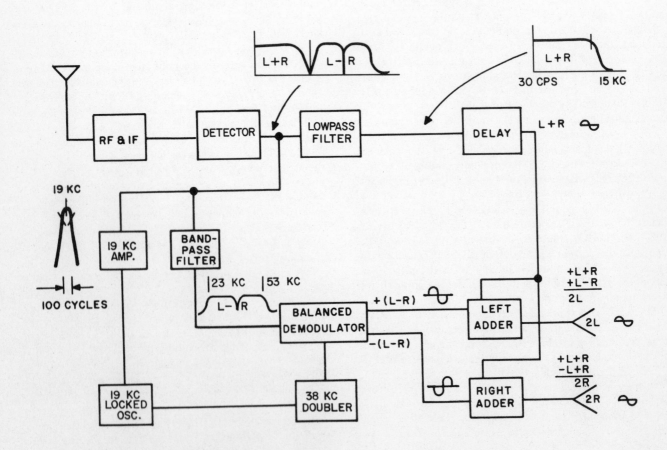

Fig. 5-8. Block diagram of a stereo multiplex receiver. (Courtesy of Motorola)

signal and, finally when only the right channel is receiving a signal. Figure 5-9 is a diagram of a stereo multiplex transmitter.

When no stereo information is present, or when both the left and right channels are receiving equal input, the L+R voltages are fed to the input of the L+R adder; the output of this adder then is one unit left plus one unit right, or a L+R signal, which is two units in amplitude. This voltage modulates the FM transmitter directly. The 19-kc pilot carrier is also fed to the transmitter input, and modulates the transmitter directly.

To obtain the stereo information, or the difference signal, L−R, the output of the left microphone (one unit L) is fed to the L−R adder, and the output from the right chan-

A diagram of the stereo receiver, showing the various waveforms as they appear under these conditions is shown in Fig. 5-10.

The output of the transmitter in the L+R channel consists of one unit L and one unit R, or two units L+R; the output of the L−R channel is zero. The signal at the output of the detector consists of the L+R signal, and the 19-kc subcarrier signal superimposed on its axis. The waveform is the same as that at the input to the transmitter.

To recover the L+R signal, the signal is fed through a lowpass filter. The response of the filter is 30 to 15 kc. The filter removes the 19-kc pilot carrier, and leaves only the low-frequency sine wave which is identical to the original voltage at the output of the L+R adder at the transmitter.

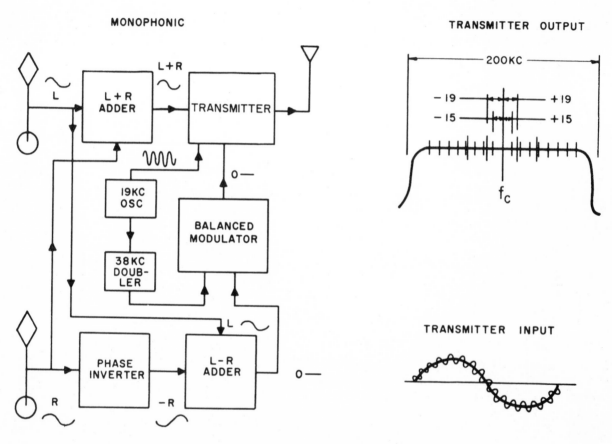

Fig. 5-9. Block diagram of a stereo multiplex transmitter transmitting a monaural signal.
(Courtesy of Motorola)

nel (one unit R) is inverted to obtain one unit −R and fed to the L−R adder. The input to the adder then is one unit +L and one unit −R. Since the voltages are 180° out of phase, and equal in amplitude, they cancel. Therefore, the L−R voltage fed to the balanced demodulator (in the case where the inputs to both channels are equal) is zero. Consequently, the output of the balanced demodulator is zero since the carrier is suppressed. The transmitter under this condition is, therefore, modulated with the L+R signal of 30 to 15 kc, and the low-amplitude 19-kc pilot carrier signal. There is no L−R signal.

When these two signals are added, they appear as a low-frequency sine wave with a 19-kc sine wave superimposed on its axis.

The L+R signal is fed equally to both the left and the right adder. The 19-kc subcarrier is passed through the narrowband 19-kc tuned circuit, is amplified, and is used to lock a 19-kc oscillator to the same frequency and phase as the 19-kc oscillator in the transmitter. The output of this oscillator is then doubled to 38 kc, and this signal is fed to the balanced demodulator. The input of the balanced demodulator from the L−R channel is zero. Therefore, the output of the bandpass filter is zero, and the +(L−R), and the −(L−R) signals at the output of the balanced demodulator are also zero. The input to the left adder is L+R and 0 + (L−R), or L+R. The input to the right adder is 0 − (L−R) + (L+R) or L+R, or the same output obtained from the left channel.

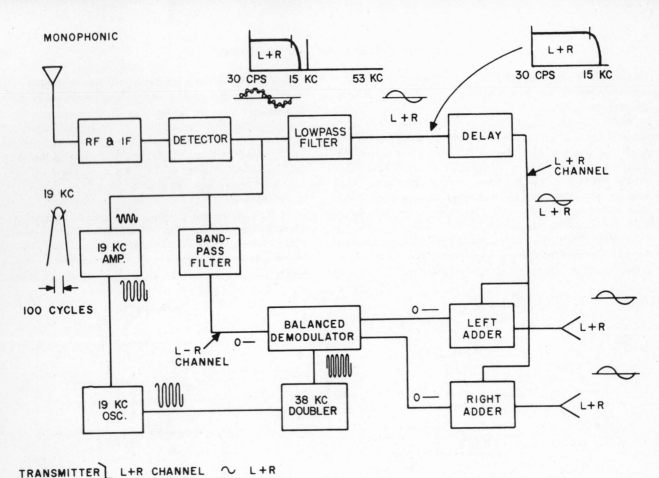

MONOPHONIC

Fig. 5-10. Block diagram of a stereo multiplex receiver receiving a monaural signal. (Courtesy of Motorola)

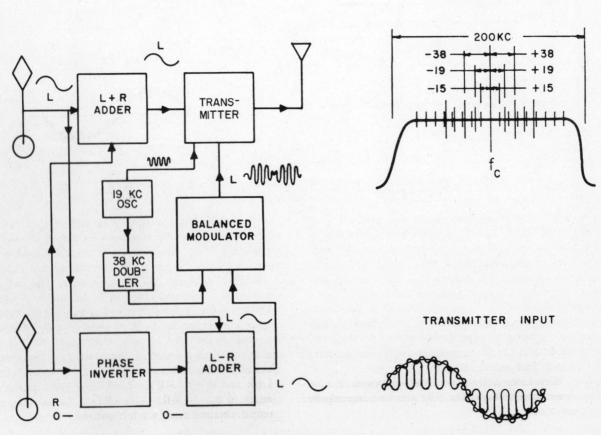

LEFT CHANNEL ONLY

TRANSMITTER OUTPUT

TRANSMITTER INPUT

Fig. 5-11. Block diagram of a stereo multiplex transmitter when the input to the right channel is zero. (Courtesy of Motorola)

Figure 5-11 is a block diagram of a transmitter, indicating the waveforms present when the output from the left channel is one unit L, and there is no input to the right channel.

Under these conditions, the input to the L+R adder consists of one unit L + zero R, or 1L. The output of the L+R adder, therefore, is one unit L or a L + R signal of one unit in amplitude. This voltage modulates the FM transmitter directly. The 19-kc pilot carrier is also fed to the transmitter input, and modulates the transmitter directly. The input to the L−R adder consists of one unit L − zero R. The output to the adder then consists of one unit L. The input to the balanced modulator is then one unit L.

side of the carrier (spaced 19 kc apart and caused by the pilot carrier), and sets of sidebands 23 to 53 kc apart (caused by the L−R signal).

A block diagram of a stereo receiver, showing the various waveforms under the condition when only the left-channel signal is being transmitted is shown in Fig. 5-12. The output of the transmitter consists of a L+R signal, consisting of one unit L, the 19-kc subcarrier, and the 23- to 53-kc sidebands representing the L−R signal or one unit L. The waveform at the output of the detector is the same as that of the waveform at the transmitter input, consisting of a low-frequency sine wave with a 19-kc tone, and the 23- to 53-kc sidebands superimposed on the axis of the sine wave. To recover the L+R signal, the wave-

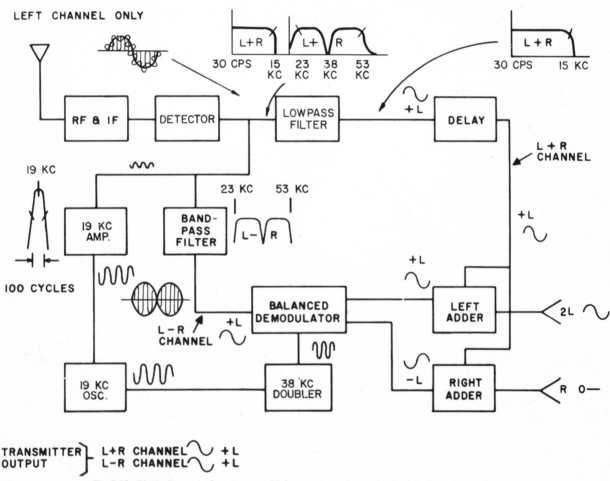

Fig. 5-12. Block diagram of a stereo multiplex receiver when only the left-channel signal is being transmitted. (Courtesy of Motorola)

A set of sidebands, representing this voltage, appears at the output of the balanced demodulator, and also modulates the FM transmitter. The input voltage to the transmitter then consists of a one unit sine wave from the L+R channel representing one unit L. Superimposed on the axis of this sine wave is the 19-kc pilot carrier, and a set of 23- to 53-kc sidebands, representing the L−R signal, or one unit L. This composite signal frequency modulates the transmitter, producing sets of sidebands on either side of the carrier (produced by the L+R signal and separated by the modulating frequency), sets of sidebands on either

form is fed through the lowpass filter, whose response is 30 to 15 kc. This removes the 19-kc pilot carrier, and the 23- to 53-kc sideband information representing the L−R, and leaves only the L+R signal. This signal is fed to both the left and right adders.

The 19-kc subcarrier is passed through the narrowband 19-kc tuned circuit, amplified, and used to lock a 19-kc oscillator. The output of the detector is also fed to a bandpass filter whose response is 23 to 53 kc. This filter rejects the low-frequency L+R signal and the 19-kc subcarrier, and passes only the L−R sidebands. The L−R sidebands are fed to the balanced demodulator input where they are combined with the 38-kc reference carrier.

The output of the demodulator consists of two phases of the L−R signal, which in this case, is one unit L. The output, therefore, is one unit +L and one unit −L.

The +L signal is fed to the left adder and combined with the +L signal from the L+R channel. The output from the left adder is, therefore, one unit L plus one unit L, or 2L. The output at the left speaker is, therefore, 2L. The input to the right channel adder is one unit −L plus one unit +L, from the L+R channel. These two voltages, being 180° out of phase, cancel. Therefore, the output from the right channel is zero.

Note that these sidebands are inverted 180° from those produced by the L channel transmission only. The input signal to the transmitter consists of one unit R from the L−R channel, a 19-kc pilot carrier, and a set of sidebands 23 to 53 kc, representing the L−R information superimposed on the axis of the L−R signal.

These signals, when combined, produce a composite modulating voltage which appears almost identical to the signal when transmitting the left channel only. This voltage at the input to the transmitter produces sets of sidebands above and below the carrier representing the L+R channel, the 19-kc pilot carrier, and the 23- to 53-kc L−R channel.

A diagram of the stereo receiver, showing the wave-

RIGHT CHANNEL ONLY

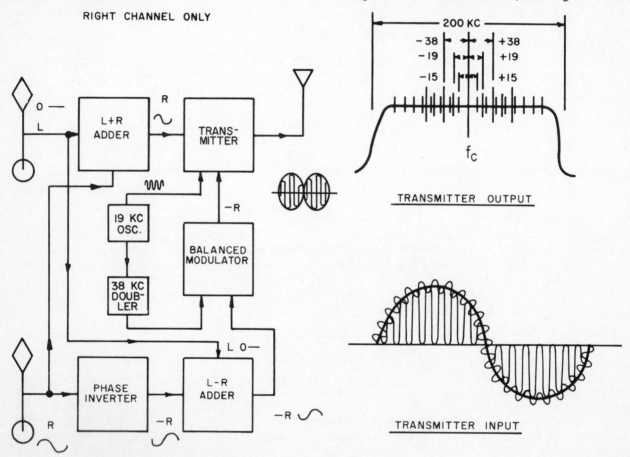

Fig. 5-13. Block diagram of a stereo multiplex transmitter when the input to the left channel is zero. (Courtesy of Motorola)

Figure 5-13 shows the waveform of a stereo multiplex transmitter when the input to the right channel is 1R and the input to the left channel is zero. These two signals are fed to the L+R adder. The signal to the L+R adder is zero L + 1R, or one unit R. This L + R signal modulates the FM transmitter directly. The 19-kc pilot carrier is also fed to the transmitter input and modulates the FM transmitter directly.

The input to the L−R adder is zero L plus one unit −R. The L−R signal at the output of the adder is, therefore, one unit −R. This signal is applied to the 38-kc balanced modulator. The output of the balanced modulator is a set of sidebands 23 to 53 kc, which represent the L−R signal.

forms present under this condition is shown in Fig. 5-14.

The transmitter output consists of one unit L+R, or +R, and one unit L−R, or −R. The output of the detector consists of the ·L+R signal, the 19-kc subcarrier, and the 23- to 53-kc sidebands representing the L−R signal. The waveform is the same as that of the transmitter input. To recover the L+R signal, the signal is fed to a lowpass filter with the response of 30 to 15 kc. This removes the 19-kc pilot carrier, and the 23- to 53-kc sidebands, representing L−R, and leaves only the L+R signal which is fed to the left and the right adder inputs.

The 19-kc subcarrier signal is passed through the narrowband 19-kc filter, amplified, and used to lock in the

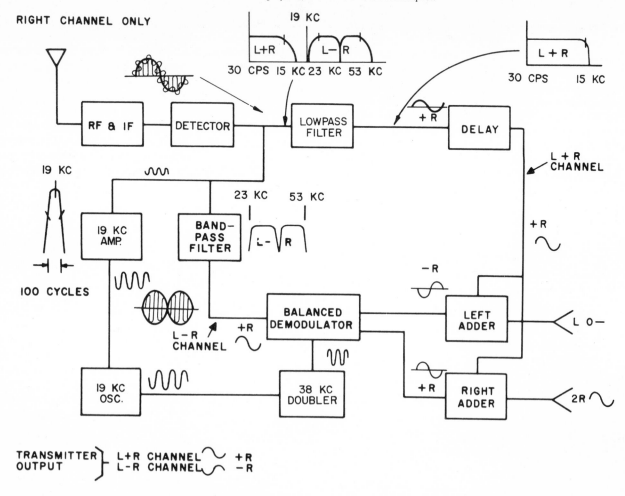

Fig. 5-14. Block diagram of a stereo multiplex receiver when only the right-hand channel signal is being transmitted. (Courtesy of Motorola)

19-kc oscillator. The oscillator is then doubled, and the output of the doubler is fed to the balanced demodulator. The detector output signal is also applied to the input of the bandpass filter whose response is 23 to 53 kc, which rejects the low-frequency L+R signal and the 19-kc subcarrier, and passes the sidebands representing the L−R signal. These sidebands are fed to the balanced demodulator input. Since L−R is one unit −R, the output of the balanced demodulator is one unit −R in the +(L−R) output, one unit −(L−R), or +R, in the −(L−R) channel.

The input to the left adder consists of one unit −R from the +(L−R) output, and one unit +R from the L+R channel. Since these voltages are equal in amplitude and 180° out of phase, they cancel. The output of the left speaker, therefore, is zero. The input to the right adder consists of one unit +R from the −(L+R) channel, and one unit +R from the L+R channel. The output of the right adder and speaker, therefore, is two units R.

This type of receiver will produce good stereo if designed and adjusted properly; however, it has some disadvantages. One disadvantage is that the time it takes the signal to travel from the detector to the speaker in the L+R channel and the L−R channel must be the same to get the proper addition and subtraction at the right and left adders.

Therefore, it is necessary to install a delay in the L+R channel. It is necessary that the filter produce a straight line delay characteristic for all frequencies involved. On investigation, we find that it is possible to take the entire output of the detector directly, take out the 19-kc pilot carrier (see Fig. 5-15), and feed the L+R signal, the L−R signal, and the 38-kc subcarrier signal, and a 38-kc oscillator reference carrier to a pair of diodes, and obtain, at the output, left and right signals directly.

Since the signal paths of L+R and L−R are identical, no delay networks are necessary. Also, since the diodes serve not only as demodulators for L+R and L−R, but adders as well, no adder circuitry is necessary.

The voltages and waveforms in Fig. 5-15 show the waveforms present when the input to the left and right channels at the transmitter are equal. Under these condiions, the L+R signal consists of one unit L, one unit R, and the L−R signal is zero. The output of the FM detector consists of the L+R signal, the 30 to 15-kc, and the 19-kc subcarrier.

We first remove the 19-kc pilot carrier through a narrowband circuit, amplify it, and feed it to the 19-kc amplifier. The output of the oscillator feeds a doubler. The output of the doubler is fed to the plates and cathodes of a pair of diodes. L−R equals 0; therefore, there is no 23- to 53-

kc subcarrier information present. Since the 19-kc pilot carrier has been removed, the input from the detector to the diodes is two units L+R.

When the 38-kc carrier is added to this low-frequency sine wave, the result is a 38-kc signal superimposed on the L+R sine wave axis. The top diode conducts only on the

Note that this envelope is in phase with the L+R voltage at the top of the waveform, or the portion detected by the diode connected to the left channel. On the bottom half of the wavefrom, or the portion of the signal detected by the right-channel diode, L−R is out of phase and equal in amplitude to the L+R voltage. They, therefore, cancel.

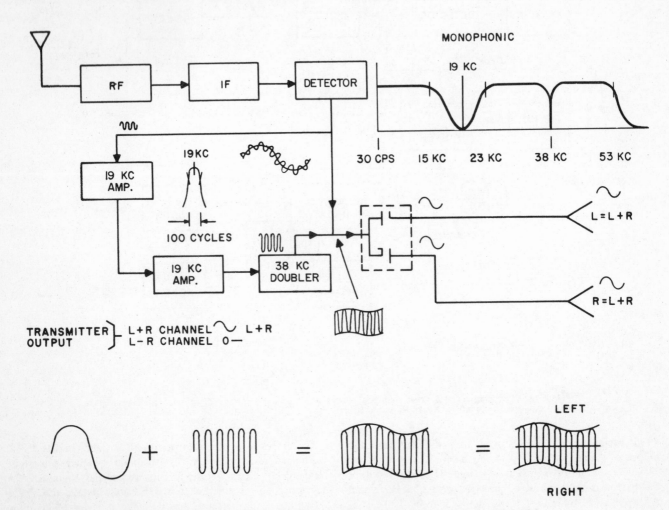

Fig. 5-15. Obtaining the left and right signals directly from the detector. (Courtesy of Motorola)

positive half cycles, and the bottom diode conducts only on the negative half cycles. Therefore, the output of diode No. 1 is one unit L+R and the output on diode No. 2 is an identical sine wave, also one unit L+R.

Figure 5-16 is the same receiver showing the waveforms present when a left-channel signal only is being transmitted. Under these conditions, the L+R signal is one unit L, and the L−R signal is one unit L. The pilot carrier is removed; the L+R signal; the 23- to 53-kc sidebands signal, representing L−R; and the 38-kc oscillator signal are fed to the input of the diode demodulators.

When this waveform is added to the 38-kc carrier, not only is the 38-kc oscillator frequency superimposed on the one unit L+R sine wave, but also when this carrier is added to the 23- to 53-kc L−R sidebands, waveform, as shown in Fig. 5-16, a conventional modulation envelope representing L−R or one unit L is obtained superimposed on the L+R.

So the output of the diode connected to the left channel is 2L. The two voltages are in phase and add. The output of the diode connected to the right channel is zero since the two voltages cancel.

Figure 5-17 shows the same receiver when the right channel only is being transmitted. Under these conditions, the L+R signal is equal to one unit R, and the L−R signal is equal to one unit −R. When the 38-kc carrier is added to this waveform, we receive the same 38-kc signal; the L+R sine wave axis, representing the L+R signal; and we also receive a conventional, double sideband modulator envelope superimposed on this signal. Since the sidebands, representing −R, are reversed 180°, the modulation envelope is also reversed. In this case, the two voltages on the bottom of the envelope detected by the diode connected to the right channel add, producing 2R. The two voltages which are detected by the left diode, are 180° out of phase; therefore, they cancel.

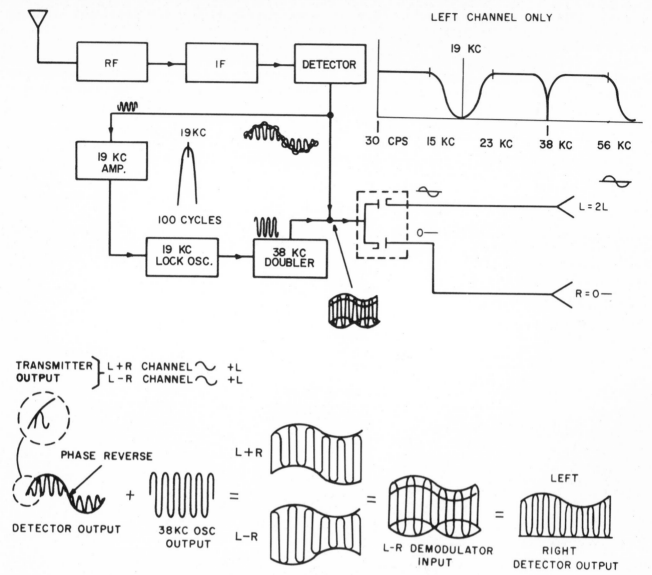

Fig. 5-16. Block diagram of the stereo multiplex receiver when a left-channel signal only is being transmitted. (Courtesy of Motorola)

Figure 5-18 is a block diagram of a typical FM receiver showing the bandpass characteristics of the various circuits in the receiver, and a schematic of a stereo multiplex demodulator of the type described.

The bandpass of the r-f and i-f amplifiers of the receiver is 200 kc. The response at the output of the detector, since the deemphasis circuit has been removed, is essentially flat from 30 cps to 53 kc. Therefore, when the receiver is tuned to a station broadcasting stereo, the L+R signal (30 to 15 kc), the 19-kc pilot carrier, and the 23- to 53-kc L−R sidebands will appear at the output of the detector. The signal first passes through two parallel tuned circuits, L1 and C1, and L2 and C2 which are tuned to 67 kc. The purpose of these two tuned circuits is to remove any SCA subcarrier that might be present on the received signal.

C3, C4, and the inductance in the primary of T1 are series resonant to 19 kc. This high-Q tuned circuit removes the 19-kc pilot carrier. The pilot carrier is coupled to the secondary of T1 and fed to the control grid of V1, which is a voltage amplifier. This amplifier amplifies the 19-kc

signal and couples it through a double-tuned transformer to provide better preselection to the grid of V2.

V2 serves as a doubler; it is biased near class-C operation. The inductance in the primary of T3 and C9 resonate to 38 kc. The 38-kc output of the doubler is coupled to the secondary of T3. Each end of the secondary of T3 is tied to the plates of diodes V3 and V4. Two 38-kc voltages appear on the plates of V3 and V4, each 180° out of phase. They serve as the 38-kc subcarrier reference voltage.

The L+R and L−R signals are fed to the centertap of the secondary of T3. The L+R and L−R voltages, therefore, apply voltage equal in amplitude and in phase at both plates of V3 and V4. Each diode rectifies the positive half of the L+R signal; therefore, L+R always appears across the diode loads, R8 and R9 of both V3 and V4. However, since the oscillator voltages on the plates are 180° out of phase, L−R sideband information appears as +(L−R) across the load of V3 and −(L−R) across the load of V4. The voltages across R9 are, therefore, L+R plus L−R. The R voltages cancel, leaving only the L signal at the output. The voltages across R8 are L+R — (L—R). The output of this diode, therefore, is always right voltages since the L signals cancel.

R10 and C14, and R11 and C15 are standard 75-μsec deemphasis networks. The output for these diodes

This serves as a stereo indicator. When a station broadcasts stereo, the lamp glows.

Automatic Switchover—Stereo to Monaural. R6 forward biases (at voltages of about 2.7 volts) the plates of V3 and V4. When the station is tuned to a monaural channel,

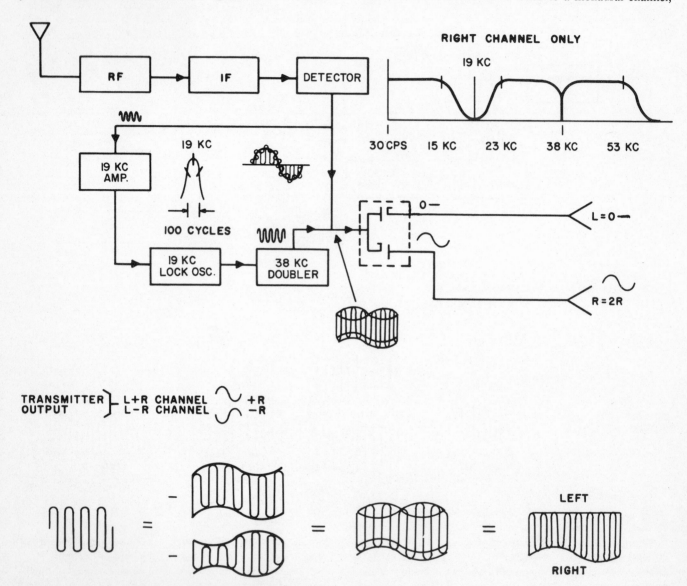

Fig. 5-17. Block diagram of a stereo multiplex receiver when a right-channel signal only is being transmitted. (Courtesy of Motorola)

feed left and right channels separately. NE1 is the stereo pilot indicator located in the front panel of the stereo receiver. When the receiver is tuned to a station that is broadcasting stereo, the lamp glows. When the transmission is monaural, it does not glow.

Stereo Indicator Lamp.

When no 19-kc pilot carrier is present, the voltage drop across R7 is zero because the 38-kc doubler, V2, is cut off. As soon as the pilot carrier appears, however, the tube goes into heavy conduction and a large voltage appears across R7. Since NE1 is connected across R7, it will glow.

this keeps V3 and V4 in conduction. Under this condition, they appear as small resistors. Since the monaural signal is tied to the centertap of the secondary of T3, then equal signal voltages, through the diode resistance, are applied across each diode load, and rectification does not take place.

When no pilot carrier is present on the signal being received, the diodes appear as resistors, and the output of the detector is connected directly to both the right and left channels. When the 38-kc sine wave is present, then the 2.7-volt bias is overcome by the rectification of the carrier, and the diodes again function as detectors, producing separate left and right signals at their outputs.

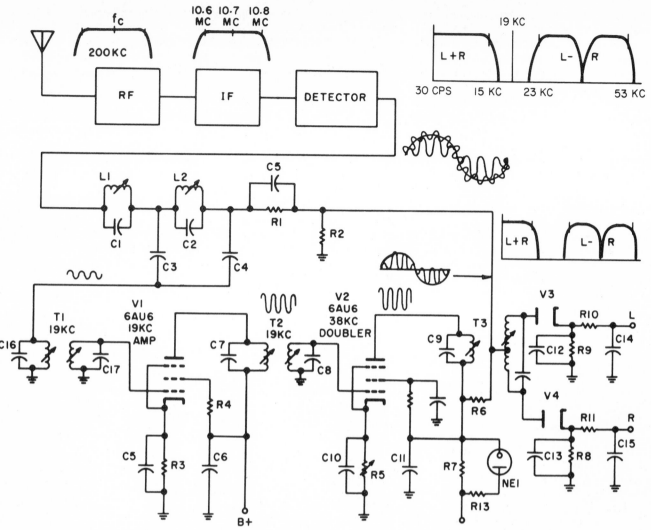

Fig. 5-18. Block diagram of an FM receiver with a schematic of the stereo multiplex demodulator. (Courtesy of Motorola)

Balanced Synchronous Detector. A variation of the detector circuit is called the balanced synchronous detector. It uses four diodes instead of two for detection of the L—R signal, see Fig. 5-19. The outputs of D1 and D2 are connected together, forming the left-channel output. D3 and D4 are likewise connected, and produce the right-channel output. The theory of operation of this circuit is identical to that of the two-diode, or unbalanced, synchronous detector.

This circuit offers several advantages over the two-diode circuit. It provides a constant load to the 38-kc oscillator, preventing pulling of the oscillator frequency when the diodes switch, which may result in a reduction in channel separation. When the polarity of the 38-kc oscillator signal in the secondary of T2 is such that terminal No. 4 is positive, then because it is centertapped, the same voltage appears on terminal No. 5, but is 180° out of phase with the voltage on terminal No. 4. Terminal No. 4 of the transformer is connected to the plate of D1, and the positive voltage on the plate of the diode causes the diode to conduct. Terminal No. 5 is connected to the cathode of D2, and the negative voltage on the cathode causes the diode to conduct simultaneously, drawing equal currents through

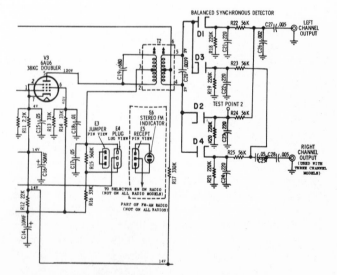

Fig. 5-19. Balanced synchronous detector.

both halves of the secondary.

When the polarity of the 38-kc signal reverses, D3 and D4 conduct. Note that regardless of whether the signal is positive or negative, there are equal currents through both halves of the primary presenting a constant load to the oscillator or doubler. Another advantage of this type circuitry, besides that of increased channel separation, is that it cancels any 38-kc component at the output of the diodes. The 38-kc oscillator signal in the output of the diodes are always 180° out of phase with each other, and because the outputs of both the left and right diodes are tied together, the 38-kc signal cancels. This makes removal of the 38-kc subcarrier much simpler.

The 38-kc carrier frequency is very close to the maximum audio frequency, which is 15 kc. It is sometimes difficult to build a filter network which will attenuate the carrier sufficiently without affecting the higher audio frequencies. If all of the 38-kc carrier is not removed in the output, then certain frequency signals will produce beat notes or birdies in the output. These beat notes are heterodyne signals between higher audio frequencies and the 38-kc carrier components and their harmonics.

lator signal on the cathode of the right-channel demodulator is 180° out of phase with that on the left-channel demodulator; therefore, when it is mixed with the L—R signal it produces a —(L—R) signal. When this signal is added to L+R, the left-channel information cancels, and only the right-channel output appears in the plate. One advantage to this type of circuit is that the detector provides amplification besides being a demodulator.

Figure 5-21 is a Zenith FM stereo decoder unit. The composite stereo signal is fed to terminal No. 2 of T12, which is the SCA or storecast trap. This trap is tuned to 67 kc, and presents a high attenuation to any storecast signal which might be present.

The composite signal less the 67-kc information is applied to terminal No. 3 of T9. The inductance of T9 and the 82-pf capacitor form a series resonant circuit sharply tuned to 19 kc. This circuit removes the 19-kc information from the composite signal, and through the resonant rise in voltage across the inductance of T9, applies the 19-kc

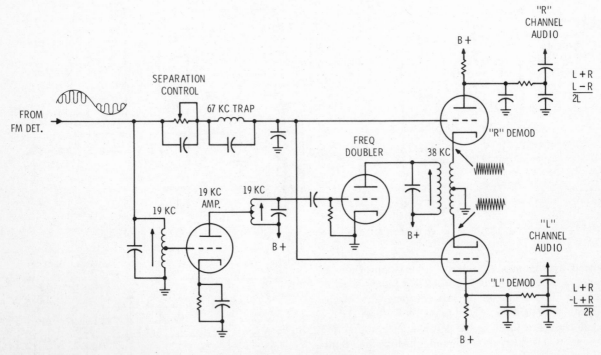

Fig. 5-20. Philco "L" series detector system.

Philco "L" Series Detector System. Another type of detector system used in the Philco "L" series FM stereo units is shown in Fig. 5-20. In this circuit, the composite signal consisting of L+R and L—R is fed to the control grid of two triode tubes. One is called the R demodulator, and one is the L demodulator. The cathodes of these tubes are fed with the 38-kc locked oscillator signal.

The L+R signal is amplified by both tubes, and appears in the output directly. The oscillator voltage on the cathodes adds to the L—R sideband signals which are present on the grids to produce the L—R signal with the carrier reinserted. The phase of the reinserted carrier is such that when it is mixed with the L—R signal on the grid of the L demodulator, it produces a +(L—R) signal. When this signal is added to the L+R signal, the right channel information cancels and produces a left-channel output only. The oscil-

signal to the grid of V8A. T10 in the plate of V8A is also tuned to 19 kc. The secondary of T10 is centertapped, and a diode is connected to either end of the secondary. Diode X1 conducts on the positive half of each 19-kc cycle, and diode X2 conducts on the negative side of each cycle. Therefore, for each cycle of 19-kc energy appearing across the secondary, two output pulses occur. The frequency of these pulses, therefore, is 38 kc.

These 38-kc pulses are applied to the grid of V8B. T11 in the plate of V8B is tuned to 38 kc. The pulses amplified by V8B cause the tuned circuit to ring at 38 kc, producing a 38-kc sine wave which is locked in frequency and phase to the 19-kc pilot carrier produced by the station.

The secondary of T11 is centertapped. The opposite ends of the secondary are connected to the cathode of two diode rectifiers. The L+R signal is applied to the centertap of

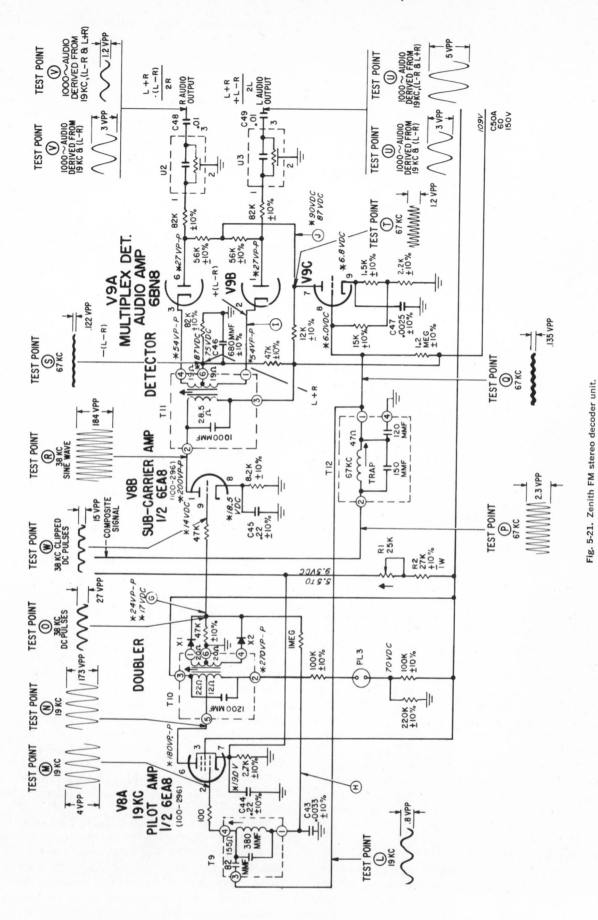

Fig. 5-21. Zenith FM stereo decoder unit.

the transformer through V9, which is a voltage amplifier. The L+R signal appears equally on both diodes, and appears directly in the output of the left and the right channels. The phase of the doubler signal is such that −(L−R) is added to the L+R signal in the right-channel diode, and +(L+R) is added to the L+R signal in the left-channel diode, producing separate left and right stereo signals.

Separation Control.

Another circuit found in some FM decoders is the separation control. Such a circuit is shown in the Philco "L" series demodulator shown in Fig. 5-20.

The operation of the detectors in this system was described above. The composite signal is coupled to the control grids of the demodulator tubes through the separation control and a 67-kc storecast trap. The purpose of the separation control is to make certain that the L+R and

FM stereo decoders. Fig. 5-22 is a complete schematic of a 38-kc locked oscillator used in the Motorola HK54-1. This circuit and variations of this circuit are used in many locked oscillator circuits.

When there is no pilot carrier present, such as when a monaural signal is being broadcast, the oscillator tube, V2, is biased to cutoff by the 12 volts on the cathode. In this condition, the tube does not oscillate, and the plate current is zero.

When the pilot carrier is received, such as when the receiver is tuned to a stereo broadcast, the 19-kc signal causes diode E1 to draw current through its load resistor, R7. The diode is connected so that the high end of R7 becomes positive. Since this point is connected to a control grid, it causes the grid to go in a positive direction, overcoming the fixed bias in the cathode, and the oscillator starts. When no stereo signal is present, there is no plate

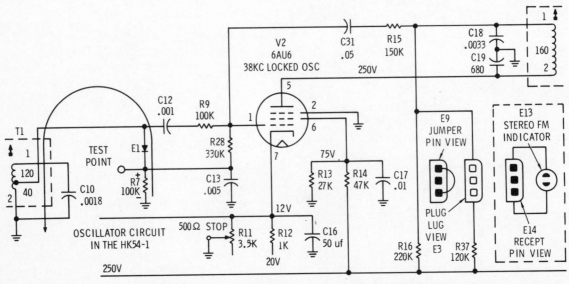

Fig. 5-22. Schematic of a 38-kc locked oscillator in the Motorola HK54-1.

the L−R signals are equal at the output of the demodulator tubes. If they are not, full cancellation of the unwanted channel will not occur. This, of course, reduces the channel separation and, hence, the stereo effect.

The reactance of the capacitor across the separation control offers little resistance to the L−R signal but is an open circuit to the low-frequency L+R signal. When the separation control is adjusted so that the resistance of R is the greatest, then the L+R signal will be reduced below that of L−R. When the resistance of the separation control is minimum, then the full L+R signal appears at the grids of the demodulator. By adjusting the resistance of the separation control, it is possible to balance the L+R and L−R signals. Proper adjustment is indicated when channel separation is maximum.

Locked Oscillator.

Some stereophonic FM decoders employ a locked oscillator to produce the 38-kc carrier in the decoder. Also to be described in the following paragraphs is the operation of the stereo indicator light used on most

current in the 38-kc oscillator tube and consequently, no voltage drop across resistance R16. However, as soon as the stereo signal is tuned in and the oscillator begins to function and draw plate current, a voltage appears across R16.

If a neon bulb is connected across this resistor, it will give an indication when a stereo broadcast is being received. When no plate current is flowing, indicating no signal, there is no voltage. When a signal is applied and plate current begins to flow, then the voltage appearing across R16 lights the stereo indicator lamp.

Another method commonly used for supplying a locked 38-kc signal is to use a frequency doubler as shown in Fig. 5-23.

The 19-kc signal is applied directly through the 0.01 coupling capacitor and 120K resistor to the control grid of a voltage doubler. The input tank is tuned to 19 kc, and the tank in the plate circuit is tuned to 38 kc. The signal on the grid of the doubler overdrives the doubler tube slightly producing harmonics. This 38-kc signal, which is produced from the second harmonic of the 19-kc

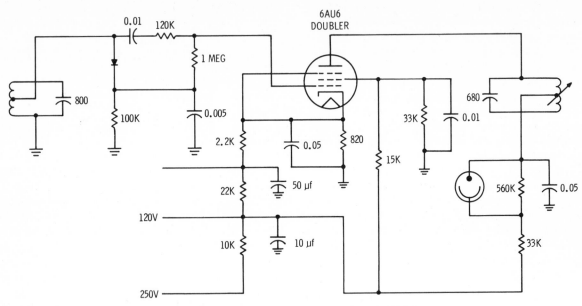

Fig. 5-23. Frequency doubler circuit of the Motorola HK54-2.

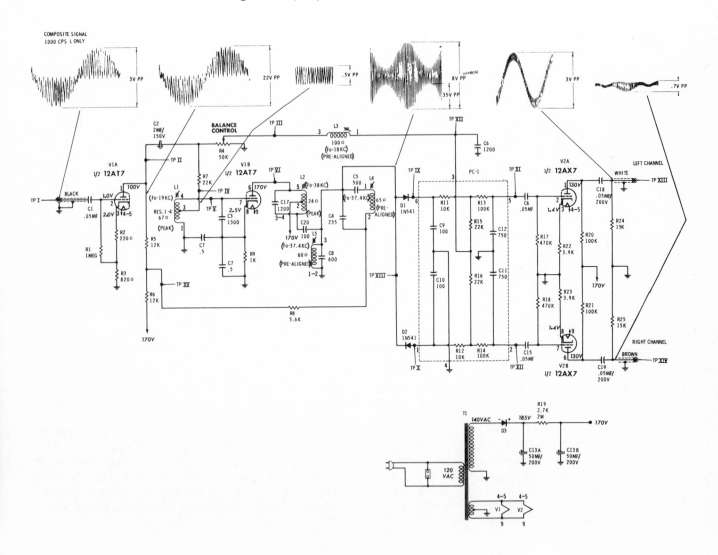

Fig. 5-24. Schematic of a GE stereo FM decoder.

pilot carrier, is automatically locked in phase and frequency. Note that the stereo indicator light circuit is the same in this circuit as in the locked oscillator circuit.

GE Stereo FM Decoder. Figure 5-24 is a schematic of the GE stereo FM decoder. This circuit differs from previous circuits discussed in that the L—R signal is separated from the L+R signal, and travels through the decoder through separate channels, and is matrixed or mixed after the demodulation of the L—R signal.

A composite signal is fed to the grid of a wideband amplifier, V1A. The L—R signal is fed through a lowpass filter consisting of a prealigned coil, L3, and the capacitor, C6, in the plate circuit of V1A. This circuit only passes the low-frequency L+R information. A balanced potentiometer, R4, is located ahead of the L+R filter. Adjustment of this control allows for the adjustment of the level of L+R so that it equals L—R at the matrix network to produce maximum separation.

The 19-kc pilot signal is separated from the composite stereo signal by the parallel resonant circuit consisting of L1 and C3 which is tuned to 19 kc. The high-amplitude 19-kc signal is developed across this resonant circuit and overdrives the grid of V1B, which operates as a doubler.

The second harmonic of the 19-kc signal is selected in the plate circuit by a resonant circuit consisting of L2 and C17, which is tuned to the second harmonic of the pilot carrier. The 38-kc frequency represents the regenerated subcarrier and is coupled into the L—R bandpass filter by C20.

The L—R signal is taken off the plate of V1A and fed through a bandpass filter, consisting of L4, C5, C4, L5, and C8. This filter is designed to pass frequencies from 23 to 53 kc only. The response of the filter over these bands must be flat for maximum separation. Diodes D1 and D2 in the L—R detector circuit are used to detect equal plus and minus quantities of L—R. Both quantities must be equal in amplitude to provide matrixing with the L+R information for maximum channel separation. The addition of L+R to the L—R information is accomplished through the 10K resistors, R11 and R12, and 22K resistors, R15 and R16. The combination of R13 and C12 in the left channel, and R14 and C11 in the right channel provides deemphasis to each audio channel. The preamplifiers, V2A and V2B, provide a gain of approximately 3 in each channel to overcome the overall circuit losses up to the grid of the preamp.

4. Servicing the FM Stereo Decoder

Although there are several variations of the circuits described, it is these basic circuits that are employed in most stereo FM decoders in use at the present time. A block diagram and schematic of a typical FM stereo decoder is shown in Fig. 5-25A.

The FM stereo decoder itself is a very simple device in comparison to the FM receiver. The decoder requires very little servicing and adjustment. Before adjusting or checking the FM stereo decoder, the technician should make a complete check of the FM receiver to make certain that it is operating properly.

The block diagram and the schematic of Fig. 5-25 show that the composite FM signal, containing both the monaural and stereo information, is separated at the output of the detector. The synchronizing information, consisting of a 19-kc signal that goes through a 19-kc amplifier, is doubled in frequency in the 38-kc doubler. The output of this doubler feeds into the stereo demodulator. The composite signal, less the 19-kc signal, and less the 67-kc storecast signal, if one is present, is also fed to the centertap of the secondary of the demodulator transformer. The output of this demodulator then consists of left and right stereo FM signals. Typical waveforms using a signal generator with right channel output only is shown at various points in the system. The waveforms represented here are typical for all stereo decoders. One possible exception would be circuits where L+R and L—R are separated and matrixed such as circuits shown in Fig. 5-24.

The signals then are split, taking two paths, and are recombined at the detector. To produce stereo, both signals must be present. For the reception of monaural only, the L+R need be present. If the receiver being tested operates normally on a monaural signal but does not operate on a stereo, the power supply is functioning normally, and the diodes in the demodulator are functioning. This means that the 38-kc oscillator signal is possibly not present, or that the phase of the signal is not proper, resulting in no channel separation or very low channel separation.

If the 38-kc oscillator signal is not present, this means that either the 38-kc doubler or oscillator is not operating or that it is not receiving a 19-kc pilot carrier signal. A wideband oscilloscope with a 10-to-1 low-capacity probe is an excellent instrument for isolating a defective stage; however, the stage can be located in most cases using a VTVM.

If the stereo FM decoder has a stereo indicator light, then this will indicate whether or not the oscillator or doubler is functioning. If the oscillator is functioning as the receiver is tuned to a stereo station, then the indicator light will glow. If the light glows, this is an indication that the oscillator is functioning, but the phase of the oscillator is probably not proper for good separation. The most probable cause for this is that the 19-kc channel is not aligned properly, and most likely the takeoff coil in the grid of the 19-kc amplifier is misadjusted, since this is the most critical and highest Q circuit in the amplifier chain.

If the stereo indicator light does not glow when the receiver is tuned to a stereo station, then this is an indication that the oscillator or doubler is not drawing plate current. There are two probable causes for this. There may be a malfunction in the oscillator itself, or the oscillator or doubler is not receiving a driving signal from the 19-kc amplifier. Again, the use of a wideband scope and a low-capacitance probe will isolate the trouble rather easily.

If the scope is not available, a VTVM may be used to determine if the oscillator is functioning. Where the 38-kc stage is an oscillator or a doubler, the grid draws current when a 19-kc signal was present. It will, therefore, swing

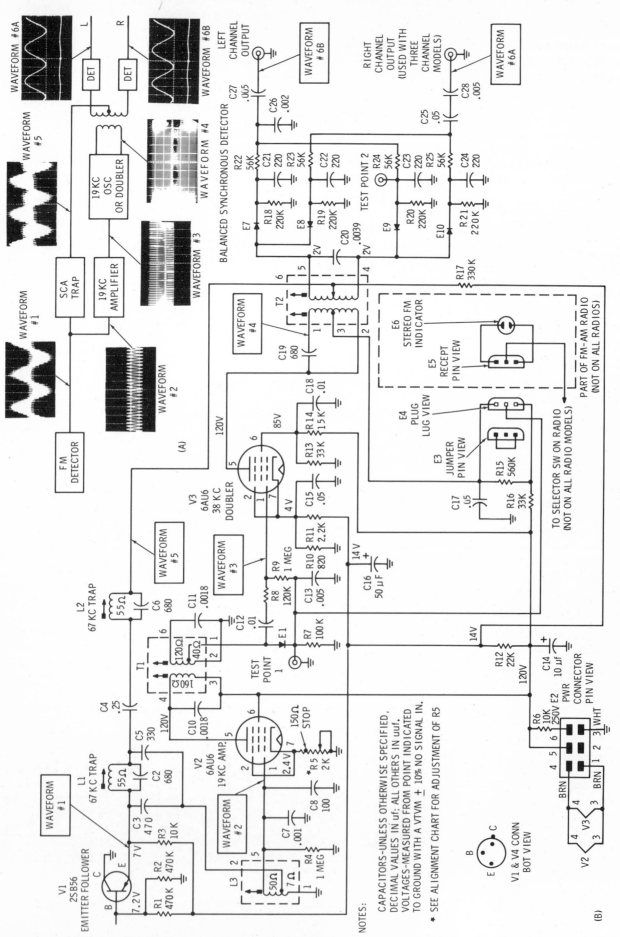

Fig. 5-25. FM stereo decoder: (A) block diagram, and (B) schematic.

negative several volts when a signal is present. First, tune the receiver to a monaural signal and measure the grid voltage on the grid of the doubler or locked oscillator. Then tune the receiver to a stereo signal. If the 19-kc amplifier is functioning, the grid should swing negative

several volts. If it is not, there will be little or no change in the grid voltage. In some circuits, the grid may swing positive when a stereo signal is tuned in. This is usually the case when noise protection is used.

5. Alignment of FM Stereo Decoder

The alignment of the FM stereo decoder is a rather simple process. To obtain good results, the technician must take considerable care in making adjustments, however. Also, the signals used must be very accurate in phase and frequency.

General Procedure

The alignment procedure is a general one. Its purpose is to describe basically the adjustments necessary on the average FM stereo unit, why the adjustments are necessary, and the general method of making the adjustments.

There are usually four basic adjustments necessary on a stereo decoder for proper operation:

1. It is necessary that the 19-kc amplifier plate and grid coils be tuned to 19 kc.

2. It is also necessary that the primary and secondary of the 38-kc transformer which feeds the L–R demodulators be tuned to 38 kc.

3. It is necessary that the 67-kc SCA trap be set for maximum attenuation at 67 kc.

4. It is necessary that the phase of the 38-kc signal be such that the L–R demodulators provide maximum channel separation.

Signals for Alignment

The FM stereo broadcast station itself supplies all the signals necessary for alignment. It is sometimes difficult to use, however, because the amplitude cannot be controlled accurately enough, and the signal which is used to modulate the transmitter cannot be controlled. It is generally not possible to adjust the 67-kc SCA trap on an "off-the-air" signal, and it is not possible, except under special circumstances, to adjust channel separation using a station signal.

The SCA carrier from the station is usually not strong enough to obtain an accurate adjustment. It is very important that this trap be set accurately as the setting will usually affect channel separation. Unless the stereo station broadcasts one channel only on voice announcements or newscasts as a special service, it is not possible to accurately adjust the channel separation. On a normal program there is usually information in both channels simultaneously. It is also very important during alignment that the input signal be kept low to prevent overload. This is sometimes not possible using "off-the-air" signals.

The stereo station may be used for alignment in an emergency. An FM stereo signal generator as described in Chapter 3 is recommended for precise alignment and best performance. The advantages of a signal generator are that the test conditions can be controlled very precisely, and the modulating signal may be controlled to provide the most accurate adjustment.

Adjustment Using an "Off-the-Air" Signal

To provide the proper signal for adjustment, tune the receiver to a station broadcasting stereo:

1. First, align the 19-kc amplifier input coil, T3, by placing a VTVM at test point No. 1 of the grid of V2, and tune L1 and T2 for a maximum negative reading. The signal should be reduced by disconnecting the antenna, or other means, so that noise is heard in the background of the broadcast continuously. The signal should be as weak as possible to obtain a meter reading, and the meter should be on the lowest possible scale.

2. The 38-kc doubler, L1, should be tuned to resonance by connecting the VTVM to test point No. 2 as shown in Fig. 5-26.

3. Tune the primary and secondary of T2 for maximum reading on the VTVM.

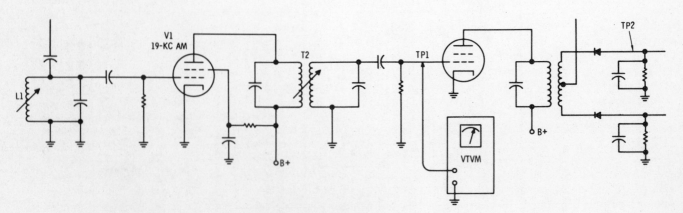

Fig. 5-26.

If a 38-kc oscillator is used instead of a doubler, the circuit will appear essentially the same as Fig. 5-27. To adjust the oscillator to 38-kc, it is necessary to remove the 19-kc pilot signal from the oscillator by either removing the 19-kc amp or detuning it.

If a d-c bias is used on the oscillator, the bias must be removed. The bias is usually a small positive voltage applied to the cathode of V1 through a voltage divider, R_x. The purpose of the bias is to keep the oscillator from running free when there is no 19-kc or stereo signal present. Once the 19-kc signal and the oscillator cathode bias is removed, the oscillator will then run free at or near 38 kc. The frequency of the oscillator is controlled by adjusting the primary of T2. The free running frequency of the oscillator should be 38 kc. Using the audio system of the FM stereo system as an indicator, adjust T2 for zero beat. The zero beat occurs between the oscillator and the 38-kc stereo signals. The secondary of T2 should then be tuned for resonance by connecting a VTVM as shown in Fig. 5-27 and tuning for a maximum meter reading.

procedure should be repeated. The adjustment of the 19-kc input coil shifts the phase of the 19 kc, and since the doubler or the locked oscillator is in phase with the 19 kc, the 38-kc signal is also shifted in phase. When the 38-kc signal is the same phase as the 38 kc used in the transmitter to create the L−R signal, the channel separator will be maximum.

It is common practice for some stereo stations presently to broadcast news and announcements on one channel only. If a station does this in your signal area, then the separation may be set easily from an "off-the-air" signal by tuning in the station when it is broadcasting one channel only, and adjusting the 19-kc input coil for minimum output in the dead channel. The speaker may be used as an indicator or an audio output meter across the speaker may be used.

Alignment Using a Signal Generator

The equipment required for FM stereo alignment are:
1. FM signal generator.

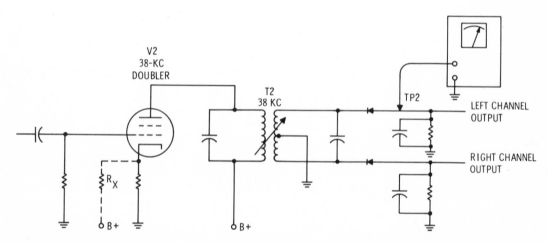

Fig. 5-27.

It is generally not possible to adjust the 67-kc SCA trap using an "off-the-air" signal. As a general rule, adjustment of this trap should not be attempted unless there is evidence that it has been tampered with. The adjustment of the trap will affect the channel separation if it is not set properly. The frequency of the trap is generally not affected by changing tubes or circuit constants except its own inductance and capacity. Unless it is tampered with, the chances of its being misadjusted are very remote.

The only other adjustment necessary on the stereo FM decoder is the adjustment of channel separation. This is usually accomplished by trimming the adjustment of the 19-kc input coil for maximum channel separation or best stereo effect. If a channel separation control is included, then this should also be adjusted for best channel separation after the 19-kc input coil has been adjusted. In the first step above, we set coil L1 to resonance at 19 kc. A very slight trimming (considerably less than a half turn) is required for adjusting channel separation. If it is necessary to adjust the slug any further than this, then the 19-kc alignment

2. FM stereo generator.
3. VTVM.
4. Wideband scope (optional).

There are two ways in which the FM stereo signal generator may be used for alignment of the decoder. The output of the FM stereo signal generator may be used to modulate the FM signal generator, which is, in turn, fed to the antenna input of the receiver to be aligned, or the output of the FM stereo signal generator may be fed directly into the input of the stereo FM decoder.

FM Stereo Generator Modulates FM Signal Generator. The best method is the one in which the FM stereo signal generator is used to modulate an FM generator, and the output of the generator is fed into the antenna terminals of the receiver to be aligned. This method indicates more precisely what the overall performance characteristics of the system are, and allows a more precise adjustment. The reason for this is that the FM receiver can sometimes introduce nonlinear phase delay to frequencies within its bandpass.

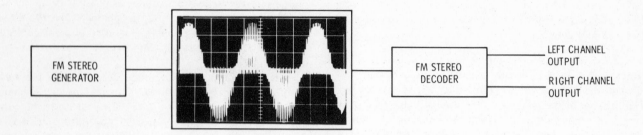

Fig. 5-28. Output waveform of an FM stereo signal generator.

The phase delays are caused by the bandpass of the system not being flat in frequency. For example, if the gain of the system is not the same for the 19-kc pilot carrier as the 38-kc sideband signals, one signal will be delayed in relation to the other. This has the same effect as if the channel separation is misadjusted.

When the test signal is fed through the entire system, the channel separation adjustment automatically minimizes any phase errors in the FM receiver.

The FM stereo signal generator generates a standard, composite FM stereo signal which consists of a 38-kc L—R signal superimposed on the axis of a low-frequency L+R signal which can be varied in frequency, and a 19-kc pilot carrier. The waveform at the output of the generator is a standard composite FM stereo signal as shown in Fig. 5-28.

If an FM signal generator is not available, the FM stereo generator may be connected directly to the input of the FM stereo decoder as shown in Fig. 5-30. The alignment procedure in either case is the same regardless of which method is used, and it is very similar to the "off-the-air" procedure. Here again there are four basic steps:

1. Adjust the 67-kc traps.
2. Align the 19-kc channel coils for peak response.
3. Tune the locked oscillator or doubler primary and secondary for 38 kc.
4. Adjust the input coil to the 19-kc amplifier for maximum channel separation.

Let us assume that the circuit which we are aligning is a circuit shown in Fig. 5-31. First, to set the 67-kc trap, set up the signal generator so that it puts out a 67-kc signal

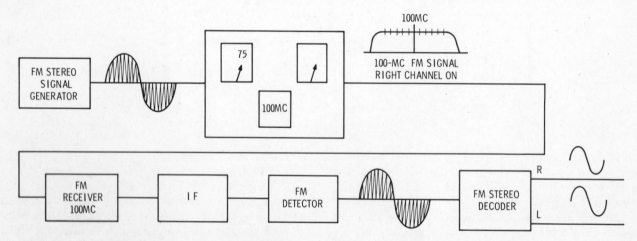

Fig. 5-29. Set-up for stereo alignment with test signal fed through a standard FM signal generator.

FM Signal Generator Fed Directly to Input. Figure 5-29 is a block diagram of a set-up for stereo alignment where the test signal is fed through a standard FM signal generator. When the FM signal generator is connected to the FM receiver, it should be properly matched. The output of the FM signal generator is usually on the order of 50 to 70 ohms. A satisfactory match can usually be obtained by the use of two 150-ohm resistors, one in series with the hot lead of the generator and one in series with the ground lead. The ground lead of the coax should not be connected to the receiver chassis.

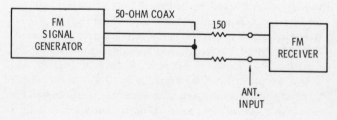

Fig. 5-30.

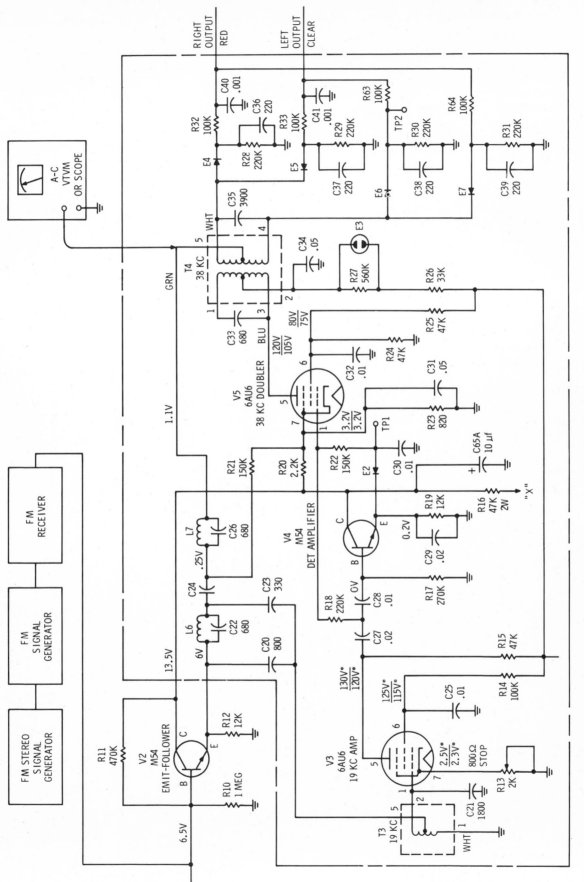

Fig. 5-31.

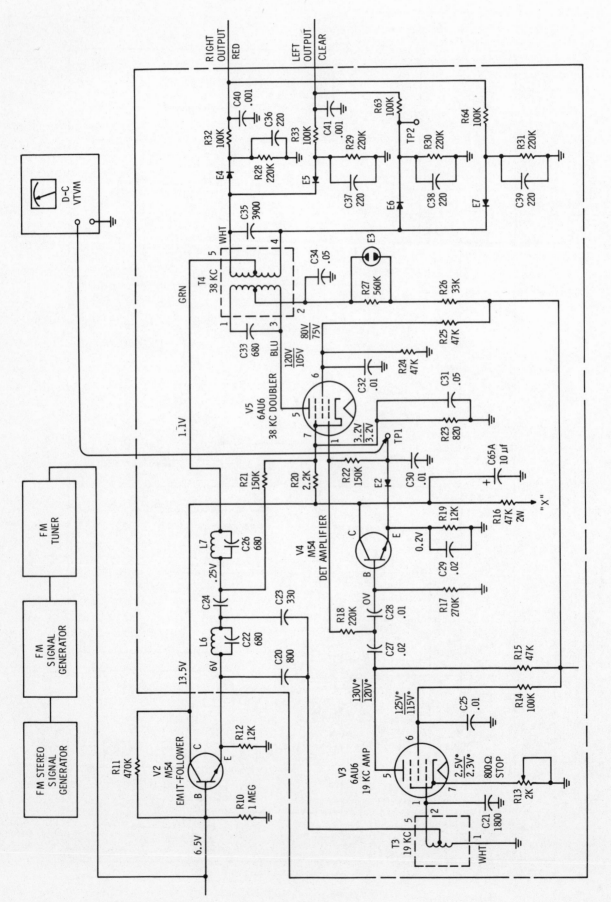

Fig. 5-32.

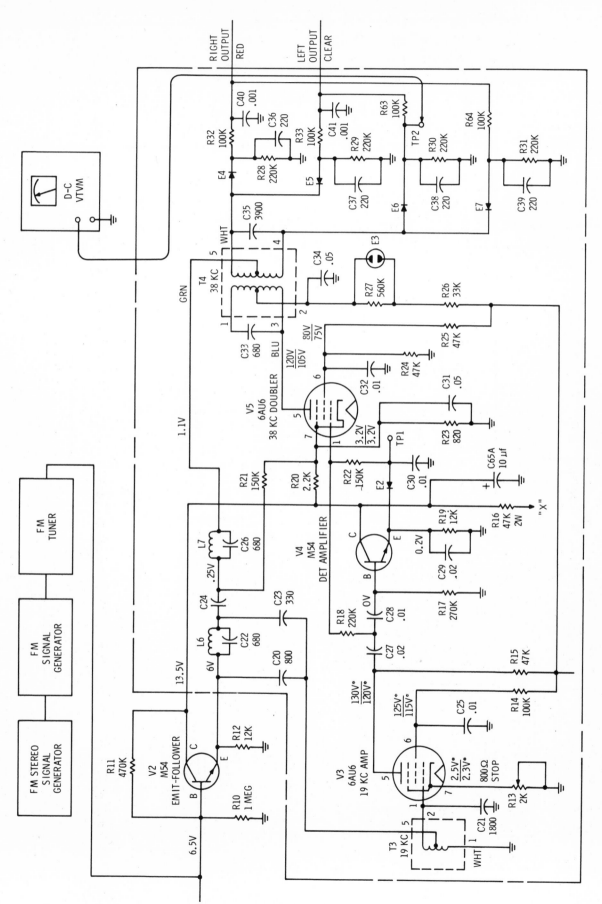

Fig. 5-33.

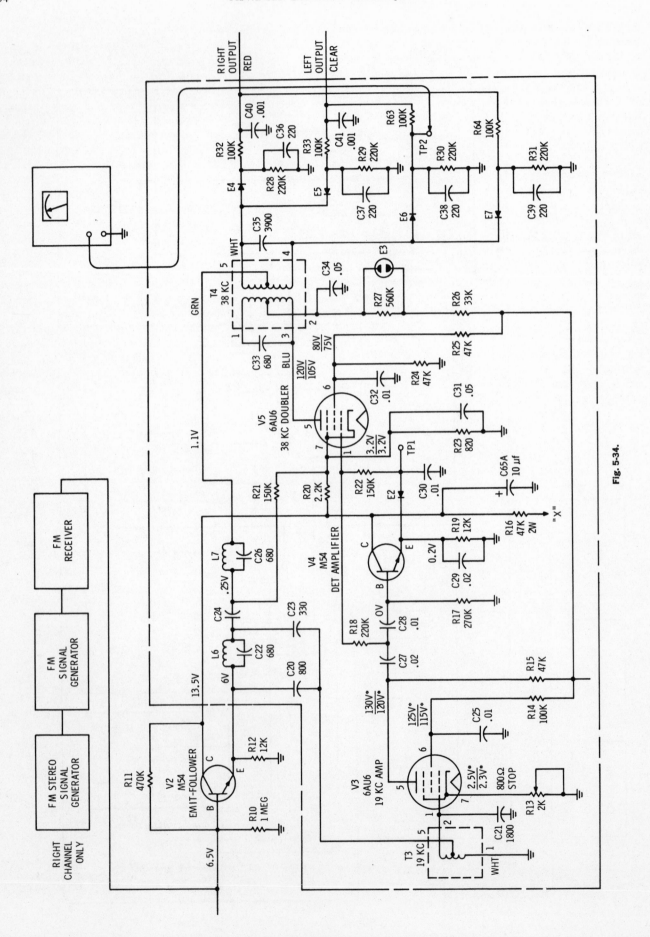

Fig. 5-34.

only. Then adjust the generator output for maximum signal. Place an oscilloscope or an a-c voltmeter at the centertap of T2, and tune L2 for a minimum response on the meter or oscilloscope.

Next, peak the 19-kc amplifier tuned circuits, see Fig. 5-32. For this adjustment, set the generator for a composite signal or a 19-kc signal only from the signal generator. It is usually more convenient to use a full composite signal for this adjustment. For an indicator, connect a d-c VTVM meter to test point No. 1. Diode E1 will rectify any 19-kc voltage available, and the voltage across R7 will be proportional to the gain of the 19-kc amplifier.

For the best possible adjustment, the meter should be placed on the lowest possible scale, and the signal generator reduced as low as possible to still obtain a reading on the meter. Under these conditions, T1 and L3 should be adjusted for maximum reading on the meter. As T1 and L3 are brought to resonance, the output of the signal generator should be reduced to prevent any possibility of overloading. The tuning on the circuits should be very sharp. If they tune broad, this is an indication that too much signal is being used for alignment. The next step would be to resonate the plate of the doubler to 38 kc. To accomplish this, move the VTVM to test point No. 2, which uses diode E6 as a detector. Adjust the primary and secondary of T2 for maximum reading on the VTVM. See Fig. 5-33.

The remaining adjustment is for channel separation. The FM stereo signal generator can usually be adjusted for a left-signal or a right-signal output. To make the channel separation adjustment, see Fig. 5-34. Set the signal generator to either the right or left channel, and connect the indicator, whether an oscilloscope, a-c voltmeter, or d-c VTVM to the opposite channel, and adjust the 19-kc input transformer, L3, for a minimum reading or minimum output.

It is sometimes an advantage to know how much channel separation that the instrument is delivering. With the signal generator putting out a signal of one channel only, the output of both channels should be read with the a-c VTVM or an oscilloscope. The ratio of the two voltages is the channel separation.

Channel separation is usually expressed in decibels. To obtain the channel separation in decibels, the standard formula of db equals 20 times the log of the voltage ratio should be used. Average separations will run approximately 20 db or 10 times. The capability of the system is approximately 30 db, and little deterioration will be noted in the channel separation by the average customer until the channel separation is below 15 db.

6 – Installation and Home Servicing Techniques

1. Installation

For AM reception, the built-in loop antenna included with the receiver should provide satisfactory reception. For monaural FM, a built-in antenna will be satisfactory in good reception areas close to the transmitter. The addition of a simple outdoor antenna, such as a folded dipole in the attic on monaural FM, will provide more consistent and more noise-free reception. The customer will usually receive the stations that he normally receives without an antenna more consistently and with less noise and fading. The chances are very good that he will be able to receive many more stations than he could without the antenna. This adds considerably to the value of the receiver, and also creates more satisfied customers.

The antenna for FM for most reception areas should be a single, folded dipole mounted in the attic of the home or some other convenient place. In extreme fringe areas, high-gain directive antennas, such as the yagi type, may be desirable to provide more noise-free reception. A good antenna installation in the long run will pay many dividends to both the customer and the serviceman. The television antenna, if one is installed in the home, usually

operates very well on FM. A two-set couple installed to the TV antenna will provide excellent reception on FM.

For stereo FM, the need for a good installation is even more critical than for monaural FM. Because of the basic characteristics of FM modulation, the signal-to-noise ratio on the multiplex channel is not as good as on the monaural channel. Therefore, in marginal reception areas where a station broadcasting a monaural signal is noise free, there may be considerable noise in the background when the station switches to multiplex. Usually the addition of a simple outdoor antenna will greatly increase the signal-to-noise ratio on multiplex under these conditions.

The use of built-in antennas on multiplex, in many cases, will also reduce the channel separation. The built-in antenna by its very nature does not provide a very good match to the input of the tuner. Therefore, the movement of objects around the receiver both in the room and traffic on heavily traveled streets can cause a tilting in the overall response of the receiver, which will reduce the channel separation. This is virtually eliminated when an outdoor antenna is installed.

2. Home Servicing Techniques

Servicing Instruments Required

Special equipment required for servicing stereo in the home are:
1. A-c VTVM.
2. Stylus pressure gauge.
3. Test record.

The average stereo console is usually a fine piece of furniture, and is rather large and bulky. For this reason it is usually more desirable to perform simple service and adjustments in the home, and to remove only the malfunctioning section of the system to the shop if this is desired.

General Procedure

A block diagram of a typical system is shown in Fig. 6-1. The first step is to determine which section is malfunctioning. If the malfunction is present on all functions, then the trouble lies either in the preamplifier or the power amplifier. If the malfunction is confined to only one function, this is an indication that the source of the problem is probably in that instrument alone.

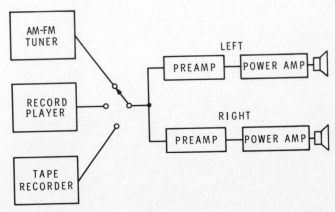

Fig. 6-1. Block diagram of a typical stereo hi-fi system.

If it is confined to only the left or the right channel, then this is an indication that the malfunction is in either the left- or the right-channel amplifier. Since there are two identical amplifier systems in a stereo amplifier, it is possible to use the amplifier itself to determine which section of the amplifier, either the preamp or the power amp, is not functioning. If, for instance, the left channel has no output but the right channel operates normally, then the right channel preamplifier may be connected into the left-channel power amplifier. If the left channel then functions normally, this indicates that the left-channel preamplifier is not functioning.

If the unit still does not function when the left-channel preamp is connected to the left channel power amp, then this is an indication that the power amplifier is not functioning. If simple voltage measurements and tubes do not repair the unit which is determined to be malfunctioning and it becomes necessary to remove it to the shop, then only that unit should removed if desired. In some cases, this may be interconnected with another chassis and it may require the pulling of two or three chassis to make the receiver operate when it is removed.

Stylus Pressure Adjustments

See Fig. 6-2. As a routine service procedure, the stylus pressure should be checked on each unit serviced. The stylus pressure is very important for good reproduction and minimum record and stylus wear. Stylus pressure on a normal ceramic cartridge will run on the order of 8 to 10 grams. On the lightweight cartridge, it may run about 5 grams. The service manual should be consulted. The stylus pressure should be set as light as possible, and still

will allow you to make a fast check of the overall performance of the system. Not only the frequency response of the amplifier and cartridge can be checked, but evidence of distortion due to improper stylus pressure, cabinet resonances, speaker rattles, cabinet rattles, and mechanical feedback may also be checked.

Fig. 6-2. Stylus pressure gauge. (Courtesy of Motorola)

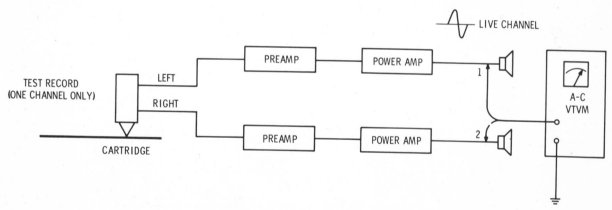

Fig. 6-3. Set-up for checking channel separation.

be able to track on all records. Tracking should be checked on both low and high frequencies, using a test record after the stylus pressure has been set, and listening for distortion or evidence of the stylus jumping out of the groove on bass notes.

Test Records

Test records for checking the performance of the cartridge and stereo amplifier system are valuable service aids. Records are available with a variety of test signals. Perhaps the most useful test signals for home service are frequency response, channel separation, quiet grooves for testing for turntable rumble, set down adjustment checks, and mechanism trip checks. The frequency response record

Channel Separation Check

Both left and right signals only are usually provided on stereo check test records to check the separation of the cartridge. Mechanical damage to the cartridge may allow it to function apparently normal, but may severely reduce the channel separation. The procedure for checking channel separation, see Fig. 6-3, is to measure the output of the live channel with an a-c VTVM reading the decibel (db) scale, then measuring the output in the dead channel. The ratio between the measurements is the channel separation. Normal channel separation on stereo cartridges should be of the order of 10 to 15 db. The lower the figure, the better the cartridge performance.

Speaker Phasing

Speaker phasing is important to good operation of the system. Most systems are coded so that the connections to the speaker may be made so that all speakers are phased in the same direction. When in doubt, a simple check to determine if the speakers are phased correctly is to connect either an ohmmeter on the low scale or a 1½-volt battery across the speaker systems which are being checked, see Fig. 6-4. All of the speaker cones should move in the same direction when the battery or the ohmmeter terminals are connected to the input to the speaker system.

Specific Troubleshooting Symptoms and Causes

Tables 6-1 to 6-3 present summary lists of specific symptoms and probable causes of troubles in the FM system.

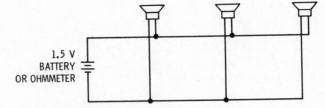

Fig. 6-4. Checking speaker phasing. All cones should move in the same direction if speakers are phased properly.

Table 6-1. Troubleshooting FM Receivers

SYMPTOM	PROBABLE CAUSE
A. Motorboating, blocking distortion on weak signals only.	1. Improper alignment. 2. Open bypass on B+ filaments, AFC buss. 3. Components around FM detector dress up away from chassis or having long leads. 4. Open screen bypass capacitors.
B. Poor AM rejection or noisy reception.	1. Low sensitivity due to defective i-f or r-f amp tube or stage. 2. Open electrolytic capacitor across ratio detector. 3. Improper alignment.
C. Oscillator drift.	1. Defective temperature compensating capacitor in oscillator. 2. Defective reactance tube or AFC diode. 3. Component in oscillator changing value with heat.
D. High-frequency distortion.	1. Improper bandpass due to misalignment.

Table 6-2. Troubleshooting Audio Amplifiers and Preamplifiers

SYMPTOM	PROBABLE CAUSE
A. Hum in both channels.	1. Open or shorted power-supply filters.
B. Hum on one channel only.	1. Heater-to-cathode leakage in amplifier tube. 2. Unbalance in output tube i-f push-pull. 3. Filament lead dressed near grid of input stage. 4. Open ground or shield or input cable. 5. Open capacitor in B+ decoupling filter in B+ to low-level stage.
C. Motorboating.	1. Open filter capacitor. 2. Open cathode or screen bypass capacitor. 3. Low-value coupling capacitors in stages having negative feedback. Change in value of components in feedback loop.
D. Severe distortion on both channels.	1. Low power-supply voltage.
E. Severe distortion on one channel only.	1. Defective tube. 2. Leaky coupling capacitor. 3. Shorted screen bypass capacitor. 4. Change in value of negative feedback resistor or capacitor. 5. Shorted cathode bypass capacitor. 6. Increased value in plate load resistor.
F. High-frequency regeneration.	1. Defective filter capacitor. 2. Change of value of components in feedback loop.

Table 6-3. Troubleshooting Stereo FM Decoders

SYMPTOM	PROBABLE CAUSE	SYMPTOM	PROBABLE CAUSE
A. Operates normally on monaural, but will not operate on stereo.	1. 38-kc locked oscillator or doubler is not operating. 2. 19-kc amplifier is not operating. 3. Phase of 19-kc signal is not correct due to severe misalignment of 19-kc input coil.		4. Leakage in diode rectifier in synchronous detector. 5. 17-kc trap coil not adjusted properly.
B. Poor channel separation.	1. 19-kc input coil not aligned properly. 2. FM if and FM detector not aligned properly. 3. Synchronous detector transformer not aligned properly.	C. Severe distortion.	1. Defective rectifier in synchronous detector. 2. Improper alignment of 19-kc and 38-kc channels (if on stereo only). 3. Improper alignment of FM if or FM detector.

Part II

Record Changers

1 – The Record Changer

1. Introduction

Most modern record changers are relatively simple electronic-electromechanical devices that can be serviced profitably by many television technicians. The mechanical operations involve simple mechanical motions, and the electronics is much simpler than that encountered in any television set. This part of the text describes mechanical and electrical operations of record changers, how to diagnose troubles, and how to repair them.

2. Components

Before progressing, it would be best to become familiar with the basic parts of the record changer—parts that are in almost every set manufactured today, see Fig. 1-1.

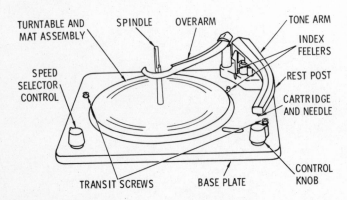

Fig. 1-1. General Electric record changer.

Tone Arm. The *tone arm* holds the cartridge and needle assembly as shown in Fig. 1-2. Its function is to: (1) trace the record grooves, and (2) reproduce the sounds in the record.

Overarm. The *overarm* (sometimes called the balance arm, the record leveler, the record support arm, or stabilizer arm) stabilizes the records on the spindle as shown in Fig. 1-3. Most present-day changers use this arm to activate the last record shut-off mechanism.

Speed Selector Control. The *speed selector control* selects the desired speed of the changer—16⅔, 33⅓, 45, or 78 rpm.

Turntable and Mat Assembly. The *turntable and mat assembly* rotates the records at the selected speed. The mat is made of rubber, or plastic, to provide friction between the turntable and the record to prevent record slippage.

Rest Post. The *rest post* holds the arm when the changer is not in use, and locks the arm in place when the unit is being transported.

Spindle. The *spindle*, or center post: (1) provides a pivot for the record when it is rotating, (2) supports the stack of records to be played, and (3) drops one record at a time to the turntable; see Fig. 1-4.

Control Knob. The *control knob* is generally used to: (1) turn the set *on* and *off*, (2) reject records, and (3) control the manual operation of the changer.

Transit Screws. The *transit screws* fasten the unit to the motor board when it is transported. Figure 1-5 shows the proper setting of these screws for transport, and playing positions.

Base Plate. The *base plate* supports the entire mechanism. It is equivalent to the chassis of a radio or television.

In general, the record changer is a complex group of individual mechanical systems integrated to perform the function of playing records automatically. The following brief descriptions of the various systems in the changers will help you to understand their operation.

Drive System. The purpose of the *drive system* is to transfer the rotating motion from the motor to the turntable. There are four ways in which this is accomplished: (1) a direct belt drive; (2) an intermediate idler, shown in Fig. 1-6; (3) multiple idlers; or (4) a combination of belts and idlers. A more detailed explanation of drive systems is found in Chapter 4.

Record Drop System. The function of the *record drop system* is to drop one record at a time, automatically, at the end of each playing sequence. The predominant part of this mechanism is the spindle, see Fig. 1-4.

Trip System. The purpose of the *trip system* is to start the cycling mechanism at the end of a record. The system is activated by an accelerated inward motion of the tone arm. A faulty trip system is indicated by no tripping at the end of the record, premature tripping (tripping before the end of the record), or late tripping (tripping after the stylus reaches the record label). See Fig. 1-7.

Tone Arm System. Although this is not a complete mechanism, as are the others, the *tone arm system* should be treated as a complete system when repairing changers. Problems pertaining to the tone arm are indicated by improper tracking, warp-wow, and any form of binding in

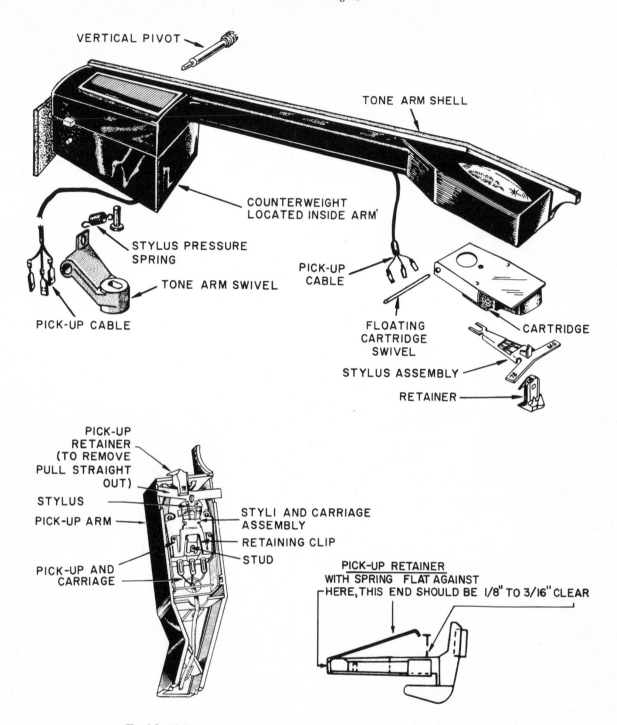

Fig. 1-2. (A) Tone arm assembly. (B) Floating cartridge assembly. (Courtesy of RCA)

the horizontal tracking of the arm. Other problems that may arise are resonance, excessive record wear, and improper stylus pressure. See Fig. 1-2.

Speed Change Assembly. The function of the *speed change assembly* is to change the record changer speeds by means of a remote knob, or lever, mounted on its base plate. Typical problems that might occur in this system are indicated by improper speeds, unusual wearing of the idler wheel, and a jammed or tight speed selector. See Fig. 1-8.

Indexing Mechanism. The *indexing mechanism* auto-

matically selects the record size, and transfers this information to the tone arm so that the arm lands correctly on the edge of the record. The basic part of this mechanism, and the most troublesome, is the record feeler as it can be bent very easily. Symptoms of problems arising in this system are wrong tone arm set-down such as tone arm landing at 7-in. position when 12-in. feelers are activated or vice-versa or any other combination.

Shut-Off System. The *shut-off system* is usually coupled to the overarm, or record balance arm, and transmits information to the mechanism so that it will shut off after the

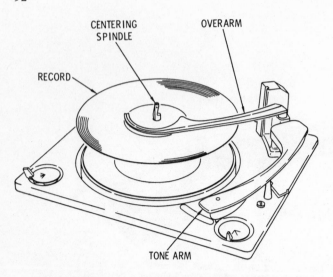

Fig. 1-3. Overarm (or balance arm) supporting a record on the spindle.

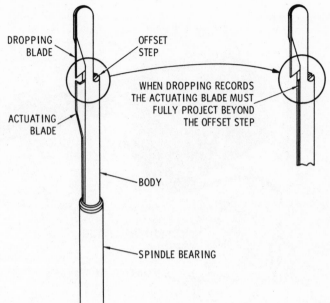

Fig. 1-4. Typical offset spindle assembly.

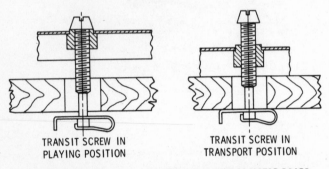

CLIP MUST BE VERTICAL WHEN ASSEMBLING UNIT TO MOTOR BOARD

Fig. 1-5. Transit screws in playing and transport positions. (Courtesy of Garrard Engineering Co.)

last record is played. This system is very closely associated with the indexing mechanism, see Chapter 13. No last record shut-off, and continuous shut-off are symptoms of a malfunction in this system. See Fig. 1-9.

The following basic troubleshooting chart will assist you further in quickly localizing specific problems in the changer.

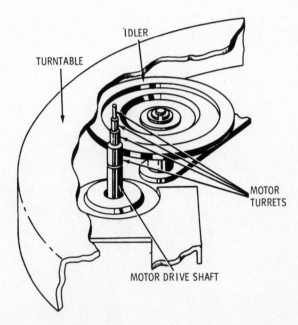

Fig. 1-6. Intermediate idler drive system. (Courtesy of General Electric)

Table 1-1. Troubleshooting Chart

SYMPTOM	CAUSE
A. Changer does not operate.	1. No power to motor. 2. Defective motor. 3. Low line voltage. 4. Idler spring broken, disengaging idler. 5. Drive belts broken, or disengaged. 6. A-c switch defective. 7. Slipping idler wheel.
B. Excessive rumble, or thumping sound.	1. Worn idler wheel. 2. Motor restrained from floating freely on its rubber mounts. 3. Defective or binding on turntable shaft, or bearing.

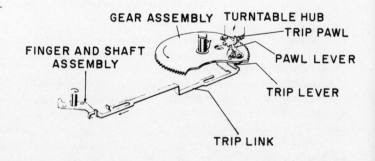

Fig. 1-7. Velocity trip mechanism. (Courtesy of General Electric)

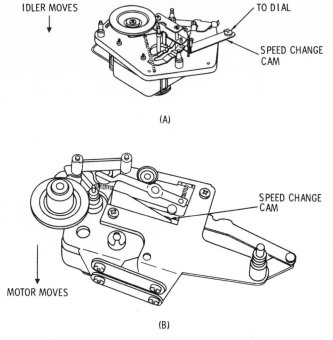

IDLER MOVES

TO DIAL

SPEED CHANGE CAM

(A)

SPEED CHANGE CAM

MOTOR MOVES

(B)

Fig. 1-8. Speed change assembly. (A) Mechanism employs a movable idler and a stationary motor; (B) mechanism employs a stationary idler and a movable motor.

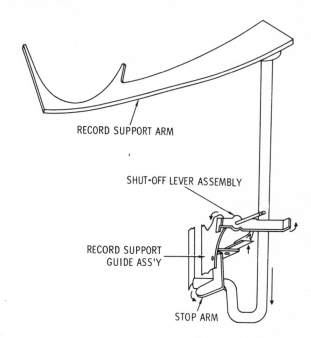

RECORD SUPPORT ARM

SHUT-OFF LEVER ASSEMBLY

RECORD SUPPORT GUIDE ASS'Y

STOP ARM

Fig. 1-9. Shut-off system.

Table 1-1. Troubleshooting Chart (Cont'd)

SYMPTOM	CAUSE
	4. Lack of lubrication on turntable shaft, or bearing.
	5. Motor pulley bent.
C. Speed too fast, or too slow.	1. Wrong size motor pulley. 2. Inadequate lubrication (slow). 3. Motor bearings out of alignment (slow).
D. Erratic speed (wow and flutter).	1. Defective turntable bearings. 2. Foreign matter on idler, or inside rim of turntable. 3. Turntable binding. 4. Idler wheel misaligned. 5. Tight tone arm pivots.
E. Changer drops two records at once.	1. Center hole in record is too large. 2. Small blade in upper portion of spindle is sticking.
F. Unit fails to drop records.	1. Center blade of spindle is not projecting beyond the offset.
G. Difficult speed change.	1. Idler arm bent. 2. Speed control linkages are bent. 3. Interference of speed linkages by a-c wires, etc.

SYMPTOM	CAUSE
H. Needle jumps first few grooves of record.	1. Changer is not level. 2. Cartridge leads are too tight. 3. Needle pressure is too light. 4. Worn needle. 5. Wrong needle size.
I. Unit fails to shut off after last record.	1. Overarm is sticking.
J. No sound during record play.	1. Cartridge is defective. 2. Open tone arm lead. 3. Defective audio cord. 4. Defective muting switch.
K. Tone arm does not land at leading groove of record.	1. Improper indexing. 2. Improper set-down adjustment.
L. Tone arm rises too high, hitting record on spindle shelf.	1. Improper tone arm height adjustment.
M. Cycling mechanism jams.	1. Check for wires caught in mechanism.
N. Tone arm repeats grooves in record.	1. Excessive horizontal friction. 2. Binding in horizontal pivot of tone arm.

2 – Servicing Information

1. Record Changer Manufacturers

Knowledge of the identity of the record changer manufacturer is important to the service technician. The following is a concise list of major record changer manufacturers currently producing record changers for all the major companies today:

1. Voice of Music (VM)
2. Garrard
3. Better Sound Reproduction (BSR)
4. Glaser-Steers (General Electric)
5. Webcor
6. R.C.A.
7. Admiral
8. Crescent (Silvertone)
9. Collaro (Magnavox)

For example, VM supplies record changers for Philco, Zenith, Motorola and several other phonograph manufac-

Fig. 2-2. BSR record changer.

IDENTIFYING MARK OF VM CHANGER 12 IN. INDEX FEELER

Fig. 2-1. VM changer.

Fig. 2-3. The Garrard Autoslim record changer.

turers. Garrard supplies General Electric and others. BSR supplies Emerson and Westinghouse with most of their units. Glaser-Steers has recently been purchased by General Electric and it is likely that all future GE phonographs will be equipped with the Glaser-Steers record changers. Webcor and R.C.A. supply only themselves. At present, Warwick Manufacturing Company (Crescent) has an exclusive contract to supply Silvertone (Sears-Roebuck Company) with their entire line of changers. Collaro, an English concern, is currently supplying Magnavox with all their

changers. Trav-ler products use both the BSR and VM changers.

This information should enable the technician to quickly identify some of the changers merely by knowing the manufacturer of the phonograph. For example, Fig. 2-1 shows some of the significant identifying features of the VM changer. Figure 2-2 shows identifying characteristics of the BSR changer; Fig. 2-3 is an example of a Garrard changer.

2. Servicing Equipment and Supplies

Purchasing and Stocking of Parts

In general, many repairs on record changers are made by merely cleaning or mechanically adjusting a linkage. Parts are very rarely replaced. However, it is advisable to stock the following standard parts.

1. An assortment of "C" lugs.
2. A group of various small springs.
3. Several cartridge mounting lugs.
4. An assortment of small metal washers.
5. A roll of tone arm wire.
6. A few standard length a-c power cords.
7. Several feet of shielded phono wire.
8. Phono lugs (R.C.A. type).
9. Needles (see Chapter 3) for stock.
10. Cartridges (see Chapter 3).

Also, in order to expedite any repairs that might require a standard replacement part, it is advisable to stock a set of idlers, a center spindle, and 45-rpm spindles for: (1) VM Models 900 and 1200; (2) Webcor; (3) BSR Models UA-8, UA-12, UA-14, and UA-16; (4) R.C.A.; and (5) Glaser-Steers. In addition to these parts certain specialized items should be stocked. These parts and quantities can only be determined by the service technician himself, and the decision depends mostly upon the changer most widely used in his area, and a knowledge of the most common faults of specific changer types. Table 2-1 lists the current manufacturers of record changers. Their service departments can help you locate local sources of parts that you may have difficulty finding.

Table 2-1. Changer Service Departments

CHANGER	SERVICE DEPARTMENT
VM (Voice of Music)	VM Corporation Benton Harbor, Michigan
Garrard	British Industries Port Washington, L.I., New York
BSR (Better Sound Reproduction)	BSR, U.S.A. College Point, L.I., New York
Glaser-Steers	General Electric Company P.S. 65 Decatur, Illinois
Webcor	Webcor Chicago 39, Illinois
R.C.A.	R.C.A. Indianapolis, Indiana
Admiral	Admiral Corporation Chicago 47, Illinois
Crescent (Silvertone)	Warwick Manufacturing Company Chicago 48, Illinois
Collaro (Magnavox)	Magnavox Company Fort Wayne 4, Indiana

Tools Needed to Repair Record Changers

It is necessary to have the proper tools to adequately perform a repair. However, most of these tools are already in the repair shop, and will require very little investment. Some tools can be made.

1. Set of standard screwdrivers.
2. Set of jewelers screwdrivers.
3. Set of Phillips screwdrivers.
4. Tweezers.
5. Crochet hooks (for hooking springs).
6. Allen wrenches.
7. Spline wrenches.
8. Needle nose pliers.
9. Hammer and punch (rivets).
10. Wire strippers.
11. Bending tool (see Fig. 2-4).
12. Hypodermic needle (lubricating motor bearings).
13. Stylus pressure gauge.
14. Stroboscope disc.
15. Multimeter.
16. Soldering iron.
17. Friction gauge.
18. 1-in. brush
19. 1000-cycle test record (R.C.A. 12-5-65).
20. 3000-cycle test record (D & R Limited, California).
21. 100-ohm, 10-watt resistor (90-volt motors).

Most of these tools need not be listed, however, there are certain items that are specialized. The *hypodermic needle* injects very light oil into the felt oil retainer in the motor.

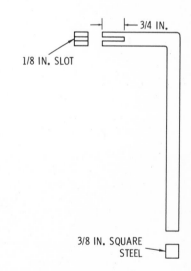

Fig. 2-4. Bending tool.

The *stylus pressure gauge* measures the force applied to the record by the needle. The *stroboscope disc*, when used with a 60-cycle-per-second light source, accurately measures the speed of the turntable within 2%. The *friction gauge* detects binding in either the horizontal or vertical plane of the tone arm pivot system. The *1000-cycle record* determines wow or speed variation in the turntable. It is advisable to use an oscilloscope in conjunction with this to accurately determine wow in a changer (see Fig. 2-5). This is accomplished by connecting the signal lead from the cartridge to the vertical plates of the oscilloscope, and observing any variation in vertical amplitude of the sine wave.

Beyond these two fixtures there are several more that are commercially available, somewhat expensive, but considered excellent. Most of these commercial stands have clamping facilities that allow the technician to rotate the changer so that the bottom of the set can be worked on easily.

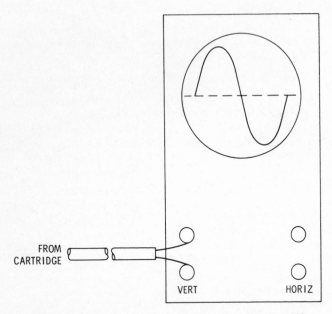

Fig. 2-5. Sine wave on an oscilloscope generated by a 1000-cycle record to determine wow in a record changer. Any difference in the amplitude of the sine wave indicates wow (speed variation).

Chemicals

The following chemicals are used in the repair of record changers.

Table 2-2.

CHEMICALS	USE
A. Trichlorethylene	1. Removing oil and grease.
B. Denatured alcohol	1. Cleaning rubber surfaces.
C. Television Tuner Spray	1. For cleaning and lubricating mechanism parts.
D. Highly Refined Grease	1. For cleaning and lubricating mechanism parts.
E. SAE 10W Lubricating Oil	1. Lubricating motor bearings.
F. 50-50 Mixture of Ammonia and Liquid Detergent	1. Cleaning painted parts.

Special Fixtures

There are several ways a changer can be mounted to enable the technician to repair it. Here are two very inexpensive fixtures that can be made quickly and inexpensively:

Changer-Drawer Slide. This mounting fixture utilizes a set of old drawer slides, four pieces of 12-in. window sash chain, and four window sash hooks. It should be mounted on an existing shelf over the workbench so that when the slides are fully expended the changer projects beyond the edge of the workbench. This enables the technician to look under the changer while it is operating.

Wooden Stands. (See Fig. 2-6.) These two wooden stands can be made from ½-in. or ¾-in. plywood. The overall height of 10 in. can be varied from about 8 in. to 14 in., depending upon the height of the workbench.

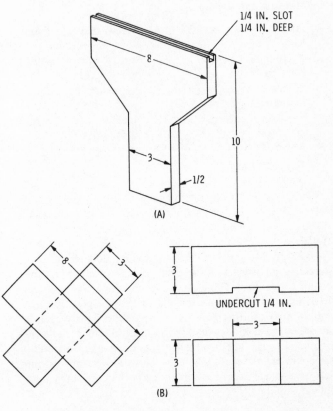

Fig. 2-6. Wooden stand fixture for mounting record changer. (A) Fixture and (B) base.

Test Bench

The table of the workbench should be about 40 in. from the floor, with about (6) a-c receptacles available. It should include two speakers, a stereo amplifier, an oscilloscope, an a-c voltmeter, and test records. It has been found to be very useful to hang all the tools on pegboard racks on either side of the bench. (See Fig. 2-7).

As the need arises, there are many pieces of sophisticated equipment that can be added to this set-up, such as a flutter meter, wow meter, motor torque gauge, stylus microscope, and a speed meter.

Test Records

There are many special test records available to the technician that will assist him in his efforts to repair a changer. The R.C.A. 12-5-35 is designed for checking landing and tripping. It is also useful for checking cartridge sensitivity, turntable flutter, and rumble. Another such useful record published by R.C.A. is the 12-5-57 which was designed for testing the landing and tripping operation. It has three various modulated bands joined by spiral grooves. The 1000-cycle modulated band starts at 6.875 in. which is the accu-

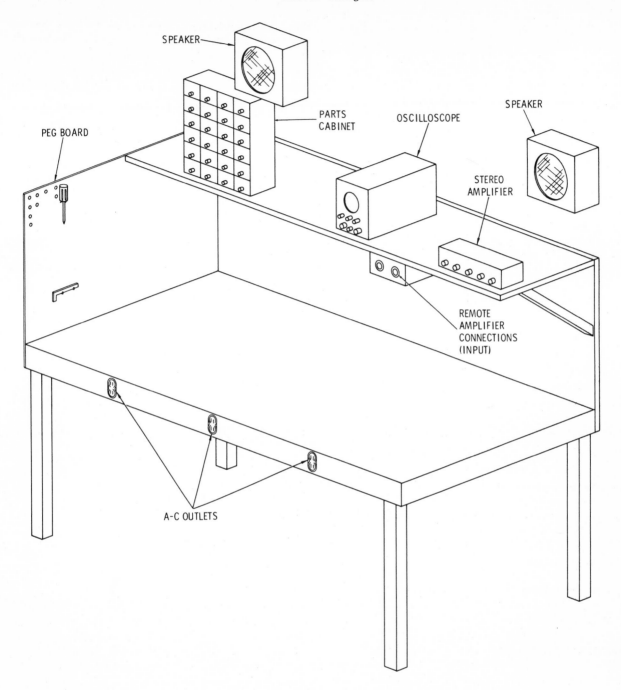

Fig. 2-7. Typical record changer test bench set-up.

rate set-down point for a 7-in. record. Another test record used quite extensively is the R.C.A. 12-5-65. It has three 1000-cycle bands recorded at 78, 45, and 33⅓ rpm, respectively. This record in conjunction with an audio generator, and an oscilloscope, will accurately measure turntable speeds. It can be utilized for checking turntable wow and flutter at the speeds.

Service Literature

There is considerable literature available from both the manufacturer and various publishers. In many cases, this literature itemizes specific defects in a changer with its cure, as supplied by the manufacturer. It is advisable that whenever large problems occur with any specific changer to contact the manufacturer directly.

3 – Cartridges and Needles

1. Introduction

The cartridge assembly plays the most important role in the reproduction of recorded sound. Actually, all the changer accessories are merely supplements to this all-important assembly. To insure that the cartridge is not damaged while working on the record changer, the following precautions should be taken:

1. Remove the stylus from the cartridge, if easily accessible, or protect it in some manner so that the arm does not slide across the turntable or record.

2. Never store crystal-type cartridges in a warm place (above 90° F).

3. Avoid magnetic fields when working with magnetic cartridges.

2. Cartridge Types

Three cartridge types presently marketed are the magnetic, the ceramic, and crystal. These all differ in their principles of operation.

Magnetic Cartridges

The magnetic cartridge, which operates on the principle of a moving wire through a magnetic field, is the best type. Because the moving system is very light and pivots about a small radius, good high-frequency response is obtained. Most cartridge manufacturers connect the stylus to the wire and, as it tracks the record grooves, a voltage is generated. This voltage is fed to the amplifier, which raises the signal to a suitable level to drive the speaker. Other manufacturers connect the stylus to the magnet, and allow this to generate a voltage by the movement of the magnetic field as shown in Fig. 3-1. The magnetic cartridge has a voltage output of approximately 5 millivolts; thus, it is necessary to use additional amplification to raise the audio signal to a useable level. This additional amplification is usually supplied by a preamplifier.

A typical magnetic cartridge housing is shown in Fig. 3-2. The mu-metal magnetic shielding, used in most magnetic cartridges, is not adequate to minimize the hum that is picked up from the stray fields of a 2-pole motor. A four-pole motor must be used to minimize hum.

Most phonograph manufacturers are hesitant to use magnetic cartridges because of the expense of a preamplifier and a 4-pole motor.

Ceramic Cartridges

The ceramic cartridge is the most versatile and most widely used cartridge in use today. Reasons for this are:
1. It has a nominal output of about 0.5 volts.
2. It eliminates the need for a preamplifier.
3. It has good frequency response.
4. It is hum free.

The principle of operation for this cartridge is based on the piezoelectric effect in which electricity is generated when pressure is applied to certain crystalline materials. Therefore, when the stylus tracks a record, applying pressure to the crystalline material, a voltage is generated which is fed to the amplifier.

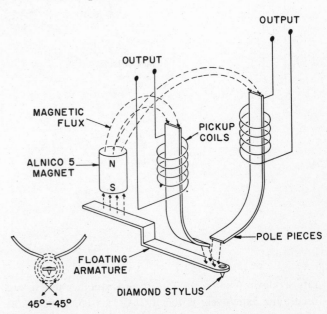

Fig. 3-1. Principle of operation of the stereo magnetic cartridge. This is a moving magnet type. (Courtesy of General Electric)

Crystal Cartridges

Crystal cartridges, although classified separately, are similar to the ceramic. The principle of operation is exactly the same; the only difference is in the crystals used. Barium titanate and lead zirconate titanate are the major

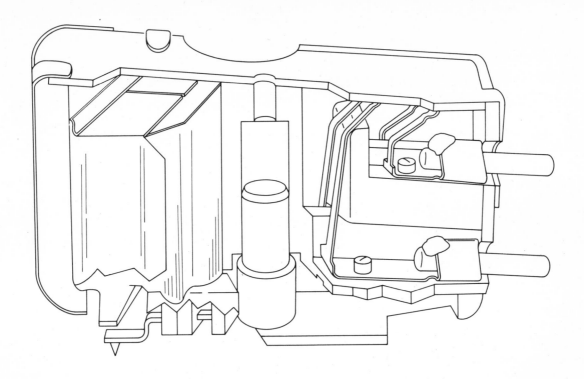

Fig. 3-2. Typical magnetic cartridge construction. (Courtesy of General Electric)

crystals used in the ceramic cartridges because they are extremely flexible, enabling the cartridge to attain better frequency response, and they resist heat damage. The crystal cartridge uses Rochelle salts, and have an extremely high voltage output, as high as 5 volts. Its disadvantages are poor frequency response, and possible breakdown caused by excessive heat. A typical crystal cartridge set-up is shown in Fig. 3-3.

Floating Cartridges

Maximum performance is derived from minimum weight and mass. As a result, cartridge manufacturers have perfected the *floating cartridge,* whose design elevates the vertical compliance of a cartridge to a height where vertical shock to the changer will not make the stylus leave the record groove. This cartridge mount is excellent, but can be a hindrance to the technician due to misadjustments of the stylus pressure by either the customer or the technician. The importance of the proper stylus pressure adjustment on floating cartridges cannot be overstressed as it will probably be the only defect that will be encountered with this unit. A typical unit is shown in Fig. 3-4.

Cartridge Defects

Defective cartridges can be detected by either signal tracing or substitution. Do not attempt to repair a defective cartridge. Replace a defective cartridge with a type recommended by the phonograph manufacturer. There are substitutes which can be used, and the replacements for most

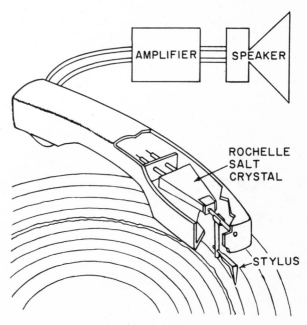

Fig. 3-3. Operation of a crystal cartridge.

of the commonly used cartridges are listed in a book published by John F. Rider Publisher, Inc.* Certain systems may indicate a defective cartridge although the unit is

*Jack Strong. *Master Cartridge Substitution Guidebook,* 2nd Edition. New York: John F. Rider Publisher, Inc., 1963.

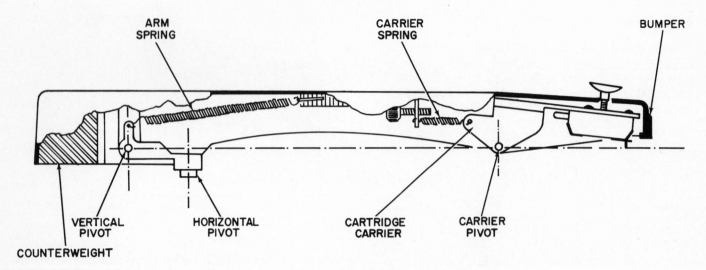

Fig. 3-4. Typical floating cartridge arm. (Courtesy of the Audio Engineering Society)

undamaged. The symptoms may include weak sound or loss of a channel. Before proceeding to replace the cartridge, check that the cartridge lugs are secure, and be sure the stylus is resting properly in the yoke. A cartridge and stylus assembly is shown in Fig. 3-5. If this checks out, proceed to replace the cartridge, making sure that no heat is applied to the contacts of the cartridge when it is installed.

3. The Stylus

Stylus Operation

The heart of the record changer, and the cartridge assembly for that matter, is the stylus. No matter how elaborate the design of the cartridge, the amplifier, or the speaker system may be, faithful sound reproduction depends on the proper junction of the stylus and the record. To initiate faithful sound reproduction, it is imperative that the stylus maintain a positive contact with the record groove *at all times*. Movement within the record groove will induce distortion in the sound output, and gouge or shave the modulation of the record grooves.

Positive contact is also lost if the stylus is in any way chipped or worn; some stylii may be so worn that they are actually tracking the bottom of the record groove instead of the intended tracking surfaces, see Fig. 3-6.

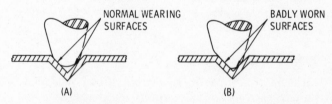

Fig. 3-6. (A) A good stylus maintains positive contact with the record changer groove; (B) a worn stylus tracks the bottom of the record, damaging the grooves.

Excessive record wear by a damaged stylus is usually the end result. We must realize that the unit pressure present at the stylus point is on the order of *25,000 pounds per square inch*. Also, the excessive heat present at the point raises the temperature to *1500° F*. These two conditions lead to excessive record wear.

To maintain long stylus life, a number of hard materials are used for the needle point. Diamond and sapphire are used today for points. The diamond stylus, which is far superior both in quality and durability, is made from synthetic diamonds. (One can distinguish the difference between a sapphire and a diamond by careful examination under a microscope. A diamond needle looks like a piece of steel; a sapphire looks like a piece of transparent glass.)

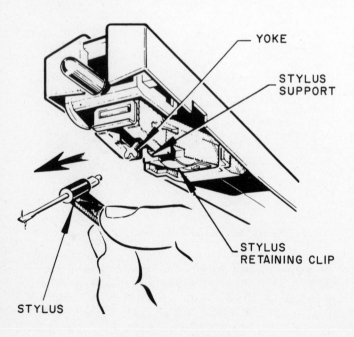

Fig. 3-5. Cartridge assembly.

Stylus Wear

While it is generally known that a diamond outwears a sapphire stylus, periodic examination is required because the life of the diamond needle depends upon the quality of the diamond in the unit. The number of hours of use, given by manufacturers, is not the most reliable guide line to actual stylus life. Periodic microscopic examination will indicate whether or not a replacement is indicated, see Fig. 3-7.

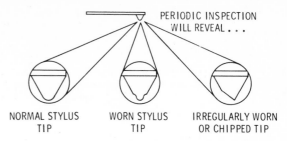

Fig. 3-7. Typical stylus tip conditions.

4 – The Drive System

1. Function

The function of the drive system is to revolve the turntable at the desired speed. This system contains several parts which may require service. The surface of many of these components are either smooth rubber or metal which cannot tolerate any oil, grease, dust, or any other foreign matter. Today's market demands that four speeds be available, and that the drive system must reduce the speed of the motor (1800 rpm for a 4-pole motor, 3600 rpm for a 2-pole motor) to the desired speed. The basic components of this system are the motor, turntable, and the coupling device. The coupling device usually consists of an idler wheel or several idler wheels, a belt or any combination of belts and idlers, to attain the proper turntable speed and coupling.

Through the years there have been many changes in the coupling method. In the early days of 78-rpm changers, this complex system did not exist. As manufacturers searched for longer playing times and higher fidelity on recordings, they discovered that records played at slower speeds gave better sound reproduction. As a result, the changer manufacturers developed several types of coupling systems: (1) the single-step idler, (2) the dual-step idler, (3) the idler-belt system, (4) the multiple idler plus single-step idler, and (5) the belt drive.

2. Coupling Systems

Single-Step Idler

This coupling has been used quite extensively in the 78-rpm players, and, with modification, it is used today in the multiple speed changers. Many of the changers produced by Voice of Music, BSR, Garrard, General Electric, Magnavox, and Silvertone have this system, see Fig. 4-1. The advantages of this system over others are reduced manufacturing cost, and ease of operation.

Dual-Step Idler

The next, and not so popular, drive coupling is the dual-

step idler, currently being used in the small R.C.A. 45-rpm players, and the most expensive Voice of Music models. This is a more expensive means of accomplishing the same job, however, there are advantages that justify the additional manufacturing cost. They are reduced motor rumble, because there is twice as much rubber from the motor to the turntable rim, as shown in Fig. 4-2, and the facility to change turntable speed by merely reducing the diameter of the motor spindle turning the idler wheel.

Idler-Belt System

The idler-belt drive system, of which there are two types,

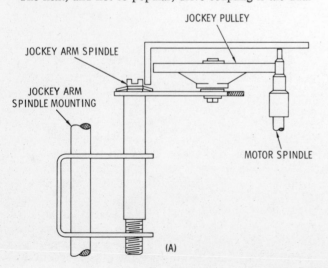

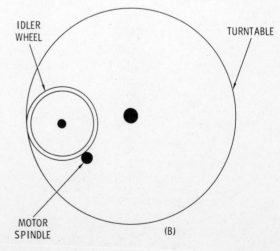

Fig. 4-1. Single step idler system. (A) Side view of the drive; (B) simplified top view.

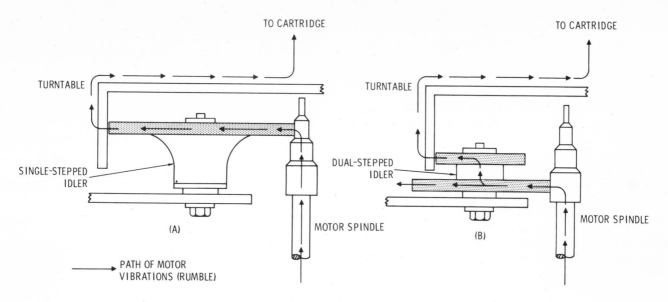

Fig. 4-2. Comparison of the rumble path between (A) single-stepped idler system and (B) dual-stepped idler system.

has the advantage of lower rumble and greater versatility in changing speeds. The lower rumble is attained because of the inability of leather or thin rubber to transmit vibrations. The modified type, as shown in Fig. 4-3, is used today in many changers, whereas the more elaborate type, as shown in Fig. 4-4, is used in many of the transcription type turntables.

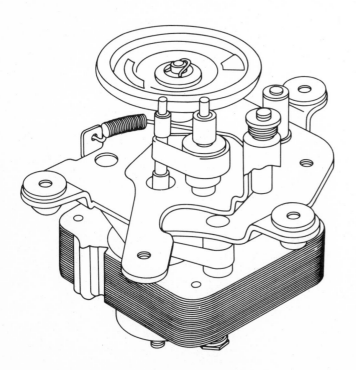

Fig. 4-3. Idler-belt drive system.

Multiple Idler plus Single-Step Idler System

Prior to the use of the single-step idler system, the multiple idler plus single-step idler was the most predominant

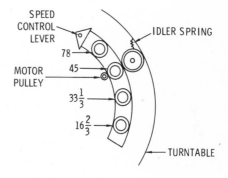

Fig. 4-4. Zenith idler-belt drive system.

coupling device used in multiple speed changers. Even today a good portion of the changers in the field utilize this system. It was used in the 900 series manufactured by Voice of Music and all three- and four-speed units made by R.C.A.

To change speed, one wheel is disengaged while another is put in its place by shifting the speed control lever.

To determine the speed to which these wheels correspond, the one with the largest diameter is the 78-rpm idler, and in descending sequences: 45 rpm, 33⅓, and 16⅔ rpm, as shown in Fig. 4-5. When determining speed, disregard the rubber diameter as it is usually the same diameter for all four wheels.

Many of the problems found in this drive are similar to those found in other drives. The only exception is when defects occur at certain speeds; the wheel that accommodates that speed should be either cleaned or replaced. Problems of this nature will occur in this particular drive system as the customer probably has a larger selection of a certain speed record, causing that particular wheel to wear out sooner than the others.

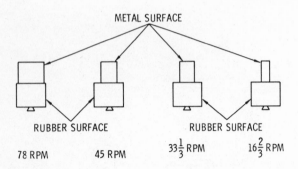

Fig. 4-5. Step drive wheels used in multiple idler systems.

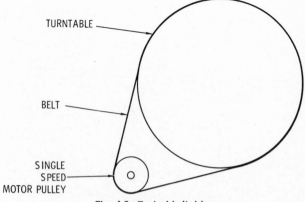

Fig. 4-6. Typical belt drive.

Belt Drive

The belt drive, see Fig. 4-6, is the least used because manufacturers have not yet designed a belt drive that is practical to construct and maintain. The greatest problem is its inability to change speeds. There are, however, many professional turntables on the market that utilize this system, but they are only single speed players, usually 33⅓ rpm. The most common fault that will be encountered by this type of drive is that the belt may stretch or become dirty. In either case, it is advisable to replace it rather than attempt to clean it. Using any of the chemicals in Chapter 2 will only cause the belt to stretch.

Maintenance

The technician will encounter a variety of problems in maintaining the drive systems, whether it be cleaning the idler wheel or replacing the motor. The following table will be of assistance when problems occur.

Table 4-1. Troubleshooting Drive Systems

SYMPTOM	DEFECT	REMEDY
A. Turntable does not turn	1. Slipping idler wheel. 2. Idler spring broken, stretched, or disengaged.	1. Clean or replace idler wheel. 2. Replace or repair spring.
B. Turntable speed too slow	1. Turntable bearings defective. 2. Slipping idler wheel. 3. Lack of lubrication of spindle or turntable bearings.	1. Replace bearings. 2. Clean or replace idler wheel. 3. Lubricate with thin oil (NO GREASE).
C. Turntable stalls during cycle	1. Idler slipping. 2. Idler spring disengaged. 3. Motor weak. 4. Gear teeth on turntable hub worn. 5. Lubricant on idler shaft hardened.	1. Clean or replace idler wheel. 2. Reset spring. 3. Replace motor. 4. Replace turntable hub. 5. Clean and lubricate with light oil.

5 – Motors

1. Function and Operation

The record changer motor is one of the most important parts of the mechanism, supplying the power that rotates the turntable as well as the power to operate the change cycle mechanism. Because of the importance of the motor, it should be cared for periodically, at least once a year.

Almost every motor that is used in changers today, whether it be a 2-pole, 4-pole, hysteresis, or otherwise, is equipped with bearings made of oil-impregnated metal, "requiring no lubrication." This claim, however, is dependent on the useage the changer receives. To be safe, the motor should be served periodically, using highly refined SAE 10W30 oil and avoiding the use of grease or heavy oil, as this will harden on the bearings of the motor and cause the motor to become sluggish. Use lubrication sparingly to avoid spillover on idler wheel.

Figure 5-1 shows the lubrication points on the motor. Be extremely careful to properly orient the lamination assembly when reassembling the motor because the armature will turn in reverse if it is not assembled properly. After the motor has been serviced, it should be checked for noise. In many cases the motor will develop a buzzing sound that is created by misalignment of its bearings. To overcome this, strike the laminations with a mallet, delivering a fairly hard blow while the motor is running. This shock will realign the self-aligning bearings in the motor, see Fig. 5-2. Misalignment may also cause the rotor to rub against the laminations. To avoid this, check the air gap around the rotor when reassembling the motor.

Operating Principles

The operation of the induction motor is simple. It utilizes the basic principle of a moving wire (rotor) in a magnetic field (lamination assembly or field). The only deviation is that these motors have shading rings that enable the motor to be self-starting. Nevertheless, the rings cause a certain amount of drag in the motor's speed, in some cases as much as 300 rpm (for a 3600-rpm motor). However, since the changer is designed with the drag taken into consideration, it will probably never be of any consequence to the technician.

One might ask, "Why the different sized motor pulleys and idlers on the same model record changer"? The answer is that some changers have 2-pole motors, others

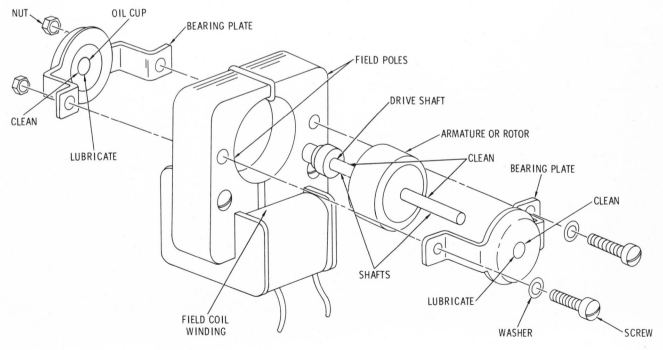

Fig. 5-1. Typical two-pole motor disassembled showing points of maintenance.

105

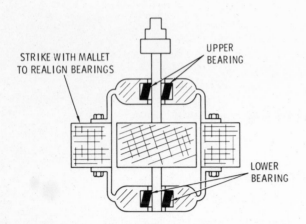

Fig. 5-2. Misaligned bearings causing buzzing sound.

4-pole, and some even have 6-pole motors. Because of this, the free running speeds of these motors are proportionately different. The formula for determining the speed of a motor is as follows:

$$Speed = \frac{2 \times (f)^2}{N}$$

where 2 is a constant, f is the frequency of the line (in cps), and N is the number of poles. For a standard 4-pole motor used in the United States:

$$Speed = \frac{2 (60)^2}{4} = 1800 \text{ rpm}$$

The speed for the same motor in Europe, where 50-cycle current is available, is:

$$Speed = \frac{2 (50)^2}{4} = 1250 \text{ rpm}$$

As can be seen, a changer that is brought to Europe from the U.S. would run much slower, and vice-versa for units purchased in Europe and brought to the U.S. Hence, the need for a 50-cycle adapter.

50-Cycle Operation

Most manufacturers that use the single step idler system can convert the changer to 50 cycles by merely increasing the diameter of the motor pulley. This is usually accomplished by using springs that slip on the existing shaft or completely replacing the motor pulley.

However, sets using stepped idlers or multiple idlers cannot do this. They must replace the idler wheel with one that has diameter dimensions to compensate for the decrease of the motor speed. In either case, when the need arises for a 50-cycle conversion, it is imperative to contact the manufacturer's service department directly to be sure that the conversion will be successfully completed. In some cases a series resistor must be included in the conversion.

2. Motor Types and Motor Defects

Types of Motors

There are many types of changer motors used today. They are all of the alternating-current type, and can be divided into three major classes: induction, synchronous, and hysteresis. While there are many modifications of these three classes, they are all similar in operation.

Induction Motor. The induction motor is the most commonly used since it is the simplest in design, and is the least expensive. The most common type of induction motor is called the "squirrel cage" because the armature resembles the wheel of a squirrel cage. In explaining the operation of this motor, it is necessary to remember the principle of induction as found in a simple transformer, and the electrical definition of *phase*. The simplest form of induction motor is the two-phase motor which can be a 2-pole, 4-pole, or 6-pole unit. In operation the poles are alternately connected so that when the two opposite poles are magnetized, the other two poles are demagnetized. The armature (rotor) has no electrical connection. Hence, the field (stator) can be compared to the primary of a transformer, and the armature as the secondary. When current flows through the field, a magnetic field forms, which sets up, by induction, a current flow in the windings of the armature. The attraction between the magnetic field of the armature and the magnetic field of the stator causes the armature to rotate.

Synchronous Motor. The synchronous motor is used on very few changers, and is very similar to an alternator

(used in many cars). In fact, an alternator connected in reverse becomes a synchronous motor. The main visible difference between this type of motor and the induction is that the armature, instead of the field, is stationary, and the field rotates. The free running speed of this motor (usually 4 pole in changers), unlike the induction type, is true to the frequency of the line. In other words, a 4-pole *synchronous* motor runs at 1800 rpm not 1600 as does the 4-pole *induction* motor. The reason for this is that if an alternating current is applied to the armature, it produces a revolving magnetic field, like that found in the field of an induction motor revolving in time with the frequency that is supplying it. In order to start this motor, a filter capacitor is used, and, undoubtedly, is the prime suspect whenever service problems occur.

The prime advantage of this motor is its ability to remain at constant speed.

Hysteresis Motor. The hysteresis motor, used only on the most expensive changers, operates on the principle of a constant magnetic field. In other words, if the voltage applied to the motor changes slightly, the speed of the motor remains constant because the speed depends not only on the amount of current applied to the field, but mainly on the previous state of magnetization of the field. Small variations in the line voltage will *not* alter the speed of this motor. This principle, when coupled with the synchronous motor, yields the best motor. It is commonly called the hysteresis-synchronous motor.

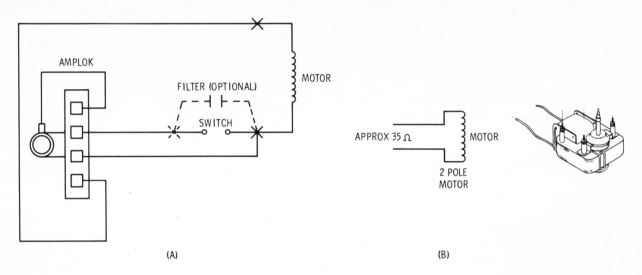

Fig. 5-3. (A) Complete power wiring of today's changers; (B) approximate resistance of a 2-pole motor.

Motor Defects

Dead Motor. With the turntable removed, apply power to the motor. If it does not revolve, try turning the armature by hand. It may have dry bearings and cannot start. If this is the case, disassemble the motor and follow the lubrication diagram of Fig. 5-1. If this is not the case, it is possible that the torque is reduced due to shorted turns in the windings. If this is true, a new motor is in order. If, on the other hand, there is no way to get the armature to turn, check the continuity of the wiring in the changer and that of the motor, see Fig. 5-3. Other possibilities may be a defective switch, an open winding in the motor, or a shorted motor.

Slow Speed. This usually means that one of the components in the drive system is not rotating freely, thus loading the motor. It may be the turntable, the idler, or the motor. If the motor is at fault, lubricate the bearings as shown in Fig. 5-1.

Thumping Sound. If the sound is localized to the motor, the only cure is to check its suspension. A twisted or frayed mounting grommet is probably at fault.

Overheating. If overheating of the motor is the case, replace the motor because it probably has shorted turns in the field winding.

Motor Buzzing. As mentioned earlier in the chapter, this defect occurs when the self-aligning bearings become misaligned. The only cure is to strike the laminations of the motor in order to reset these bearings, see Fig. 5-2. Also check to see that the rotor is balanced.

Rumble. Rumble is a low pitched sound usually detected when a silent passage is played, and is usually caused by one of the components in the drive system. If the problem is pinpointed to the motor after checking the mounting grommets, clean the motor or, if the situation demands, replace it.

6 – The Change Cycle

1. Function and Operation

The change cycle, in many instances, is the least understood segment of the automatic record changer. It consists of various gears, cams, and linkages, which, when connected together, perform specific functions. Two typical cycling mechanisms are shown in Figs. 6-1 and 6-2. The functions, in sequence, are as follows:

1. To drop the record.
2. To sense the record size.
3. To place the tone arm at the beginning of the record.
4. To allow the record to play to the end (unless actuated manually).
5. To trip and repeat the sequence if another record is on the spindle. If not, the mechanism shuts the changer off automatically.

To follow each sequence of the changer cycle, it is advisable to manually rotate the turntable, and observe the

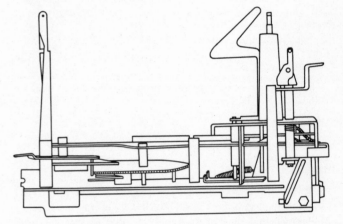

Fig. 6-1. Complete cycling mechanism featuring unitized construction.

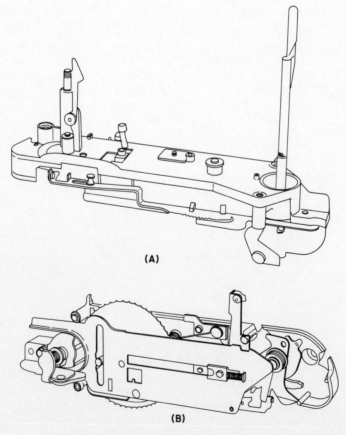

(A)

(B)

Fig. 6-2. Complete cycling mechanism of the type used in VM changers. (Courtesy of General Electric)

action that takes place. Most changers have a velocity-trip mechanism which starts the mechanism by the fast, inward motion of the tone arm when the needle enters the lead-out grooves at the end of the record. As the trip is actuated, the large slide (commonly called the main slide) moves in the direction of the tone arm, depressing a pin upward that allows the tone arm to raise.

After the tone arm is pivoted toward the rest post, clearing the record, the mechanism activates the spindle, allowing the next record to drop. As the record drops, it will either hit or miss a sensing device that tells the mechanism where to deliver the tone arm, whether it be a 12-in., 10-in., or 7-in. record. Usually, there are only sensing devices for 12-in. and 10-in. records. If none of the sensors are activated, changers will automatically deliver the tone arm to the 7-in. position.

Change Cycle Drives

There are basically two classifications for the change cycle drive—independent drive and turntable drive. The least common of the two is the independent drive found in many models of the Collaro, Glaser-Steers, and Crescent changers. Both Collaro and Glaser-Steers utilize a rubber pinion gear to drive the main gear when the cycle is activated, while Crescent uses an eccentric, rubber main gear that is activated by the hub of the turntable. Both of these cycle drives are excellent because they are somewhat trouble-free, inasmuch as they provide more of a direct drive to the mechanism, and are less likely to cause a problem such as sluggish change cycle.

The second type of cycle drive commonly used is the turntable gear type and, by far, the most widely used today, offering simplicity and reduced manufacturing cost. It can become troublesome if the rubber (idler wheel) becomes glazed, hard, and brittle, or if any foreign matter falls on any of the drive surfaces.

Although the trip mechanism, the shut-off mechanism, and the indexing mechanism, etc., are integrated parts of the cycling mechanism, we will treat them independently in the following chapters.

2. Maintenance

Problems in the Change Cycle Drive

Although turntable stopping, or slowing down during the change cycle, gives the appearance of trouble associated with the drive mechanism of the change cycle, the trouble is more likely to be found in the drive mechanism of the changer. (Refer to Chapter 4 for a remedy.) In any event the change cycle drive should be checked at every opportunity. When cleaning and lubricating, it is wise to inspect all of the drive parts. If the unit does not perform satisfactorily after cleaning, replacement of the drive wheel may correct the problem.

Lubrications

There are certain parts in the change cycle that should be lubricated, and certain parts that must be absolutely clean. As mentioned in Chapter 4, the drive surfaces, such as, the idler drive wheel, motor pulley, and inside rim of the turntable, must be absolutely free of any dirt or oil. Also, all the parts that pertain to the trip system must be

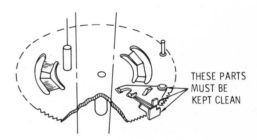

THESE PARTS MUST BE KEPT CLEAN

Fig. 6-3. Parts for a velocity trip mechanism.

clean. These parts are usually a part of the main gear assembly, see Fig. 6-3. To lubricate points that are inaccessible, a brush should be used to apply grease, and an oil can with a long, thin nozzle should be used to apply oil. Apply a sufficient amount of grease to all gear teeth, cam surfaces, slots, and rollers. Oil should be applied to shafts and pivot studs. Never apply an excess of oil because oil thins under heat, and may tend to run or splatter, coating critical surfaces.

7 – Trip Mechanisms

1. Function and Categories

The trip mechanism used in present-day changers are extremely sensitive. The most widely used mechanism is the *velocity trip* which has been used in many forms for the past years, but has been incorporated with other types. Basically, the trip mechanisms can be divided into three categories:

1. The position trip, or positive trip.
2. The oscillating trip, or eccentric trip.
3. The velocity trip.

The Position Trip

The position trip, or positive trip, was the first mechanism used for initiating the change cycle, see Fig. 7-1. Basically, it incorporates a fixed actuating lever, rigidly fastened to the tone arm pivot, so that the pivot moves in unison with the tone arm. At a predetermined point in the lateral movement of the arm, the actuating lever will strike a pawl, and start the change cycle.

The Oscillating or Eccentric Trip

The eccentric trip was developed for a more positive tripping action. It uses the eccentric lead-out grooves at the end of the record, with the backward motion of the tone arm starting the eccentric trip mechanism, see Fig. 7-2. The trip finger in the device employs a series of saw teeth.

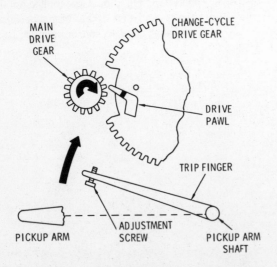

Fig. 7-1. Position trip mechanism (positive trip mechanism) is the device used for starting the change cycle. The main drive gear is mounted on the turntable shaft.

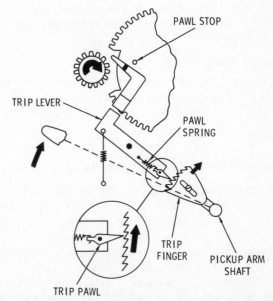

Fig. 7-2. Eccentric trip mechanism. Inset shows details of trip pawl and saw teeth on the trip finger.

About half way through the recording, the teeth contact the trip pawl, keep progressing inwardly until the tone arm reverses itself due to the eccentric lead-out grooves, and then release the trip pawl, starting the change cycle. Although this method is more efficient than the positive trip, it has the disadvantage of a long change-cycle actuating time. A trip system, whereby the tone arm upon entering the lead-out grooves would actuate the change cycle immediately, is required. The velocity trip was developed to perform this function.

The Velocity Trip

The velocity, or acceleration, trip is the most widely used today. Velocity trip action derives its name from the increased velocity of lateral motion of the tone arm when it enters the eccentric lead-out grooves.

Let us now follow a typical sequence of events in a VM mechanism, see Fig. 7-3. The tone arm, and the finger and shaft assembly are connected so that they move in unison. As the tone arm nears the end of a record, the finger and shaft assembly pulls the trip link, thus engaging and pivoting the trip lever. As the trip lever pivots, the pawl lever pivots with it, and carries the trip pawl toward the turntable hub. While the tone arm is in the modulated grooves,

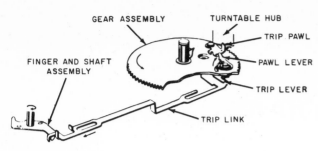

Fig. 7-3. Trip mechanism parts. (Courtesy of General Electric)

the small motions of the trip pawl are not sufficient to cycle the mechanism because with each turntable revolution, the wiping contact (caused by the hub projection on the turntable gear) moves the trip pawl back.

When the needle enters the lead-out grooves, the trip pawl is moved far enough to properly engage the projection on the turntable hub. The contact between the trip pawl and the turntable hub projection gives the push required to engage the teeth on the gear assembly, with the teeth on the turntable hub causing the gear assembly to rotate.

2. Maintenance

VM Trip System

The VM trip system, although very durable under normal handling, may jam. In most cases, the aluminum trip link bends, and in order to restore the changer to proper working order, this link must be replaced. It is good practice for a service shop to have a few trip links available. Some of the other service problems that might occur in this mechanism are found in Table 7-1.

Garrard Trip System

Because the Garrard trip link is made of steel, it is un-

likely that it would present any serious problems. Should it bend, it would be a simple task to straighten it. Should trouble develop in this system, it is recommended to check the freedom of movement of all the linkages in the trip system. Make sure the pick-up leads are free, check for defective stylus, etc.

Webcor Trip System

Along with VM, Webcor also jams. Their trip link is also a part that would be worthwhile stocking, as it bends beyond repair whenever the changer jams.

Table 7-1.

SYMPTOM	CAUSE	REMEDY
A. Changer continues to cycle.	1. Trip mechanism binding.	1. Check up to see that the trip link is not bent or frozen. It should move freely. 2. Make sure that the control shaft (connected to the reject knob) is not binding. 3. Check for a binding trip pawl, trip lever, and pawl lever. These should have surfaces free from grease or oil.
B. No trip.	1. No finishing grooves on the record.	1. Check record for trip groove. Some old records have none.
C. No trip.	1. Needle jumps out of grooves in record.	1. Check trip pressure. Lateral friction of arm should not exceed stylus pressure. 2. Insufficient stylus pressure.

SYMPTOM	CAUSE	REMEDY
		3. Defective record. 4. Defective needle. 5. Tone arm pivot, or velocity trip mechanism binding.
D. No trip.	1. Trip pawl binding on gear face.	1. Check for burrs or binding on trip pawl.
E. No trip.	1. Bent finger and shaft.	1. Straighten or replace.
F. No trip.	1. Trip link bent.	1. Straighten or replace.
G. Changer trips before needle reaches end of record.	1. Hole in record too large.	1. Replace record.
H. Changer trips before needle reaches end of record.	1. Trip link binding.	1. Check for freedom of movement of the trip link.
	2. Trip link bent.	1. Straighten or replace.
	3. Trip pawl bent.	1. Straighten or replace.

8 – The Shut-Off System

The shut-off mechanism is an assembly which (1) controls the movement of the tone arm so that it does not return to the record at the end of the last record play, and (2) shuts off and/or disengages the motor so that the turntable does not continue to turn after the last record play. The most common difficulties encountered with the shut-off system are (1) complete operational failure, and (2) premature shut-off. The troubleshooting procedures for difficulties encountered with the shut-off system are discussed later in this chapter. Three types of shut-off systems are described in the following paragraphs.

1. Typical Shut-Off Systems

Overarm Shut-Off Mechanism

The overarm shut-off mechanism is the most commonly used automatic shut-off device contained in record changers. It represents the most sophisticated, positive mechanical shut-off system developed for modern-day record changers.

A typical shut-off mechanism is shown in Fig. 8-1. When the last record drops to the turntable, the overarm or record support arm returns to its lowest position with reference to the turntable(horizontal axis). The lower end of the record support arm shaft is now allowed to press on the quadrant lever, forcing it to pivot in an upward direction. This changes the pivot point of the stop pawl. The change of pivot point of the stop pawl causes the index pawl to move inward to engage the last notch on the index ratchet assembly. This action prevents the index ratchet assembly (which controls the position of the tone arm) from pivoting, and allows the tone arm to return to and remain at rest after the last record has played.

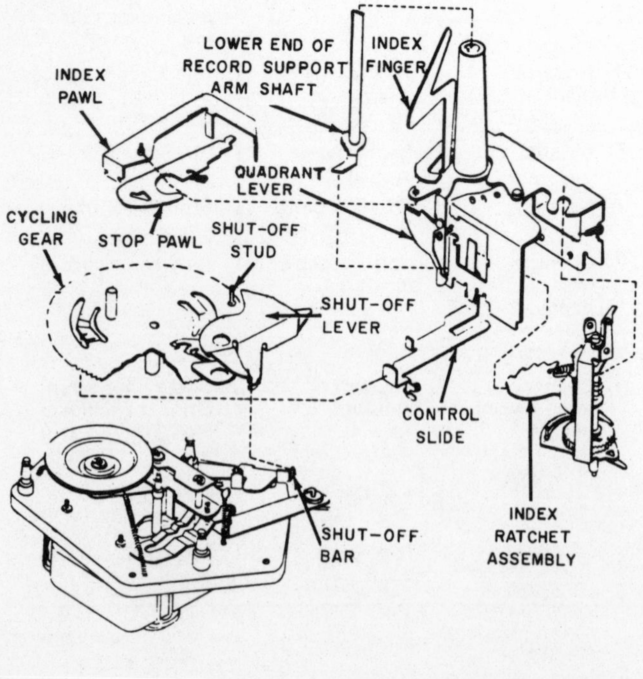

After the record has played and the tone arm has returned to the rest post, the index ratchet assembly holds the control slide assembly in position so that the cycling gear cam contacts the tab which is protruding from the control slide. This causes the cycling gear to move to a raised position as it rotates. When the cycling gear is rotating in the raised position, the shut-off stud on the cycling gear actuates the shut-off lever. The shut-off lever contacts and engages the shut-off bar which moves the slide switch to the OFF position, and disengages the idler wheel.

The slide switch will remain in the OFF position (removing electrical power from the motor), and the idler wheel will remain in the disengaged position until their respective positions are changed manually by correctly positioning the record start control. When the record start control is actuated (manually), the slide switch is set to the ON position, and the idler gear is once again engaged.

Spindle Shut-Off Mechanism

The spindle shut-off mechanism is similar to the overarm shut-off mechanism. The basic difference is that in the spindle type, a lever in the spindle actuates the mechanism for returning and setting the tone arm at the rest post and shutting off and/or disengaging the motor from the turntable; in the overarm type, the position of the overarm causes the cycling gear to perform this function.

A basic spindle shut-off mechanism is shown in Fig. 8-2. When there are records on the spindle, pressure is applied on the spring-loaded lever. As long as there is pressure on the lever, it will remain disengaged from the stop arm. When the last record has dropped to the turntable, the pressure is removed from the lever, permitting it to move in the upward direction. When the opposite end of the lever follower pivots in the downward direction, it forces

Fig. 8-1. Automatic shut-off mechanism. (Courtesy of General Electric)

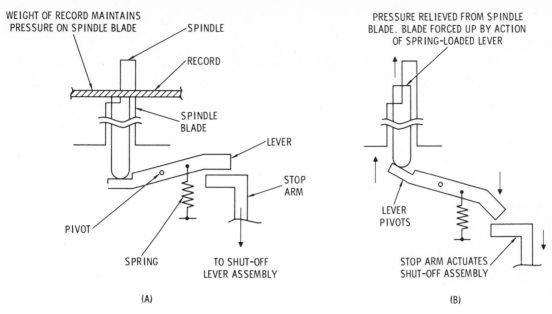

Fig. 8-2. Spindle shut-off mechanism.

the stop arm down. The stop arm contacts and actuates the shut-off lever assembly. From this point, the mechanical action that takes place is similar to the overarm shut-off mechanism.

Feeler Shut-Off Mechanism

The feeler shut-off mechanism is not commonly used in modern record changers; however, they are manufactured and used, and, therefore, it is necessary to have a know-ledge of their operation.

In this assembly, a mechanical lever is mounted somewhere in the record area, usually at the perimeter of the turntable. The pressure applied by the records resting on this lever keeps the lever disengaged from the shut-off mechanism. When the pressure is removed, the lever engages and actuates the shut-off mechanism in a manner similar to those discussed in the overarm and spindle shut-off mechanisms.

2. Maintenance

In maintaining the shut-off mechanism, there are two major areas to be considered, the electrical and the mechanical. The electrical portion of the shut-off system is the motor shut-off switch. It is a good idea to check the opera-tion of the switch before proceeding with any trouble-shooting procedures. The following table will be of assistance when problems occur.

Table 8-1. Troubleshooting Shut-Off Mechanisms

SYMPTOM	DEFECT	REMEDY	SYMPTOM	DEFECT	REMEDY
A. Changer will not shut off automatically after playing the last record.	1. Overarm does not move to its full downward position. 2. Bent overarm. 3. Bent quadrant lever. 4. Overarm shaft may have some oil or dirt on it. It must be free to move with gravity.	1. Clean overarm shaft and lubricate with light oil. 2. Straighten overarm. 3. Straighten quadrant lever. 4. Clean overarm shaft.		2. Control slide not retracting.	2. Bend control slide so it can move freely, or clean foreign material from surface between control slide and base.
B. Unit continuously shuts off.	1. Quadrant lever is not dropping.	1. Clean foreign matter from surface between quadrant lever and index bracket, or bend quadrant lever slightly to allow it to drop freely.	C. Changer shuts off prematurely.	1. Bent overarm.	1. Bend overarm so it is level with records.
			D. Tone arm does not return to rest post after shut-off.	1. Pawl does not latch in fourth ratchet notch.	1. Adjust pawl stop. 2. Check freedom of movement of the index pawl assembly.
			E. Tone arm returns to rest post for shut-off, but turntable continues to rotate.	1. Shut-off lever not latching shut-off bar.	1. Adjust shut-off lever to contact and actuate shut-off bar.

9 - Record Dropping System

The function of the record dropping mechanism is to release one record from the stack at the top of the spindle at the end of each record play. The following section will examine typical record dropping mechanisms.

1. Typical Record Dropping Mechanisms

Spindle Record Dropping Mechanism

The spindle mechanism utilizes the most basic mechanical device, the lever. Figure 9-1 shows the spindle in action. When the tone arm is directly above the rest post, the mechanical assembly (usually the cycling gear) causes the spindle actuator to raise the spindle actuating rod. This is accomplished by (1) an eccentric cam forcing the spindle actuator rod to rise at it rotates, or (2) a lever forcing the spindle actuating rod to rise as it pivots, or (3) a rotary- or screw-type action causing the spindle actuating rod to rise as it rotates in a thread.

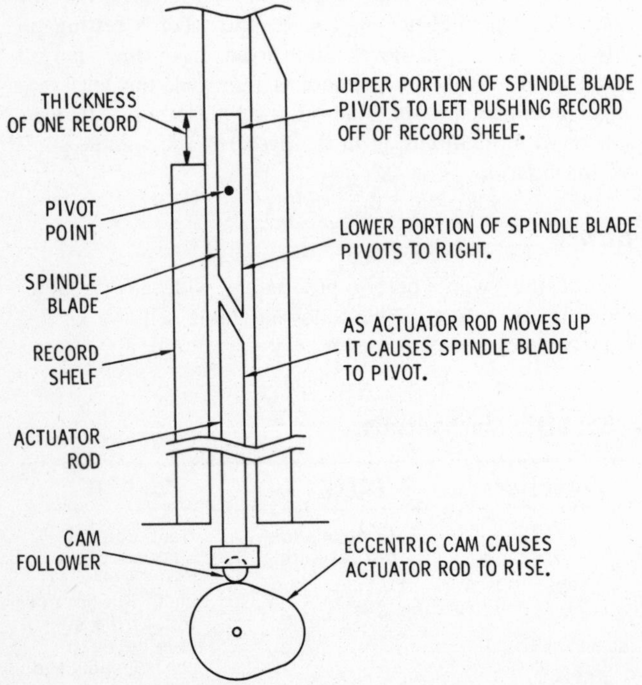

The upward motion of the spindle actuating rod causes the spindle blade to move into the spindle record shelf area. Because the spindle blade protrudes above the spindle record shelf (as much but not more than the thickness of one record), it pushes the lowest record off the spindle record shelf. When this happens, the hole in the center of the record is forced over the lower portion of the spindle. With nothing to support it, the record drops, guided to the turntable by the lower portion of the spindle. Once this is accomplished, the controlling mechanism (cycling gear) causes the actuating rod to lower. As the actuating rod lowers, the spindle blade pivots in the opposite direction, retracting from the record shelf area. When the spindle blade retracts from the record shelf area, the next record drops to the record shelf.

Pusher Record Dropping Mechanism

The pusher record dropping mechanism utilizes the spindle and the pusher platform to support the records. This type of mechanism may be used with 10- or 12-in. records only, and the records may not be intermixed.

Figure 9-2 illustrates the basic pusher record dropping mechanism. When the tone arm is directly over the rest

THICKNESS OF ONE RECORD

PIVOT POINT

SPINDLE BLADE

RECORD SHELF

ACTUATOR ROD

CAM FOLLOWER

UPPER PORTION OF SPINDLE BLADE PIVOTS TO LEFT PUSHING RECORD OFF OF RECORD SHELF.

LOWER PORTION OF SPINDLE BLADE PIVOTS TO RIGHT.

AS ACTUATOR ROD MOVES UP IT CAUSES SPINDLE BLADE TO PIVOT.

ECCENTRIC CAM CAUSES ACTUATOR ROD TO RISE.

Fig. 9-1. Spindle operation.

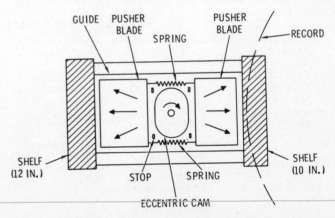

Fig. 9-2. Pusher type record dropping mechanism.

post, the cycling gear, through a series of gear reductions, causes the record drop cam to turn. The cam is constructed so that when it is in the normal position it does not engage the record drop blade. As the cam turns it engages the record drop blade, and causes it to move into the record shelf area. When the blade moves into the record shelf area, it pushes the record off the record shelf and off the eccentric part of the spindle. The record is guided to the turntable by the lower portion of the spindle. As the cam continues to rotate to complete its cycle, the spring-loaded record dropping blade retracts, allowing the next record drop to the record shelf.

This record dropping mechanism is usually mounted on a pivot so that it may be turned to accommodate either 10- or 12-in. records.

Slicer Record Dropping Mechanism

The slicer record dropping mechanism was one of the first record dropping systems used in record changers. Few, if any, modern record changers utilize this method.

Figure 9-3 illustrates the basic slicer mechanism. The

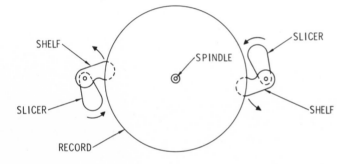

AS THE SHELVES MOVE OUT OF THE RECORD AREA, THE SLICER BLADES MOVE INTO THE AIR SPACE BETWEEN THE LOWEST TWO RECORDS.

Fig. 9-3. Slicer type record dropping mechanism.

records are supported on two selector posts, and are guided by the spindle. When the tone arm is in position over the rest post, the actuating mechanism (usually the cycling gear) causes the selector arms to turn simultaneously. As they turn, the selector blades of the selector arms (which are raised slightly above the lever of the selector arm) will separate the lowest record from the stack. When the selector arm has reached its maximum rotation, there is no support for the record, and so it drops. As the selector arm rotates back to its neutral position, the next record on the stack falls to rest on the selector arm shelf.

45-rpm Record Dropping Mechanism

The 45-rpm record, because of its large center hole, requires a special adapter to permit it to be played on a standard three-speed record changer. The large hole is compensated for by either an adapter disc which fits the center hole of the record, allowing it to be placed on a standard spindle, or by a special adapter spindle which is usually supplied with the record changer.

Figure 9-4 shows the operation of a basic 45-rpm adapter spindle. When the spindle actuator rod rises, and the spindle

blade moves out to the spindle shelf, the spindle blade actuates the mechanism in the adapter spindle, causing the record shelves to withdraw into the housing, and simultaneously causes the slicer blades to protrude into the space between the lowest two records. The lowest record drops, and the remainder of the stack then rests on the slicer blades. As the spindle blade withdraws from the record shelf area, the spring loaded slicer blades withdraw into the housing, and, simultaneously, the record shelves return to their normal position. When the slicer blades retract, the remainder of the stack falls to rest on the record shelves. This type of adapter spindle and the standard 45-rpm spindles operate in the same manner.

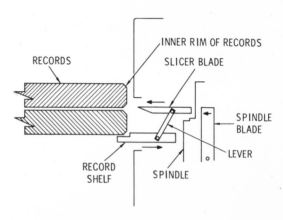

Fig. 9-4. 45-rpm adapter spindle operation.

Table 9-1. Troubleshooting Record Dropping Mechanisms

SYMPTOM	DEFECT	REMEDY
A. Record does not drop when changer cycles.	1. Spindle actuator rod broken or bent.	1. Replace actuator rod.
	2. Spindle blade not moving far enough to eject a record.	2. The spindle blade should move flush with, or a maximum of 0.010 in. beyond the lower portion of the spindle body. If adjustment of the actuator rod fails to move the blade far enough, the spindle should be replaced.
	3. Spindle actuator assembly malfunctioning.	3. Replace.
B. Two records drop at once.	1. Hole in record too large.	1. Check the diameter of the hole in the record. An oversize hole will cause two records to drop at once.
	2. Small blade in upper portion of spindle is not fully down.	2. Clean slot of foreign matter. Blade must be free to fall of its own weight.

2. Maintenance

Two difficulties are most frequently encountered with the spindle record mechanism. They are: (1) record fails to drop, and (2) two records drop at one time. These difficulties are discussed in detail in Table 9-1.

10 – Indexing Mechanisms

1. Introduction

The indexing mechanism detects the size of the record when the record falls to the turntable or is in position to fall to the turntable, and transfers this information to the tone arm positioning mechanism so that the tone arm lands in the correct position, on the edge of the record. In some of the more complex record changers, the indexing mechanism also performs the function of changing the speed of the turntable, according to record size.

There are two different indexing mechanisms: the intermix and the nonintermix types. The nonintermix indexing mechanism does not permit the mixing of different size records in the same stack on the spindle. The intermix indexing mechanism allows mixing of *all* size records on the same stack on the spindle. The basic difference between the two is that in the nonintermix type, the record feeler is positioned and fixed for each size record stack. This is usually accomplished by a record feeler which is positioned when the records are placed on the spindle. In the intermix type, as the record drops to the turntable, the outer perimeter of the record strikes the record feeler, which in turn transmits position information to the tone arm positioning mechanisms. The following section examines the intermix indexing mechanism because basically the operation of the

two types is the same, except that the record feeler position is fixed for each record size in the nonintermix type. See Fig. 10-1.

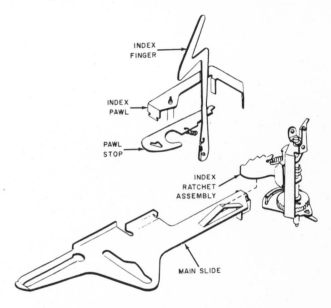

Fig. 10-1. Indexing mechanism. (Courtesy of General Electric)

2. Intermix Indexing Mechanism

7-Inch Landing

When a 7-in. record drops to the turntable, it does not touch the record feeler (index finger). The record feeler remains in its normal position. In this position, the feeler and its associated mechanism are engaged with the 7-in. step on the index ratchet assembly. When the feeler mechanism and the index ratchet assembly are engaged this way, the tone-arm positioning mechanism will position the tone arm correctly for 7-in. record play.

10-Inch Landing

When a 10-in. record drops to the turntable, it strikes the record feeler, causing the record feeler mechanism to engage the 10-in. step on the index ratchet assembly. When the feeler mechanism and the index ratchet assembly are engaged in this way, the tone arm positioning mechanism will position the tone arm correctly for 10-in. record play.

12-Inch Landing

When a 12-in. record drops to the turntable, it strikes the record feeler, causing the record feeler mechanism to engage the 12-in. step on the index ratchet assembly. When the record feeler mechanism and the index ratchet assembly are engaged in this way, the tone arm positioning mechanism will position the tone arm correctly for 12-in. record play.

Record Size Vs. Speed Change

In the more common changers with intermix indexing mechanisms, records of only one speed may be stacked on the spindle at one time. In some of the more complex record changers, the indexing mechanism is mechanically linked to the speed change mechanism. This is accomplished by a mechanism linkage between the record feeler and the speed change mechanisms. When the record drops to the turntable and strikes the feeler arm, the record speed will change according to the record size.

Both the automatic speed change and the nonautomatic speed change record changers have their distinct advantages and disadvantages.

1. Because records of *all speeds* are being manufactured in *all sizes,* the automatic speed change type is not desirable. This type of changer is usually designed to change speed for (1) 45 rpm for 7-in. records, (2) 78 rpm for 10-in. records, and (3) 33⅓ rpm for 12-in. records. If you wanted to play three 33⅓-rpm records of different sizes, each record would have to be manually placed on the turntable.

2. If you intend to play records that fall into the three categories described in step 1, the automatic speed change record changer would have an advantage over the nonautomatic speed change type.

3. If you own a nonautomatic speed change type, you may only stack records of the same speed on the spindle at one time.

3. Maintenance

While the indexing mechanism is not very complex, its component shape and position configurations are very critical. The following table will assist the technician in localizing malfunctions.

Table 10-1. Troubleshooting Indexing Mechanisms

SYMPTOM	CAUSE	REMEDY	SYMPTOM	CAUSE	REMEDY
Improper indexing.	1. Record feeler not moving properly.	1. Check for binding record feeler or spring disconnected. Clean and lubricate as required.		3. Bent or broken pick-up lever.	3. Replace.
				4. Broken pick-up lever spring.	4. Replace.
	2. Record feeler bent.	2. Bend record feeler slightly forward or backward as required.		5. Broken record feeler.	5. Replace.
				6. Mechanical linkage malfunction.	6. Adjust, repair, or replace as required.

11 – The Tone Arm

1. Function and Operation

The tone arm moves the cartridge and stylus assembly to the record at the beginning of record play, and removes the cartridge and stylus assembly from the record at the end of record play. The mechanisms associated with the tone arm are responsible for actuating the trip mechanism, the shut-off mechanism, and the record change mechanism.

After the record dropping mechanism places a record on the turntable, and the record feeler has programmed the tone-arm positioning mechanism to set the tone arm down in the proper position on the record, the tone arm lifts off the rest post and cycles to the lead-in grooves of the record.

During record play, the mechanical motion of the stylus, which is moving in the record grooves, is converted to electrical energy in the cartridge. This energy is of a very low level, and so it is transferred to the amplifier through the electrical wiring.

Some time during or immediately after record play, the movement of the tone arm causes the trip actuator to engage the trip lever. At the end of record play, the movement or the position of the tone arm causes the trip actuator to actuate the trip lever, recycling the record changer.

2. Maintenance

The critical areas of concern for the tone arm are the pivot, tracking, cartridge mounting, and counterbalance. Chapter 13 contains adjustment procedures for each of these critical areas. Table 11-1 will be of assistance when problems occur.

Table 11-1. Troubleshooting the Tone Arm

SYMPTOM	CAUSE	REMEDY	SYMPTOM	CAUSE	REMEDY
A. Tone arm does not track in record grooves.	1. Worn stylus.	1. Replace.		4. Cartridge leads interfering with motion of tone arm.	4. Check for ample slack in tone arm leads so that lateral travel is not effected.
	2. Improper tracking pressure.	2. Check tracking pressure for cartridge used and adjust to to recommended value. Refer to Chapter 13.	B. Tone arm wobbly on hinge assembly.	1. Vertical pivot out of place.	1. Tighten or replace as required.
	3. Changer not level.	3. Relevel changer. Refer to Chapter 13.	C. Tone arm does not land at lead-in groove of record.	1. Improper set-down adjustment.	1. Adjust as described in Chapter 13.

12 – Circuit Troubleshooting and Cycling Analysis

1. Circuit Troubleshooting

Checking and troubleshooting record changer circuitry consists of continuity checks and a signal presence test. Figure 12-1 illustrates a basic record changer circuit. Perform electrical circuit troubleshooting as follows:

1. Check for continuity between the a-c input and the motor. If there is no continuity, replace the a-c wiring.

2. Check for continuity between the inputs of the motor. If there is no continuity, replace the motor.

3. Check for continuity between ground and the windings of the motor. If there is continuity, replace the motor.

4. Connect a test amplifier to the outputs of the cartridge, and check for signal presence during record play. A vacuum-tube voltmeter may be used to check that the signal level meets the specifications of the manufacturer.

5. Close the a-c switch and check for continuity. If there is no continuity, replace the switch.

2. Cycling Analysis

The modern-day record changer is a complex automated device. To perform successful troubleshooting and repair procedures, the technician must fully understand the operation of the overall equipment as well as the subassemblies

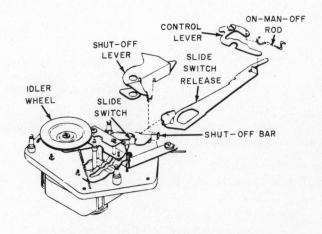

Fig. 12-2. Starting the cycle. (Courtesy of General Electric)

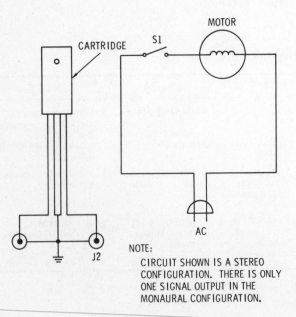

Fig. 12-1. Record changer circuit.

NOTE:
CIRCUIT SHOWN IS A STEREO CONFIGURATION. THERE IS ONLY ONE SIGNAL OUTPUT IN THE MONAURAL CONFIGURATION.

that make it up. The following paragraphs contain a complete cycling analysis of a typical General Electric record changer.

Note. The following cycling analysis begins in the middle of record play and with a stack of records on the spindle.

Start the changer into the cycling sequence (see Figs. 12-2

and 12-3) by setting the ON-MAN-OFF control to the ON position. The ON-MAN-OFF rod activates the control lever which, in turn, pushes the slide switch release against the shut-off bar. The shut-off bar is unlatched from the shut-off lever. The shut-off bar then releases the idler wheel so that it engages the motor moller shaft and turns the slide switch ON, starting the motor, and rotating the turntable.

The linkage formed by the ON-MAN-OFF rod, the control lever, and the slide switch release causes the velocity trip release to move toward and strike the velocity trip lever, which, in turn, moves the velocity trip catch into engagement with the projection on the turntable hub. This action turns the cycling gear counterclockwise, engaging it with the gear teeth on the turntable.

A stud on the top of the cycling gear (see Fig. 12-4), which is positioned in a slot in the main slide, drives the slide toward the center of the changer. As the main slide

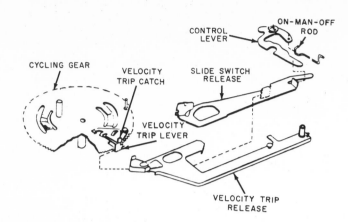

Fig. 12-3. Actuating the mechanisms. (Courtesy of General Electric)

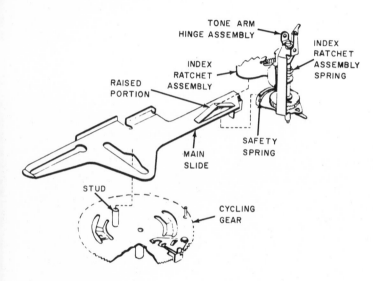

Fig. 12-4. Cycling. (Courtesy of General Electric)

first notch on the cam of the index ratchet assembly. When this happens, the tone arm will move out to the 7-in. set-down position.

When a 10-in. record drops to the turntable, it strikes the index finger, causing it to be caught between the first and second notch on the pawl stop. This allows the index pawl assembly to engage the second notch on the index ratchet assembly. When the index pawl is engaged with the second notch on the index ratchet assembly, the tone arm will move out over the 10-in. set-down position.

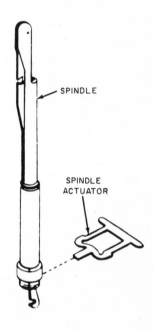

Fig. 12-5. Spindle mechanism. (Courtesy of General Electric)

In the case of a 12-in. record, the action is the same as described above, except the movement of the index finger is beyond the second notch of the pawl stop, and the pawl stop will engage the third notch on the index ratchet cam, causing the tone arm to move out over the 12-in. set-down position.

The main slide now reverses direction of travel. As it

begins to move, the index ratchet assembly moves down off the raised portion of the main slide. The index ratchet assembly is forced down by the action of the index ratchet assembly spring. As the assembly moves down, it pulls the rear end of the tone arm hinge assembly downward, lifting the front end of the tone arm up and off the record.

The tab on the rear of the main slide engages the spring. This forces the spring forward. Since the spring, the tone arm, the bracket assembly, and the tone arm hinge assembly are secured together, they move in unison. This movement causes the tone arm to pivot toward the rest post.

As the tone arm reaches a point above the rest post (see Fig. 12-5), the bottom end of the eccentric pin on the cycling gear has rotated into contact with the spindle actuator. The spindle actuator moves the spindle blade, dropping a record.

As the record drops toward the turntable (see Fig. 10-1), it either strikes or misses the index finger (record feeler). When a 7-in. record drops (missing the index finger), the pawl stop catches the index finger adjacent to the first notch. This allows the index pawl assembly to engage the

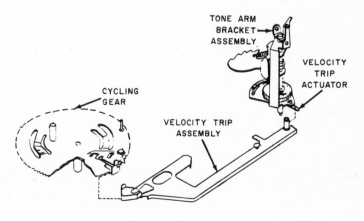

Fig. 12-6. Velocity trip mechanism. (Courtesy of General Electric)

does so, the index ratchet assembly pivots and moves the tone arm out over the record. At this time the index ratchet assembly rides up on the raised portion of the main slide. This action allows the tone arm to lower on to the record, and also disengages the antiskate spring. The cycling gear now completes its rotation to the out-of-cycle position, allowing the tone arm to travel freely in the record grooves.

After the completion of the recorded portion of the record (see Fig. 12-6), the tone arm enters the lead-out grooves. The velocity trip actuator, located on the tone arm bracket assembly, moves the velocity trip assembly toward the center of the changer, actuating the velocity trip lever and the velocity trip catch, thus starting another cycle.

When the last record of the stack drops to the turntable (see Fig. 8-1), the lower end of the record support arm rod causes the quadrant lever to pivot upward. This changes the pivot point of the stop pawl, moving the index pawl assembly inward, engaging the last notch on the index ratchet assembly. The action prevents the index ratchet assembly from pivoting, and allows the tone arm to return to the rest post.

When the tone arm returns to the rest post, the index ratchet assembly holds the control slide assembly toward the cycling gear. The cycling gear cam contacts the tab on the control slide. The cycling gear is raised as it rotates and the shut-off stud on the cycling gear actuates the shut-off lever. The shut-off lever engages the shut-off bar which moves the slide switch to the OFF position, and disengages the idler wheel.

13 – Adjustment and Checkout Procedures

To perform a qualified and accurate checkout and adjustment procedure, the technician should make reference to the service manual for the changer undergoing repair. It has been this author's experience that the manufacturers in the record changer industry are more than cooperative in supplying these manuals to qualified technicians.

Because all record changers are different, the following section contains *typical* checkout and adjustment procedures.

1. Typical Procedures

Leveling the Changer

Most changers are equipped with springs to allow the changer to float on the changer base board assembly. Leveling screws are located at key points on the changer base plate to facilitate leveling. Perform the leveling procedure as follows:

1. Place a small carpenter's level or torpedo level on the turntable perpendicular to the front of the changer.
2. Adjust the leveling screws on the front and back of the base plate until the level indicates the turntable is level.

Note. The leveling screws should never be turned so tight so that the changer does not float freely (adequate spring action between the base plate and the base board is recommended).

3. Place the level parallel to the front of the changer on the turntable.
4. Adjust the leveling screws on the left and right sides of the base plate until the level indicates that the turntable is level.
5. Repeat steps 2 and 4 until the turntable is completely level.

For changers without leveling screws, place shims under the springs. If the leveling screws are the transit, they should not be used to level the changer as they will cause noise and microphonics.

Tone-Arm Height Adjustment

The tone-arm height adjustment is not critical but is important. Too low adjustment can cause the tone arm to hit the side of the record and the stylus will strike the changer base during record play. After record play, the tone arm will not come to rest on the rest post. Too high adjustment will prevent the stylus from setting in the record groove, causing a no-play or skating condition.

Most changers have a tone-arm height adjustment screw located under the rear of the tone arm. Some changers have this screw located on the tone arm casting itself, while others have it mounted on the tone arm hinge and bracket assembly. No matter where the tone-arm height adjustment screw is located, the operation of each is basically the same.

The height adjustment screw will mate with a flat surface, maintaining constant tone-arm height throughout the cycling operation.

While most record changers require a different tone-arm height adjustment, a general rule is to set the tone arm height (during the cycling operation) so that the stylus rides approximately ⅛ in. above the maximum number of records the changer is designed to hold. The tone-arm height adjustment is made by lifting the tone arm, locating the tone-arm adjustment screw, and adjusting the screw until the proper tone arm height is obtained.

Stylus Set-Down Position

If the stylus set-down position is not adjusted properly, you may only hear part of the record or if the stylus sets down before the record, the result may be a broken or prematurely worn stylus. These two conditions are needless, especially since the adjustment is simple and easily accesible.

In most record changers, the set-down adjustment screw is located on the tone arm hinge assembly. Perform a typical tone arm set-down adjustment as follows:

1. Lift the tone arm and locate the set-down adjustment screw.
2. Place a 10- or a 12-in. record on the turntable.
3. Cycle the changer.
4. If the stylus sets-down prematurely, turn the screw counter-clockwise. This will make the stylus set-down closer to the spindle.
5. Repeat steps 3 and 4 until the correct set-down position is obtained.
6. If the stylus sets down after the lead in grooves, turn the adjustment screw clockwise. This will move the set-down point away from the spindle.
7. Repeat steps 3 and 6 until the correct set-down position is obtained.

Stylus Pressure

The pressure that the stylus exerts on the record during play is often the difference between good and poor quality sound reproduction, long and short record life, and long and short stylus life. It is for these reasons that a stylus pressure gauge is an invaluable tool to have in the work shop.

There are basically two methods for adjusting and maintaining good stylus pressure. The first method, and the less common of the two, is the use of external balance weights located at the rear of the tone arm. By manipulating these weights (usually they are threaded on a long screw at the rear of the tone arm), as one would the weights on a balance scale, the pressure that the tone arm exerts on the record may be adjusted.

The second, and by far the most commonly used method in record changers, is a balance spring located under the tone arm attached to the underside of the tone arm and the hinge bracket. Moving the spring toward the front of the tone arm decreases the stylus pressure. Moving the spring toward the rear of the tone arm increases the stylus pressure. In some changers, the spring is moved from hole to hole on a stylus pressure clip, while in others the spring is moved by turning a pressure adjusting screw. Refer to the changer service manual for recommended stylus pressure and method of adjustment.

Cartridge Replacement

If local troubleshooting indicates a faulty cartridge, the cartridge and stylus assembly may be replaced as follows:

1. Remove electrical connecting lugs from lugs on cartridge (two for monaural, four for stereo cartridges). Be sure to mark the position of the wires.

2. Unscrew attaching hardware, and remove the cartridge.

3. Obtain exact or equivalent replacement.

4. Secure replacement to tone arm with attaching hardware.

5. Reattach the electrical connectors to the lugs on the replacement cartridge in the same configuration as when they were removed. If soldering is necessary, be sure to use heat sinks on the lugs to prevent the heat from damaging the cartridge.

Stylus Replacement

Each cartridge manufacturer has its own stylus positioning technique. Generally it is a good idea to make note of the method that the stylus was removed to facilitate easy replacement. Most styli are mounted on a wire arm which is shaped to fit a corresponding groove in the cartridge. In most cases all that is required to remove a stylus is to apply pressure to the holding spring and slip out the stylus, being very careful not to damage the contacting mechanism.

Checking Turntable Speed

The easiest and most economical method for checking turntable speed is with the use of a stroboscopic disc. This type of disc is usually made of paper, cardboard, or light plastic, and comes in various sizes and different types of markings. No matter what the size or markings, the method for use and results are the same.

When a stroboscopic disc is placed on a turntable, illuminated with a fluorescent light or neon lamp, and rotated, the pattern for the speed being tested will appear stationary. If the turntable is rotating too slowly, the pattern will have the effect of moving counterclockwise. If the turntable is rotating too fast, the pattern will have the effect of moving clockwise.

To accurately test the speed of a turntable, the stroboscopic test should be performed under the following conditions:

1. With only one record on the turntable without the tone arm in place.

2. With only one record on the turntable with the stylus on the record.

3. Add one record at a time (to the maximum number of records the changer will hold), and perform the stroboscopic test each time.

Record Dropping Adjustment

The record dropping adjustment must be checked whenever the spindle or associated components have been removed or changed. Automatic record drop is accomplished by the movement of the spindle blade pushing the record onto the lower portion of the spindle. To adjust the action of the spindle blade, the spindle actuator mechanism must be moved so that the spindle blade will travel the correct distance to eject the record. When possible, refer to the changer service manual.

Tripping Adjustment

If the tripping mechanism of the changer is not functioning, the whole purpose of the record changer is defeated. At the end of each record, the changer must be cycled to start a new record or turn off the machine. Any malfunction, whether it be too soon or no tripping at all, can usually be traced to a poor trip mechanism adjustment. As discussed in Chapter 7, trip mechanisms vary from machine to machine.

A malfunction in a positive trip mechanism is corrected by adjusting the trip actuator to contact and actuate the trip lever at the end of the modulated record play.

A malfunction in an eccentric trip mechanism is corrected by adjusting the trip actuator to actuate the trip lever at the end of modulated record play. The trip actuator contacts the trip lever somewhere in the middle of modulated record play.

The velocity trip mechanism must be adjusted so that only the rapid movement of the trip actuator, at the end of modulated record play, when the stylus is in the lead-out grooves, will actuate the trip lever. Refer to the changer service manual.

Indexing Mechanism Adjustments

The basic part of the indexing mechanism, and the most troublesome, is the record feeler. Because of its shape and consistency, the record feeler can be bent or distorted very easily. Most malfunctions of the indexing mechanism are caused by this condition, and consequently may be remedied by reshaping the record feeler and adjusting it for 7-, 10-, and 12-in. records. The procedure for performing this adjustment is as follows:

1. When a 7-in. record is being cycled onto the turntable, the record should not in any way touch the feeler mechanism. Place a 7-in. record on the spindle and cycle the changer. If the record touches the record feeler, bend the feeler so that it does not touch.

2. Place a 10-in. record on the spindle and cycle the changer. The record should touch the feeler just enough to engage the 10-in. step on the pick-up lever. If the record does not touch the record feeler, bend the feeler toward the spindle until the record causes it to engage the 10-in. step

on the pick-up lever. If the record moves the record feeler too far and it engages the 12-in. step on the pick-up lever, bend the feeler away from the spindle until the record causes the record feeler to engage the 10-in. step on the pick-up lever.

3. Place a 12-in. record on the spindle and cycle the changer. The record should touch the record feeler to move it enough to engage the 12-in. step on the pick-up lever. If the record does not touch the record feeler, bend the feeler toward the spindle until the record causes it to engage the 12-in. step on the pick-up lever. If the record causes the feeler to move past the 12-in. step on pick-up lever, bend the feeler away from the spindle until the record causes it to engage the 12-in. step on the pick-up lever.

2. Final Checkout Procedure

The procedures contained in the following steps should be performed before returning a repaired changer to the customer to ascertain that the changer is performing according to maximum performance standards.

1. Place a 7-in. record on the spindle and cycle the changer. Check that the record drop mechanism is functioning correctly, and that the stylus set-down position is correct.

2. Repeat step 1 using a 10-in. record.

3. Repeat step 1 using a 12-in. record.

4. If the changer is capable of handling records of mixed sizes, place several records of each size on the spindle, and cycle the changer. Check that the indexing mechanism is functioning properly by noting that the stylus sets down in the proper position for each record size. If the changer is capable of changing speed with each record size change, check that the proper speed is selected for each record size.

5. Place a stroboscopic disc on the turntable, and check the turntable speeds. If possible, use a test record, oscilloscope, and audio generator to perform this check and also check for wow, rumble, and flutter.

6. Check that the cartridge is seated properly in the tone arm.

7. Check that the stylus is properly seated in the cartridge.

8. Check the condition of the stylus for wear.

9. Using a stylus pressure gauge, check that the stylus pressure is according to manufacturer's specification.

10. Check the tone arm height.

11. Check that the tripping mechanism is functioning properly.

12. Check that the shut-off mechanism is functioning properly.

Part III

Tape Recorders

1 – The Tape Recorder

1. General Information

The ever-growing use of tape recordings has resulted in an increasing need for technicians skilled in troubleshooting and repairing the tape machines. The following sections, based upon that need, present the basic fundamentals of tape recording and, while they cannot completely cover every malfunction, present guide lines by which a skilled electronics technician can locate and repair any machine.

The types of tape recorders discussed include home tape recorders, both monaural and stereo; dictating and letter-writing machines; and pocket-size units.

Introduction to Tape Theory

Tape recording involves conversion of audio signals to electrical signals, and the subsequent conversion of electrical signals to magnetic patterns. The steps of the recording process are shown in the block diagram of Fig. 1-1A. Tape playback, essentially the reverse or reproducing process, is shown in Fig. 1-1B.

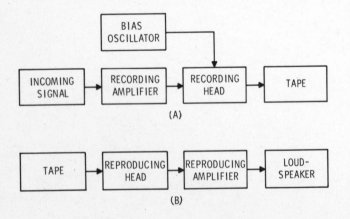

Fig. 1-1. Block diagram of the tape recorder. (A) Recording process. (B) Reproducing process.

A microphone converts the audible input signal to a varying electrical signal. The electrical signal energizes an electromagnet that in turn magnetizes the metallic oxide on the tape.

Recording

Conversion of Sound into Electricity. Sound and electrical waves can be pictured in terms of their amplitude and frequency as shown in Figure 1-2. Sound intensity (loudness) is determined by the wave amplitude; pitch is determined by the wave frequency. A high-pitch sound, for example, is one at, say, 10 kc.

When the sound waves produced by the audio source impinge upon the surface of a microphone diaphragm, the diaphragm vibrates at the same frequency as the sound. In the example cited above, this would be 10 kc. The microphone is constructed so that the vibration sets up voltage which alternates positively then negatively at the same rate as the applied sound wave. Thus, sound energy is converted into electrical energy. The *value* of voltage produced is dependent upon the intensity of the applied sound.

Conversion of Electricity into Magnetic Patterns. The output of the microphone is amplified, then coupled to the recording head, which is a form of electromagnet. Several shapes and placements of the recording heads are possible; Fig. 1-3 shows the three major types. Figure 1-3A illustrates the ring head and its magnetic pattern. Figure 1-3B illustrates the double pole piece, with one pole on each side of the tape. The poles can be directly opposite each other, or staggered as shown. Figure 1-3C illustrates the single pole piece type. The typical construction shown in Fig. 1-4 is that of the ring type, which will be used throughout the discussion.

The heads have pole pieces made of magnetically "soft" iron wound with coils of wire through which the recording signal current flows. The air gap in the pole structure ensures that there will be a strong magnetic field outside of the metal pole, since it is this field through which the tape passes.

Whenever a surge of *positive* current flows in the coil it magnetizes the head in *one* direction. The reverse occurs with negative flow. Thus, the polarity of the head changes with each alternation in signal current.

When the tape is in contact with the head, the tape's "hard" coating offers an easier path for the magnetic flux lines than does the air gap. Thus, most of the lines flow through the coating. Further, while the magnetically "soft" head rapidly loses magnetism when no current flows, the magnetically "hard" coating does not. The small magnetized area becomes, in effect, a small bar magnet, with its north pole pointing as shown in Figure 1-5A.

At the point of alternation, see Figure 1-5B, current flow through the coil drops to zero (ideally, not actually). Therefore, no magnetic field is created at that time. As a

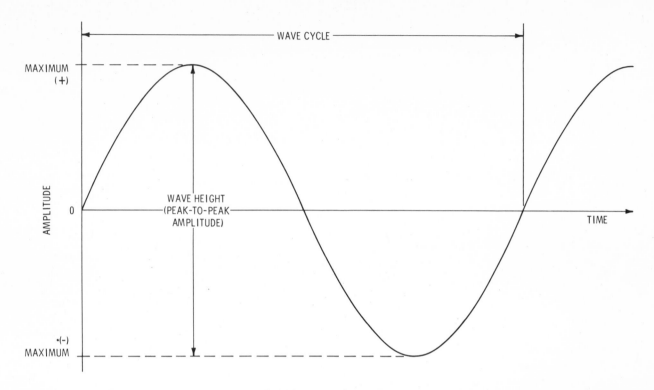

WAVE CYCLE

MAXIMUM (+)

AMPLITUDE

0

WAVE HEIGHT (PEAK-TO-PEAK AMPLITUDE)

TIME

•(-) MAXIMUM

Fig. 1-2. Waveform diagram.

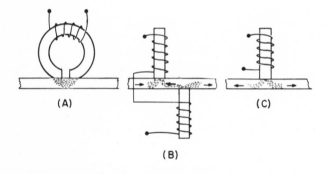

(A)

(B)

(C)

Fig. 1-3. Magnetic heads: (A) Ring, (B) double pole piece, and (C) single pole piece. (Courtesy of RCA)

result, the tape moves a fraction of a length without any additional magnetization.

When a negative surge enters the coil, see Fig. 1-5C, the polarity of the electromagnet (head) is reversed. Again the iron oxide coating is magnetized, permanently, but in the opposite direction. Then, see Fig. 1-5D, zero current occurs as did at Fig. 1-5B, and no magnetization occurs at this point.

As a result, the tape now contains a series of small bar magnets on its coating. Because the tape is moving, the magnets occur at intervals along the tape, as shown in Fig. 1-6. Tape speed and input-current frequency determine the distance between the magnets; input-current amplitude determines the magnetic strength of each segment. Thus, for example, the 10-kc sound would produce 10,000 bar magnets with a north-pointing polarity and 10,000 with a south-pointing polarity. In effect, there are 20,000 bar magnets end to end for every second of time the tape moved across the head gap. On a tape recorder moving at,

say, 3¼ inches per second (ips), these 20,000 bar magnets would occupy 3¼ inches. If the speed were 7½ ips, the 20,000 magnets would occupy 7½ inches. (High-fidelity recordings are usually obtained at the higher speed, since there is less compression of the magnets, hence less distortion.)

The foregoing is true only in the case of a steady tone. If the pitch changes, the magnetic pattern changes. Since, in normal recordings, sounds other than simple tones are used, the magnetic pattern on the tape consists of a wide variation in both pitch and intensity.

Linearity and Biasing. The magnetization curve for mag-

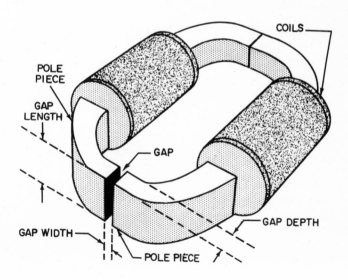

COILS

POLE PIECE

GAP LENGTH

GAP

GAP DEPTH

GAP WIDTH

POLE PIECE

Fig. 1-4. Typical ring type head. (Courtesy of the Ampex Corp.)

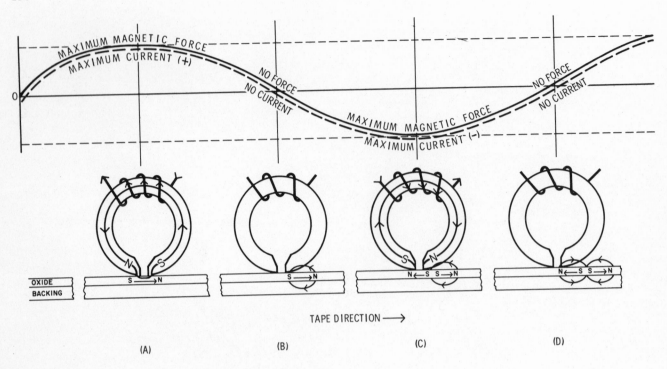

TAPE DIRECTION ⟶

(A)   (B)   (C)   (D)

Fig. 1-5. Direction of flow-record function. (Courtesy of the 3M Co.)

netic tape is highly nonlinear, as shown in Fig. 1-7. With such a characteristic, audio signals will be distorted during the recording process. Thus, some sort of biasing must be used, so that only the linear portion of the characteristic is utilized.

Both d-c and a-c biasing are employed, the latter being the most prevalent. The ac is of the high-frequency type, anywhere from 30-150 kc, and is furnished by a bias oscillator, as shown in Figure 1-8. When such a method of biasing is employed a straight-line recording characteristic is obtained.

In some cases the bias oscillator is used as the erase oscillator. This is explained later in detail.

Playback

Playback more or less reverses the recording process,

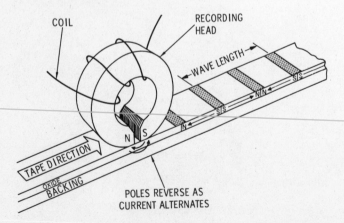

Fig. 1-6. Magnetic pattern caused by recording head. (Courtesy of the 3M Co.)

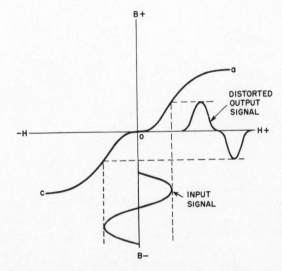

Fig. 1-7. Distorted signal on demagnetized tape with no bias current applied.

i.e., a magnetic field moving through a coil creates an electric current. The magnetic field is the tape recording, the coil the playback head.

Figure 1-9 illustrates what occurs on playback. The recorded tape moves past the playback head. The changing polarity in the magnetic patterns on the tape induces a current in the coil, which is amplified and coupled to the speaker.

What goes on the tape during recording does not necessarily come out on playback. When recorded signals of equal amplitude but different frequencies are reproduced, the outputs at different frequencies will be unequal; they will vary directly as the frequencies vary. Thus, with two

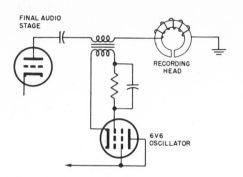

Fig. 1-8. Typical method of applying audio and high-frequency bias signal to recording head. (Courtesy of Brush Development Co.)

signals, say 200 and 400 cps, recorded under equal conditions, the 400-cps signal will produce double the output (6-db increase) of the 200-cps signal.

This is true up to about 3500 cps; above this point the increase in output is nonlinear. The increase in nonlinearity is caused by two factors: (1) tape self-demagnetization, and (2) a combination of gap width and tape speed.

When a magnet is wider than it is long, it tends to de-magnetize itself. This is the case in high-frequency

frequency response, therefore, indicates that a good check of the equalization network is in order.)

As for the tape speed and gap width, the higher the speed and the narrower the gap, the greater the fidelity. A check, therefore, of the condition of the motors, drive belts, capstan, etc., might well bring to light the cause of poor playback. Also, a check for proper gap width and dirty heads is in order.

Erase

Erase is accomplished by either of three methods: permanent magnets, d-c, or a-c heads. The major requirement is that the head be capable of magnetizing the tape sufficiently to saturate, in the opposing direction, the existing magnetic patterns on the tape. However, going to saturation without any other action leaves the tape full of noise. Hence, some process must occur which leaves the tape clean. Figure 1-10 illustrates how this is done in the case of a bar magnet.

The bar magnet is positioned so that the field through the tape is sufficient to saturate the tape in the direction opposite to the recorded patterns. As a point on the tape, indicated at A, reaches the magnet's north pole, the tape is brought to saturation, as shown by A' on the curve. As

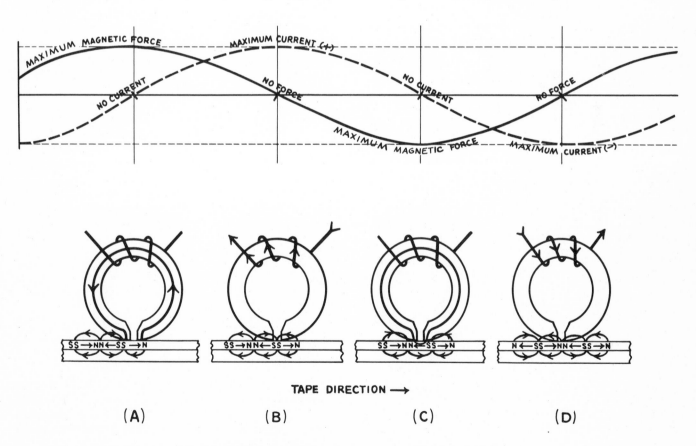

Fig. 1-9. Direction of current flow during playback. (Courtesy of the 3M Co.)

recordings, where the magnets deposited on the tape are short and wide. Most good recorders, therefore, have equalizing circuits built in to offset this effect. (Poor high-

the point moves from A to B, so the curve decreases from A' to B'. When the moving point on the tape reaches point C, the effect of the magnet's south pole has changed the

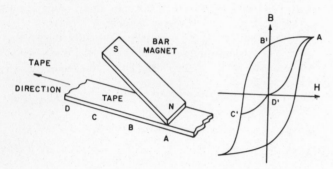

Fig. 1-10. Single-magnet tape erasure. (Courtesy of RCA)

induction from saturation at A' to a lesser value at C'. Then, when the point reaches D on the tape, where the magnet has no effect, the induction changes again from C' to D'. The residual induction is now almost zero, and the tape is fairly free of noise.

Better d-c erasure, actually a form of low a-c erasure, is shown in Fig. 1-11. Two magnets are used, each applying strong, oppositely polarized magnetic fields to the tape.

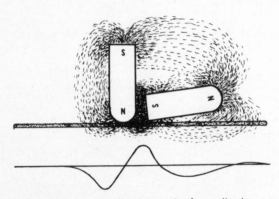

Fig. 1-11. Erasure by two permanent magnets of opposite sign. The resultant alternation field reduces residual magnetism left by the single pole piece type of erasure. (Courtesy of the Brush Development Co.)

The second magnet, with its opposing field, reduces the amount of residual magnetism left by the first. However, this method still leaves some noise.

The best and most commonly used method of erasure is by means of a high-frequency a-c signal. Here a high-power, ultrasonic signal is applied to the tape by the erase head. The frequency of the erase signal is usually from 80 kc to 100 kc, but is not critical. In fact, some recorders use the same oscillator for both erase and bias functions,

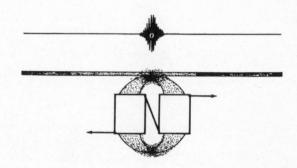

Fig. 1-12. Improved modern method of high-frequency erasure. The tape is demagnetized to a neutral condition. (Courtesy of the Brush Development Co.)

with the latter being a much weaker voltage.

Another factor in high-frequency erasure is the gap width. In this method the gap of the erase head is much wider than that of the record head, about 0.02 inches (20 mils). This is a must, as erasure requires complete magnetic saturation to ensure clean tapes.

The principle of high-frequency erasure is as follows. As the recorded tape approaches the high-frequency field of the erase head, the magnetic particles on the surface of the tape become magnetized in alternate directions due to the rapidly reversing field of the head. As these particles pass the center of the gap, they become saturated, as shown in Fig. 1-12. This completely erases any previous recording. As the tape continues to move, the particles are still under the influence of fringe fluxes. These fringe fluxes rapidly lose their effect as the tape continues to move, with the result that all residual magnetism is removed. Tapes erased in this manner have only a negligible amount of noise remaining, and for all practical purposes, are equivalent to newly-purchased tapes.

2 - Mechanisms

1. Recording Mechanisms

The mechanics of a tape recorder are in many ways similar to those of a record player. The motion must have a correct and constant speed, with no binding or irregularities in the mechanism. The motor(s) must be sufficiently powerful to pull much more than the maximum expected load. The capstan (the equivalent in the tape recorder of the main drive shaft in the record player) must be fly-wheel loaded, and must be set into smooth bearings.

To assure constant and smooth tape motion, slippage and slack must be held to a minimum. A pressure device (roller or pad) against the capstan minimizes slippage, while slack is eliminated by the use of smooth drive and take-up mechanisms.

Table 2-1 and Figs. 2-1, 2-2, and 2-3 describe the basic transport mechanism. Figure 2-1 is a basic mechanism; Figs. 2-2 and 2-3 are those of actual machines, the R.C.A. Victor model 6HF1, and the Ampex model 1250, respectively.

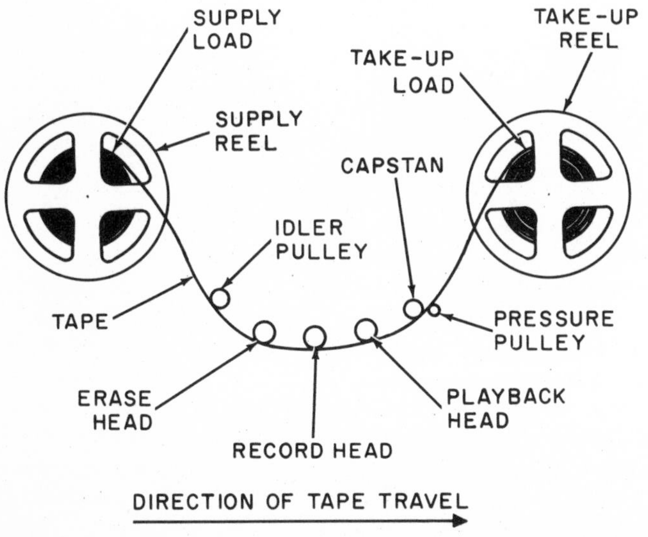

Fig. 2-1. Basic tape transport mechanism.

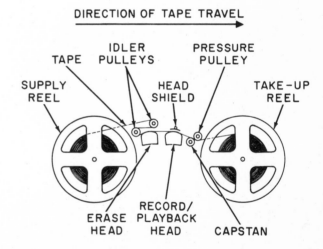

Fig. 2-2. RCA type TR-1 tape transport.

2. Reel Drive

The tape transport mechanism must permit extremely smooth tape movement past the heads with no slack at the reels. To do this, the supply reel must gradually speed up as the take-up slows down, all while the tape moves at an *absolutely* constant speed past the heads. Three methods of doing this are in general use, as described below.

Spring-Belt Drive

The spring-belt drive is one of the most common drives. The spring belt connects the drive to both the supply and take-up reels, and the pulleys are made so that the take-up will be driven at a slightly higher speed than necessary at

the innermost edge of its diameter. The stretch in the spring allows slippage so that the reel can rotate only at the speed of the tape past the capstan. The drive to the supply reel is usually released from the main drive, and the belt slippage acts as a drag because the drive pulley is anchored.

Friction-Clutch Drive

The friction-clutch drive is similar in principle to the spring-belt drive, except that slippage is supplied by a clutch mechanism which utilizes leather or some other material for slippage. Figure 2-4 illustrates a take-up clutch used by Westinghouse in their recorders.

133

Motor-Drag Drive

The motor-drag drive uses separate, torque-type induction motors on each reel shaft. Motors are connected so that the one driving the take-up runs as fast as allowed by the speed of the tape across the capstan. The supply-reel motor is torqued in the reverse direction; the amount of torque is inversely proportional to the speed of the take-up reel. Thus, as the take-up slows down, the supply-reel motor has increased torque in the reverse direction, increasing the drag on the supply reel.

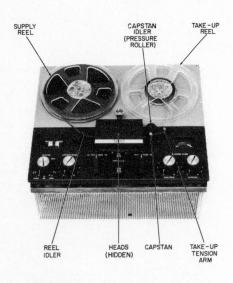

Fig. 2-3. Ampex model 1250 transport.

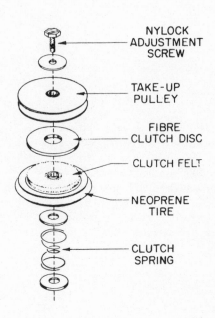

Fig. 2-4. Typical take-up clutch. (Courtesy of the Westinghouse Electric Corp.)

3. Flutter, Wow, and Drift

Flutter is defined as: the deviation of frequency which results, in general, from irregular motion during recording, duplication, or reproducing.*

Flutter, wow, and drift are all caused by variations in tape speed which frequency modulate the input signal. The speed of variation (modulation rate) defines which of the three is present. Thus, flutter is defined as that variation which produces a frequency variation in the input signal at a rate of 10 cps or greater. Slow-speed variations, at about 0.5 cps are termed wow; below 0.5 cps they are termed drift.

No mechanism is entirely flutter-free. Flutter specifications usually indicate the total flutter that can be expected during recording and subsequent playback. Some of the more expensive machines are rated at 0.1%. Since the playback signal frequency is a direct function of tape speed, any deviation in that speed will result in a frequency deviation. Thus, since most home recorders are used for both record and playback, a 0.1% change in speed usually results in a total frequency change of about 0.2%.

For example, consider a 7500-cycle tone recorded at 7½ inches per second (ips). The recorded wavelength is then 0.001 inch. Now, suppose that the playback speed, while *averaging* 7½ ips, deviates about one percent from the average during operation. That is, the speed deviates from the center of 7.5 ips to a high of 7.575 ips and a low of 7.425 ips. Since the center playback frequency is 7500 cycles, it, too, will deviate; from 7500 up to 7575 and down to 7425 cycles. This fluctuation manifests itself as a wavering or quavering (falsetto, vibrato, etc., depending upon frequency) in the reproduced sound.

Some of the more common causes of flutter include: line frequency or voltage change; variations in the friction of the drive system; eccentricities in any of the parts of the drive system; nonuniform bearing friction; wobble; inaccurate gearing; drive belt irregularities; changes in spring tensions; wear on rubber wheel surfaces; nicks, chips, dust, dirt, etc., on rubber-rimmed driving units. Although there are many causes, a good technician using proper equipment should have no trouble in locating the specific fault, because each cause results in its peculiar characteristic, which, after some experience is gained, is readily identifiable to the technician.

---

* IEEE Sound Recording and Reproducing Committee, "I.R.E. Standards on Sound Recording and Reproducing: Methods for Determining Flutter Content, 1953," p. 537, *I.R.E. Proceedings,* March, 1954.

Table 2-1. Transport Components

ITEM	DESCRIPTION	FUNCTION
Supply or Load Reel	Metal or plastic reel vertically or horizontally mounted. Friction or other slippage and braking means is used for controlling unwind speed. Reel is keyed and locked to shaft.	Furnish tape to heads and take-up reel during recording. Receive and store recorded tape during rewind or playback.
Take-up Reel	Same as and interchangeable with supply reel. Directly or indirectly driven, often by the capstan drive motor.	Reverse of supply reel during operation.
Record Head	Balanced-winding magnet, precision ground to very narrow gap width. Poles are polished for uniform contact across entire tape width.	Generate magnetic fields proportional to signal current in windings. Resultant fields rearrange particles on magnetic tape, leaving a recorded magnetic pattern.
Playback Head	Similar to record-playback heads, but with much head for record and playback by means of switching circuits.	Pick up deposited field pattern. This induces corresponding voltage variations in head windings. Outputs drive playback amplifier.
A-C Erase Head	Similar to record-playback heads, but with much wider gap, and heavier windings to handle higher current. Generally energized by ultrasonic frequency (anywhere from 30-100 kc, usually about 80 kc), and must be shielded to prevent stray pick-up.	Generate diffused fringing flux, much more powerful (approximately 300 volts) than highest recording peaks, to demagnetize and neutralize recorded tape.
D-C Erase Head	Permanent magnet with field strong enough to saturate tape. Mechanically removed to prevent influencing record or playback.	Single head saturates and neutralizes tape, but leaves high noise content. Two staggered heads better, with lower noise content. A-c heads superior to both types.
Capstan	Concentric, power-driven, highly-torqued, rotating element. Circumference usually rubberized to assure firm tape contact.	Maintain proper tape tension while drawing tape past heads at constant speed.
Capstan Pressure Pulley (Idler Roller)	Freely-rotating pulleys (or idlers) press tape evenly against capstan surface. Static pressure pads, made of felt or other like material, are often used instead.	Maintain tape firmly against capstan during all operations.

4. Tape Construction

Today there is a magnetic tape for virtually any recording purpose. Whatever the purpose, the tape used is basically the same, whether it be sound or electronic signal recording. Magnetic tape is composed of a plastic "ribbon" coated with finely-powdered iron oxide. This, however, is where the simplicity of magnetic tape ends.

The iron oxide used by all manufacturers today is a non-magnetizable, yellow, synthetic pigment: alpha ferric oxide monohydrate. Three different grades of oxide are available, based on the fineness of the oxide particles and coating smoothness.

The oxide, in pigment form, is mixed with a binder (a complex blend of resins and plasticizers) before deposition on the backing material. The coated tape is then oven-dried, which causes evaporation of solvents in the binder, leaving the oxide particles uniformly coated in a permanent bond. Coating thickness is normally ½ mil (0.0005 inch) for standard tape.

Most magnetic-tape backings comprise one of two plastic materials: cellulose acetate and polyester (Mylar®) film. Normally, tape is available in three backing thicknesses.

For maximum strength, 1½-mil backing is used; this is the type found on 1200-foot tapes on the standard 7-inch reel. For 50% more playing time, 1-mil backings are used, allowing 1800 feet of tape on the same 7-inch reel. The reduction in thickness reduces tape strength, but 1-mil polyester is actually stronger than 1½-mil acetate. However, it has greater stretching tendencies.

Decreasing the backing further to ½ mil permits a 100% increase over the 1200-foot length. However, this further reduces the strength. To compensate for this, and for the stretching problem, pre-stretched, "tensilized", polyester-backed tape has been developed. This tape is twice as strong as the 1-mil polyester tape (1800-foot length), but is also more expensive.

The number of shapes and sizes of magnetic tape varies. The most familiar, no doubt, is the ¼-inch width found in home recorders. Other tapes used for audio recording come in ½-, ¾- and 1-inch widths on reels ranging in diameter from 3 to 14 inches. Lengths can vary anywhere from 150 to 7200 feet.

3 - Maintenance and Repair

1. Introduction

Tape recorders differ from other audio equipment in that they are just as much mechanical as electrical. Thus, the service technician must be adept in both areas. Also, he must keep in mind that, as far as the customer is concerned, the tape recorder is a piece of high-fidelity equipment, and must perform as such when it emerges from the shop. This, of course, pertains to the home tape recorder; to a lesser degree for office recorders and pocket-size machines.

All tape recorders are similar in principle; the major differences lie in the mechanical arrangements and the complexity of the electronics. Hence, the following information is of a basic nature; specific problems can be solved only through the use of manufacturer's service manuals, then, later on, by the technician's familiarity with the machines.

2. General Techniques

Before anything else is done, once a machine comes in, the main problem should be determined. Since only the machine's owner can tell this, do not ignore him. He can save time and trouble with the explanation of his complaints, even though it may require a superman to translate his layman's terms into technical sense.

Next on the agenda, become familiar with all the manufacturer's data, such as exploded views, mechanical flow diagrams, circuit schematics, and any other information. Who knows, tucked away in a corner of the service manual may be the one little "cure" that will solve the problem.

Item three, be sure all the necessary tools are handy and clean. The tools generally used by radio and record-player servicemen are applicable also to tape recorder servicing. However, the test equipment may not be. For proper servicing the test equipment listed in the chapter on high fidelity should be available. Table 3-1 lists additional servicing musts. Figure 3-1 shows fixed or adjustable service racks.

3. Routine Maintenance

Preliminary Checks

Preliminary checks of the electrical components, i.e., amplifiers and oscillators, present no unusual problems. The same techniques prevail here as with any electronic circuits, i.e., visual checks for burned resistors, bulging capacitors, cracked tube bases, loose or broken connections; tube transconductance and short tests; voltage and current checks against manufacturer's specifications; signal tracing; etc. The fact that there are high-fidelity circuits does not change the techniques; it just means that the tolerances are much more critical and must be adhered to.

Servicing the mechanical portions is another matter. As explained in the section on flutter, almost any mechanical part can cause trouble. And, since tape recorders are relatively new on the audio scene, few technicians are wholly familiar with their mechanical workings. However, as with all equipments, some general techniques pertain. These include visual checks for dust, dirt, excess grease, broken or loose switch contacts, cracked rubber, loose or broken springs or other belt drives, etc.; checks for wobble or binding of moving parts; and checks that slide switches are sliding properly.

Cleaning and Inspection

Following the preliminary checks, a good cleaning of the transport mechanism is in order. During normal operation, oxide loosened from the tape builds up on the tape heads, guides, pressure roller, pressure pads, and capstan. This accumulation can result in poor playback response, weak and/or distorted recordings, and poor erasure. It can also cause an up-and-down travel of the tape between the pressure roller and capstan. These oxide deposits, and any other dirt, grime, oil, etc., should be removed by means of denatured alcohol and cotton swabs; "Q-Tips" or pipe cleaners make handy tools for this purpose. In some cases, specific cleaning procedures are recommended by the manufacturer; however, a good general procedure is given below.

Note. Cleaning and lubricating kits containing all needed items are sold by most big supply houses.

1. Dip the applicator ("Q-Tip", or equivalent) into the cleaning solution, then squeeze excess solution from applicator.

2. Apply applicator to the faces of the heads, swabbing back and forth until all traces of oxide are gone. Use a dry applicator to remove any excess solution after cleaning is complete.

3. Repeat the same procedure on the pressure roller.

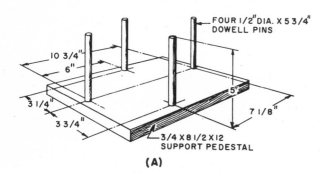

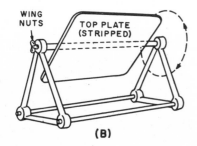

Fig. 3-1. (A) Fixed pedestal for servicing tape mechanisms. (Courtesy of the Bell Sound Systems, Inc.) (B) Adjustable service rack with stripped top plate in place.

4. Turn the machine "on," and hold wet applicator firmly against pressure roller. This will cause the solution to contact the capstan, thus wiping off the oxide. Continue the process until removal of all traces of oxide is assured.

5. Using a cloth tape, such as Allied Radio "Kleen-Tape", Stock No. 91R846, or Lafayette Radio Tape Cleaner, Stock No. PK-283, operate the machine as though it were in "playback." This will not only clean again all the critical parts, but put a high, smooth polish on them.

While cleaning, inspect all parts for wear. The oxide coating on the tape is an abrasive, causing wear on the heads. As they wear, the gaps widen, causing both lower output level and poorer high-frequency response. The gaps must be inspected with a magnifying glass; they are too narrow for ordinary visual checks. The record and playback head(s) gap(s) should appear as a fine, uniformly wide line. The erase head has two gaps, each of which is about five times as wide as the record and playback gap(s). Any increase in gap width, or irregularities in the gaps, such as shown in Fig. 3-2, indicate the need for replacement of the heads.

Check the tape guides for excessive wear. Worn guides can cause misalignment of the tape with the heads.

Check the pressure pads to be sure they hold the tape flat against the heads but not too tightly. Pads too tight produce rapid head wear and can cause tape speed variations. Pads packed too tightly, or with glazed or hardened surfaces can be "fluffed out" again by judicious use of an emery board or a small file. The file used for the points on an automobile distributor will do just fine. Care must be used, however, not to scratch the heads. Should the pressure pads require recementing due to looseness, care should be used in applying the adhesive. Excess cement will saturate the pads and harden them. (R.C.A. recommends that pads *not* be recemented; they suggest replacing the entire pad assembly.)

Lubrication

Most manufacturers have specific instructions about lubricating their machines. Basically *do not* lubricate them unless absolutely necessary, such as when a moving part is being replaced. Most machines are factory lubricated; this lubrication is good for approximately one year. Knowing how long the customer has had the machine can help determine whether lubrication is necessary or not. Also, the manufacturer's service manual for the particular ma-

Table 3-1. Required Shop Equipment

ITEM	FUNCTION
A. Flutter and Wow Indicator (RCA MI-9763B or equivalent)	Determine the extent of flutter and wow against manufacturer's specs. Reads: @ 1⅞ ips, 0.8% average, 1% peaks @ 3¾ ips, 0.6% average, 8% peaks @ 7½ ips, 0.5% average, 7% peaks
B. Fixed or adjustable service racks (See Fig. 3-1)	Mount mechanism for inspection, test and repair.
C. Flashlight	Check dark corners of mechanism.
D. Tape Splicer	Edit/repair tapes.
E. Standard Test Tapes	For comparison checks and overall system check after repair.
F. Speed Check Tapes (3M Co. No. 43)	Check tape transport speed. For example, @ 7½ ips, an 18.75 foot tape should run 30 ± 0.5 seconds.
G. Tachometer	Check motor speed.
H. Lateral Adjustment Tapes	Adjust heads in azimuth.
I. Highpass Filter Distortion Meter (General Radio GR-732B, or equivalent)	Eliminate flutter and wow during checks for distortion.
J. Magnifying glass (high-powered)	Check head gaps.
K. Demagnetizing Tool	Demagnetize heads.
L. Miscellaneous: Tape Lubricant Tape Cleaner Splicing Tape Head Lubricant Light Machine Oil	Care and maintenance of tape; lubrication of bearings and heads.

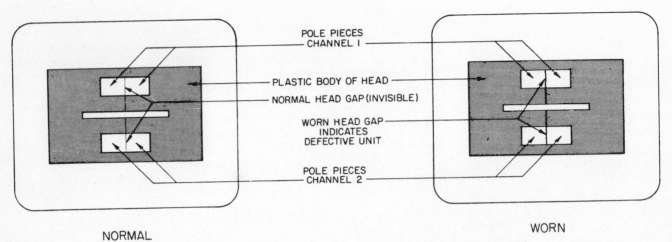

NORMAL   WORN

Fig. 3-2. Normal and worn stereo heads. (Courtesy of the Westinghouse Electric Corp.)

chine may provide special instructions as to where, when, how much, and what to use. In the final analysis, the service manual should be the guide on all repairs. However, some general procedures can be observed, such as:

1. Never use lubricants that can oxidize and harden.

2. Never use oil or grease on the capstan and pressure roller.

3. When necessary to lubricate, be sure that no oil or grease covers any of the rubberized parts or any parts which might transfer the oil or grease to the tape or drive surfaces.

4. Heads can be lubricated with a silicone-base lubricant, such as Lafayette Radio Stock No. RT-346. This type of lubricant will not affect rubberized surfaces or the drive components.

Head Demagnetization

The more the machine is used, the greater the residual magnetism picked up by the heads. This residual magnet-

ism decreases the machine's high-frequency response while increasing both noise and harmonic distortion. Thus, one of the first items on the service agenda should be head demagnetization (following cleaning). Heads should also be demagnetized any time they have been checked for continuity with an ohmmeter, or if magnetic tools have been used in the near vicinity.

Heads can be demagnetized with the use of a demagnetization tool, Allied Radio Model HD-3JR, Stock No. 90R948, or the Robins HD-6 available from Radio Shack and from Lafayette Radio (Stock No. RT-336). A good idea is to cover the tool's tip with cellophane tape to avoid scratching the head.

To demagnetize the head, proceed as follows:

1. Insert the tool tip between pressure pad and head.

2. Turn on current to tool and press it *gently* against the head.

3. *Slowly* pull the tool tip away from the head. Don't turn off the tool until it is completely away from the vicinity of the head.

4. Preliminary Tests and Adjustments

Mechanical Tests

Tape recorders are electromechanical devices, hence are subject to both mechanical and electrical failures. Mechanical failures occur more often because of the constant wear on moving parts.

Certain mehanical failures, such as defective switches and worn heads, directly affect the recorder's electrical performance. Defective switches are a common source of trouble because of their continual use. The record and playback heads deteriorate in high-frequency response and output-voltage level as they wear. Thus, a mechanical condition, head wear, is indicated by an electrical condition, output-signal deterioration. However, loss of high-frequency response and low output level may also be caused by head misalignment, or by excess record bias. Wow and flutter, rumble, and improper tape speed are other mechanical malfunctions that show up in degraded electrical performance.

The first step in any test procedure is to become familiar with the normal operating procedure of the equipment under test. You should know what happens, or is supposed to happen, when each control is operated. Then, if possible, an overall performance check should be made with a standard test tape. The latter is a tape recorded under exacting NARTB standards, and can be obtained in various frequency ranges.

To return to the operating procedure, the following is a general procedure, applicable to most machines.

1. Operate the "stop" control and turn on the power. Mount both supply (full) and take-up reels. Using about a foot of tape from the supply reel, thread the tape through the drive and head assemblies and fasten the end to the take-up reel. In the "stop" position, neither reel should turn. If either has a tendency to do so, check the brake mechanism, i.e., rollers, springs, etc., for proper operation.

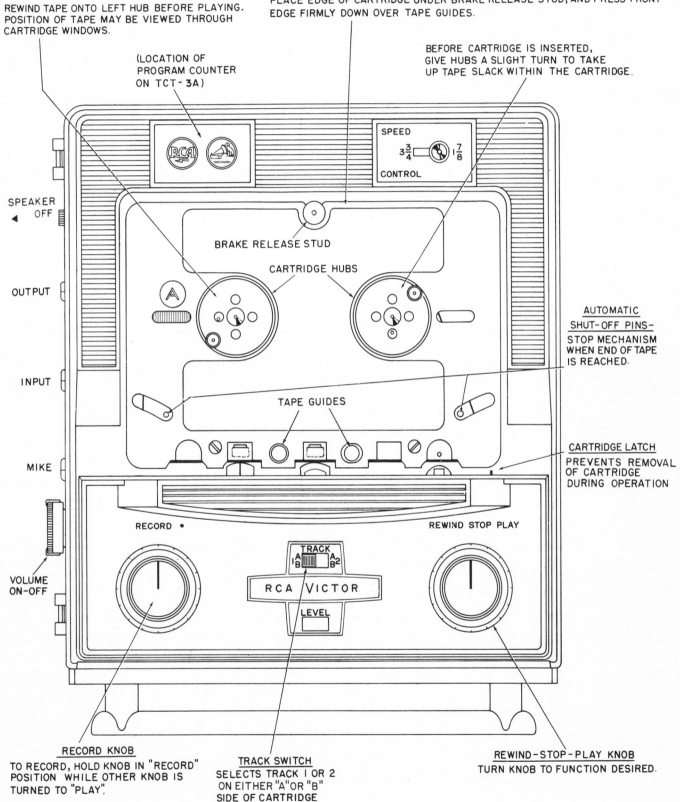

CARTRIDGE
THE CARTRIDGE IS SYMMETRICAL. WITH EITHER SIDE "A" OR SIDE "B" UP,
EITHER TRACK MAY BE RECORDED OR PLAYED. TO INSERT THE CARTRIDGE,
PLACE EDGE OF CARTRIDGE UNDER BRAKE RELEASE STUD, AND PRESS FRONT
EDGE FIRMLY DOWN OVER TAPE GUIDES.

REWIND TAPE ONTO LEFT HUB BEFORE PLAYING.
POSITION OF TAPE MAY BE VIEWED THROUGH
CARTRIDGE WINDOWS.

(LOCATION OF
PROGRAM COUNTER
ON TCT-3A)

BEFORE CARTRIDGE IS INSERTED,
GIVE HUBS A SLIGHT TURN TO TAKE
UP TAPE SLACK WITHIN THE CARTRIDGE.

SPEED
$3\frac{3}{4}$ $1\frac{7}{8}$
CONTROL

SPEAKER
OFF

OUTPUT

INPUT

MIKE

VOLUME
ON-OFF

BRAKE RELEASE STUD

CARTRIDGE HUBS

AUTOMATIC
SHUT-OFF PINS-
STOP MECHANISM
WHEN END OF TAPE
IS REACHED.

TAPE GUIDES

CARTRIDGE LATCH
PREVENTS REMOVAL
OF CARTRIDGE
DURING OPERATION

RECORD •

REWIND STOP PLAY

TRACK
A A²
B B¹

RCA VICTOR

LEVEL

RECORD KNOB
TO RECORD, HOLD KNOB IN "RECORD"
POSITION WHILE OTHER KNOB IS
TURNED TO "PLAY".

TRACK SWITCH
SELECTS TRACK 1 OR 2
ON EITHER "A" OR "B"
SIDE OF CARTRIDGE

REWIND-STOP-PLAY KNOB
TURN KNOB TO FUNCTION DESIRED.

Fig. 3-3. RCA TCT-3 cartridge recorder.

2. Operate the "play" control. This causes the head assembly to move forward against the tape. The drive mechanism should start immediately without any tape spillage. If the tape does not move at all, or moves erratically, check the capstan drive mechanism and take-up clutch for proper operation. If the head assembly fails to move forward (no sound output) check the assembly parts, usually some sort of spring mechanism, for proper operation.

Check that the footage counter operates properly. Listen for flutter and wow, or periodic squeaking or scraping. If either is heard, check all moving parts. A touch of lubricant may be all that is required to eliminate the defect. Either that, or some oxide may remain after cleaning, causing drive eccentricities.

With the motor running, move the speed-change switch, and check that the speed changes correctly. (Never switch the speed-change control while the motor is not running; to do so may cause a jam in the drive mechanism.) Check both speeds by means of a tachometer pressed against the shaft of the pressure roller or capstan. Speed checks also can be made with a speed-timing tape (Table 3-1) as separate tests.

3. Operate the "stop" control. The reels should stop with no tape spillage. If they do not, recheck the braking mechanism.

4. Operate the "rewind" control. The tape should wind rapidly and smoothly on the take-up reel. If not, check the fast-forward mechanism in the machine.

5. Stop the machine, then rewind the tape back onto the supply reel. Some machines have an automatic cutoff switch. Make sure this shuts off the motor after the tape is completely past it.

6. Operate the "stop" control again, and remove the supply reel and tape. Mount and thread a clean tape, or one which has "erasable" material on it.

7. Operate the "record" control. As in "play", the tape should move smoothly from reel to heads to reel.

8. Make a tape recording on the tape. Depending upon the level indicator, adjust the volume control so that the loudest sound inputs won't cause distortion. (On neon-bulb indicators, the proper level is that which causes only *half* the bulb to light when normal speech is recorded.)

9. Operate the "stop" control, then rewind to approximately the point on the tape where you started the recording.

10. Operate the "play" control and check carefully for noise and distortion. Operate the volume and tone controls, and clean if necessary.

11. Operate the "stop" control, then rewind the tape again, as in step 9.

12. Operate the "record" control, and record right over the previous recording.

13. Operate the "stop" and "rewind" as in step 9.

14. Operate the "play" control. Only the new recording should be heard. If not, the erase function is not operating properly.

15. Operate the "stop" control and shut off the power.

The foregoing procedure applies in general to machines with removable supply and take-up reels. However, R.C.A. manufactures a machine, see Fig. 3-3, which operates in a slightly different manner. Instead of the supply and take-up reels, this machine utilizes a cartridge load. (Many office recorders are also of this type.) To play or record all that

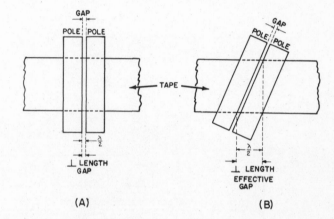

Fig. 3-5. Air-gap tilt effect (Courtesy of RCA)

is required is to drop the cartridge in place, as shown. No threading procedure is required. To record on this machine, however, both the "record" and "play" controls are operated simultaneously. Aside from these two differences, the general procedure given above holds true.

Mechanical Adjustments

Take-Up Clutch Adjustment. If the clutch develops too much drag it can cause wow or excessive tape speed. Insufficient drag will cause tape spillage. In the Westinghouse take-up clutch, the clutch adjustment is made by means of a Nylock screw. In the R.C.A. clutch shown in Fig. 3-4, adjustment is made by moving the collar on the clutch spring assembly inward or outward (increasing or decreasing torque, respectively) while holding the turntable firm. A set screw locks the spring in the desired position.

Almost all machines have clutches similar to one or the other of the foregoing. All use some sort of felt or leather

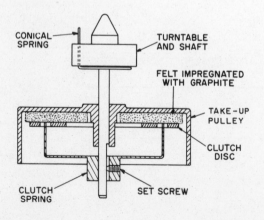

Fig. 3-4. Clutch assembly of the cartridge recorder. (Courtesy of RCA)

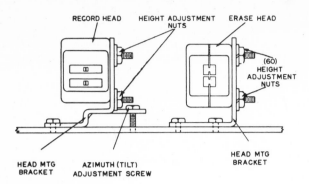

Fig. 3-6. Typical head mounting and mounting adjustments. (Courtesy of RCA)

pad as part of the clutch. If correct adjustment cannot be made, these pads should be replaced. All clutch parts must be cleaned thoroughly before reassembly and adjustment.

Head Alignment. Improper head alignment can cause several problems, such as low output, poor high-frequency response, and, in stereo recorders, sound track overlap. The record and playback heads must be exactly perpendicular to the tape, while the line of the gap must be perpendicular to the edge of the tape, as shown in Fig. 3-5A. When the gap is not perpendicular, as in Fig. 3-5B, the effective gap length is much longer. This, in turn, lowers the frequency range capable of being recorded; as a result, high frequencies are cut off.

The top edge of the pole piece of the tape must be even with the top edge of the tape.

Three different head arrangements are shown in Figs. 3-6, 3-7, and 3-8. Figure 3-6 shows the layout for the

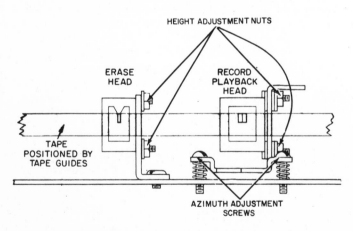

Fig. 3-7. Head alignment of the Westinghouse half-track monaural heads. (Courtesy of the Westinghouse Electric Corp.)

R.C.A. TCT-3 and TCT-3A transport mechanisms. Figure 3-7 is the layout of a Westinghouse half-track, monaural head assembly. Figure 3-8 is the layout for the Curtis Mathes R3-R4 chassis. All require the use of prerecorded test tapes; R.C.A. uses their number 12-5-64T, Westinghouse requires a 5-kc tape, and Curtis Mathes a 6-kc tape. Some other recorders go as high as 12 kc for their test-tape requirements. Whatever the machine, exact align-

ment instructions are given in the manufacturer's service manuals.

Worn Heads. If the head alignment does not do the trick, the next step is to replace the head or heads. Worn heads can cause any number of discrepancies in a test of frequency response. The heads are not expensive, and are as easily replaced as a tube in a radio. Head replacement must be followed by head alignment.

Torque and Drag Adjustments. Most machines have specific amounts of torque in their play, record, rewind, and fast-forward mechanisms. These range anywhere from 2 ounces in play and record up to 5 ounces in fast-forward. Precise amounts, and the means for their attainment are given in the service manual applicable to the machine under repair.

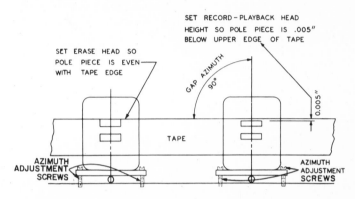

Fig. 3-8. Head alignment of the Curtis Mathes models R3 and R4

Capstan Adjustment. Unless the capstan and pressure roller are in perfect parallelism, the tape will tend to ride up and down during its travel, or even cause tape wrinkle and possible tear. Figure 3-9 shows what can happen when the capstan is out of true alignment, and what it should look like when properly adjusted. All machines are provided with capstan adjustments; the exact method depends on the mounting arrangement.

Following readjustment of the capstan, the pressure roller pressure should be checked. The average pressure is anywhere from 3-5 pounds. If the pressure is incorrect, the pressure roller spring is usually to blame; replace it.

Automatic Cutoff Switch Adjustment. The cutoff switch provided in some machines is usually a microswitch in series with the drive motor(s). The tension of the tape during operation is enough to keep the switch in the "off" position. When the tape runs out or breaks, the switch arm releases, turning off the motor. Adjustment of the switch merely calls for loosening the mounting screws and repositioning the switch until the normal tape tension during operation is sufficient to keep the switch off. If the switch is an immovable one, simply bend the switch arm until the same effect is obtained.

On the R.C.A. cartridge machine, automatic shut-off is provided in the cartridge itself, as shown in Fig. 3-10. The shut-off pins react to tape tension, in turn actuating a toggle link system which controls the play-rewind-stop functions. During normal operation, tape tension is insufficient to trip the pins. However, the drag at the end of the run pulls the shut-off pins to their "off" position, which causes the machine "stop" switch to be actuated. Malfunction of the automatic shut-off in this case calls for check and readjustment of the toggle link system and, possibly, a touch of the proper lubricant.

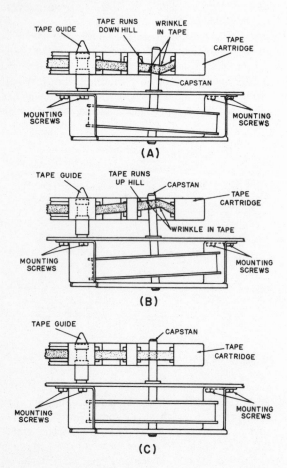

Fig. 3-9. Effects of incorrect flywheel position. (Courtesy of RCA)

Electric Motors. Defective motors are often detected by speed-timing tests. Subnormal speeds indicate that motor bearings, or directly-driven rotating parts, may need cleaning and/or lubricating. On the other hand, there may be low line voltage to the motor. This can be checked at the customer's house/office only. What to do about it is his problem. (You can recommend a Variac®, of course.)

Check the motor shaft concentricity. Where the motor shaft connects to the first rotating part, usually the flywheel, runout should be a maximum of 2 mils (0.002 inch). If beyond this, the motor must be replaced. If not, excess oil on the motor shaft or on the rotating parts may be causing slippage and consequently subnormal speed.

Rubber Driver Components. One of the causes of wow is the slippage of the rubber drive surfaces. These surfaces harden with age, tending to become smooth and polished, hence the slip. Trying to rough up the surface as a temporary expedient is useless; not only does the surface quickly smooth again, but the surface may lose its roundness because of the roughening process. The best repair

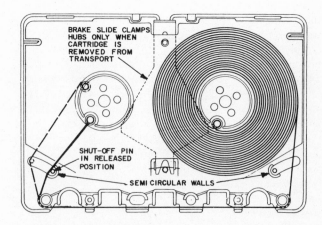

Fig. 3-10. End of tape; automatic shut-off. (Courtesy of RCA)

in this case is replacement of the entire unit.

As for rubber belts, their age is evidenced in looseness or spots which become hard and tend to cause slippage during operation. Here, again, unless there are adjustments, such as the idler wheel, which enable you to take up the slack, replacement is the only remedy. Here, at least, you can save time and money by making your own belts. Rubber belt material is obtainable in almost any size and length. All you need do is thread the replacement belting through its operating position, cut it (make the cut a trifle shorter than required; this will ensure a tight fit and no slippage), then remove it and bond the ends together. Once the bond sets, the new belt can be snapped into place. (In some cases, the same process can be used to replace the rubber drives around mechanical parts. Care must be used, however, to make sure that the bonded joint is smooth, or you will have a periodic bumping during operation, and possible out-of-round condition of the part after a short time.)

Tape Repair. Due to mechanical malfunctions, the tape may become stretched in spots, or broken. If such is the case, before attempting repair, remind the customer that the repair will result in a small cut-out of the recorded data. Telling him later won't help; he'll be sure you goofed. Especially if the tape is a two- or four-track one.

Stretched sections are treated similarly to badly-torn tapes. Simply cut out the stretched (or broken) section, as shown in Fig. 3-11A. Butt the cut ends together, with

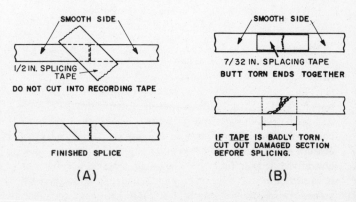

Fig. 3-11. Tape splicing. (Courtesy of RCA)

the splicing tape at a 45° angle as shown. Be sure that you use the *shiny* side of the magnetic tape for the splice.

For torn tapes not too badly broken, simply butt the broken ends together, as shown at the top of Figure 3-11B, again with the *shiny* side up, and mend with the splicing tape. The 7/32-inch splicing tape to use is 3M Co. No. 41, or equivalent. *Never* use ordinary cellophane tape; the adhesive will bleed through the magnetic tape and cause the latter to stick together on the reel.

Although the instructions given above are fairly simple, several tape-splicing machines are commercially available which can make the job even easier. Since these are not too expensive, their purchase price is quickly made up by the time and trouble they can save.

A good idea, following the splicing process, is to lubricate the tape with a good commercial tape lubricant. This will eliminate friction which can cause flutter, wow, squeal, and rapid wear on the heads.

facturer's specs, or to those given by a standard test tapes. If any differences are noted, the individual circuits will then have to be checked.

Distortion Tests. To determine whether distortion is present, measure the distortion with a highpass filter distortion meter (Table 3-1). Once the fact is established that there is distortion, tests to isolate the malfunction may be made.

Distortion tests call for stage-by-stage checking with an oscilloscope. Waveforms must be checked at each plate and grid, or collector and base, as applicable, until the defective stage is found. Remember that a defective power supply can upset all readings, so a check of the supply voltages may be in order first. Also, a leaky coupling capacitor in one stage can affect the following stage, throwing you off the track.

Bias Tests. Bias troubles can be determined simply. Whereas the recorder amplifier is used in both record and

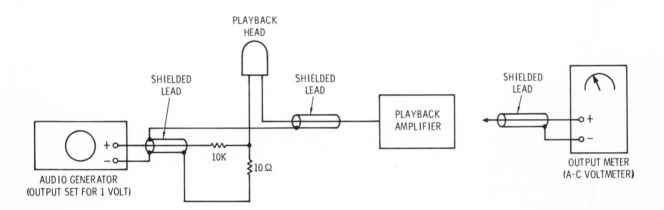

Fig. 3-12. Test set-up for measuring frequency response of the playback amplifier.

Electrical Tests

Several major checks should be made before any electrical repairs are attempted. These checks will either help pinpoint any troubles, or determine that particular circuits are operating satisfactorily. Again it must be remembered that these are high-fidelity circuits, with critical levels and tolerances. Hence, constant reference to schematics, parts lists and tolerances, and any other data available from the manufacturer, is a must.

In all the tests listed below, the machine should have a pre-test warm-up of at least 15 minutes.

Frequency Response Tests. Differences in response between standard test tapes and those recorded by the machine under test are often caused by the playback amplifier. These can be checked by making gain and frequency tests. One way of doing this is to connect the machine to a test set-up such as that of Fig. 3-12 and record the machine's full frequency spectrum. Be sure all control settings, especially the equalizer settings, are correct, and the generator is furnishing the proper levels. Once the recording is completed, connect an output meter (a-c voltmeter) across the machine's output terminals and play back the recording. Compare the meter readings against the manu-

playback, the bias oscillator is used only in record. Hence, if the recorder doesn't record properly, but plays back satisfactorily a previously-recorded tape, the trouble is in the oscillator.

In quite a few recorders the bias and erase oscillators are one and the same tube. Hence, a defective tube can disturb both operations. The best way to check this is to replace the tube with a new one; tube checkers do not check oscillator operation.

Other failures that cause the loss of record bias can originate in the oscillator circuits, in the coupling circuits between the heads and the oscillator, and in the heads themselves. Failures in the circuitry result in loss of bias, and low, distorted recordings.

To determine that the oscillator is operating, check the amount of grid bias against that called for by the schematic. Any discrepancy denotes a bad tube, or a defective part in the surrounding circuitry. Voltage checks can be used to isolate the trouble.

The oscillator frequency should also be checked. This is done by comparing the specified frequency against that of a calibrated signal generator. To perform the check, proceed as follows: Connect the high side of the erase head through a shielded lead to the vertical input of an oscilloscope. Connect the signal generator, set to the oscillator frequency specified by the manufacturer, to the oscilloscope's horizontal input. Set the scope to "External Sync," then readjust the generator frequency until a Lissajous pattern (see Fig. 3-13) appears on the scope. The generator frequency is now the oscillator frequency, and should be within 10% of that specified. Demagnetize the erase head when the test is finished.

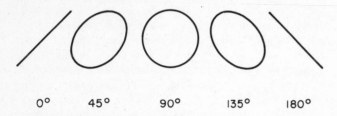

Fig. 3-13. Lissajous patterns. (Courtesy of the Westinghouse Electric Corp.)

Equalization Tests. Equalization networks are those used to compensate for frequency-response irregularities in the tape recorder. Pre-emphasis and de-emphasis networks make up the equalization circuits. Pre-emphasis is used during recording, de-emphasis during playback. Pre-emphasis is usually provided following the first amplifier stage, to improve the S/N ratio.

Equalizers are essentially highpass or lowpass, RC filters, often just tone control circuits, such as that shown in Fig. 3-14. Sometimes, the bias oscillator coil is switched in, to form a compensating IC circuit during playback.

There are no specific tests to determine a defective equalizer. One way of checking is to compare the responses of a test tape and a newly recorded tape, played under the same conditions. Any differences can be detected easily. If differences are found, check the playback circuits first, then the record circuits.

Hum Tests. Hum tests should be performed with the motors running, volume all the way up, and all shields in place. If the unit has a hum-bucking (balance) control, a slight readjustment may be all that is necessary to eliminate the problem. Sometimes a slight repositioning of the power supply transformer will do the trick.

Tube Checks. As mentioned previously, tube checkers cannot really check oscillator tubes. To a somewhat lesser extent, this holds true for amplifier tubes, especially those in high-fidelity circuits. The best check is to substitute a new tube for a suspected one. Failing this, an operating check can be done. A milliammeter in the plate circuit and voltage tests at critical points, when compared to the specification in a tube manual, will provide an adequate test. Grid and cathode bias should be checked against the applicable schematic.

Electrical Adjustments

Few electrical adjustments can be made, aside from front-panel controls already provided. However, record/

playback and erase head adjustments can be performed to peak the recorder's response.

Record/Playback Head Adjustment. The following procedure will align the record/playback heads with each other:

1. Disconnect the record and playback connecting leads, and connect the leads formerly from the playback head to the record head.

2. Connect an output meter across the output of the playback amplifier.

3. Playback an azimuth adjustment tape, using the former record head as the playback head. Adjust the head for maximum output, then lock it in place.

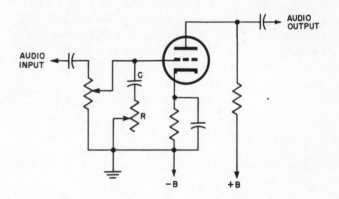

Fig. 3-14. Typical tone control for variable retardation of higher audio frequencies.

4. Reconnect all leads to their original head connections.

5. Remove the test tape and thread in a tape which can be erased.

6. Connect an audio generator to the input and record a signal at the highest rated frequency of the machine.

7. Now play back the recorded signal and adjust the playback head for maximum output. Lock the head in place.

Erase Head Adjustment. In some recorders a balance control is provided to minimize erase and hiss. When such is the case, hiss can be minimized as follows:

1. With the machine operating in "record," insert a thin piece of cardboard or plastic, about the thickness of a business card, between the record head and the tape. Reposition the erase head for minimum hiss; lock, then remove the cardboard.

2. Reset the balance control to the midpoint of its range, then let the machine run until thoroughly warmed up.

3. Readjust the balance control for minimum hum.

Troubleshooting

Table 3-2 lists some common symptoms of reel recorders, their possible causes, and remedies. Table 3-3 is a troubleshooting chart for RCA cartridge recorders, but is applicable to other recorders of this type.

Table 3-2. Troubleshooting Chart: Reel Recorders

SYMPTOM	PROBABLE CAUSE	REMEDY
Mechanical		
A. No tape drive in "Record" or "Play"	1. Jammed, slipping, or broken drive belt.	1. Clear jam; replace belt.
	2. Disconnected or broken pressure roller spring.	2. Reconnect or replace spring.
	3. Oil on pressure roller or capstan.	3. Clean.
B. No tape drive in "Fast Forward" (Wind)	1. Fast-forward spring (or belt) broken or disconnected.	1. Replace or reconnect.
	2. Oil on take-up reel rest or on drive parts.	2. Clean.
	3. Reels binding.	3. Clean and lubricate reel shafts.
C. No tape drive in "Rewind"	1. Rewind spring (or belt) broken or disconnected.	1. Replace or reconnect.
	2. Oil on supply-reel rest or, idler, or other drive parts.	2. Clean.
	3. Reels binding.	3. Clean and lubricate reel shafts.
D. No tape drive in "Rewind" and "Wind"	1. Slipping or broken belt.	1. Replace.
	2. Pressure roller stuck against capstan.	2. Check pressure roller spring, and replace if necessary.
E. No tape drive at all	1. Jammed or broken belts.	1. Check and clear jam or replace belts.
	2. Defective motor.	2. Replace.
	3. On models with automatic cutoff, check for inoperative shut-off microswitch.	3. Repair or replace.
	4. On pocket-types, check for low battery voltage.	4. Replace batteries.
F. Take-up reel doesn't turn (Supply O.K.)	1. Loose take-up clutch.	1. Readjust or replace clutch pads.
	2. Broken or disconnected take-up spring.	2. Replace or reconnect.
	3. Take-up belt broken or slipping.	3. Replace.
G. Tape Spillage	1. Loose take-up clutch.	1. Readjust or replace clutch pads.
	2. Defective braking.	2. Check brake springs, rollers, etc. Replace defective parts.
	3. Oil on reel rests or brakes.	3. Clean.
	4. Supply-reel drag not operating properly.	4. Check for wear or oil; clean or replace worn part; check and replace broken spring.
H. Tape continually breaks	1. Tight take-up clutch.	1. Adjust clutch.
	2. Brakes not releasing sufficiently.	2. Check brake springs for stretch or break and replace.
I. Machine squeals	1. Tape is brittle and dried out.	1. Try lubricating.
	2. Incorrect tape tension.	2. Entire drive must be checked for binds, lubrication, or slippage.
	3. Reels are warped.	3. Rewind tape on new reels.
	4. Tape guides or reels improperly aligned.	4. Check and adjust or repair guides/reel shafts.
	5. Dirt on heads.	5. Clean.
	6. Dry or worn bearings.	6. Lubricate or replace.
	7. Dirt on pressure pads, or pressure pads too tight.	7. Clean or replace pads.
J. Speed selector defective	1. Loose control knob.	1. Check and tighten set screw.
	2. Spring broken or disconnected.	2. Replace or reconnect.
K. Tape counter not operating	1. Broken counter.	1. Replace.
	2. Broken or slipping drive belt or spring.	2. Replace loose or broken parts.
L. Uneven tape speed; Flutter Wow	1. Take-up clutch too loose or too tight.	1. Readjust or replace pads.
	2. Bearings are binding.	2. Lubricate.
	3. Oil on drive components.	3. Clean.
	4. Friction drags worn.	4. Replace.
	5. Defective motor (intermittent).	5. Check insulation for grounds; replace motor.
Electrical		
M. No "Playback"	1. Open head.	1. Check continuity; replace.
	2. Defective function switch.	2. Check for bent, broken contacts; replace switch.
	3. Defective amplifier.	3. Check and replace defective part(s).
	4. Low battery voltage on pocket types.	4. Replace batteries.
	5. Open speaker.	5. Check continuity and replace.
	6. Defective output connector.	6. Check for loose or bent contacts, and repair.
N. Distorted or weak "Record"; no "Record"	1. Defective microphone.	1. Check with new microphone; repair or replace.
	2. Bias/erase oscillator not functioning properly.	2. Check voltages, resistance, etc.; replace defective parts.

Table 3-2. Troubleshooting Chart: Reel Recorders (Cont'd)

SYMPTOM	PROBABLE CAUSE	REMEDY
	3. Defective coupling capacitor, oscillator-to-head.	3. Replace defective part.
	4. Function switch defective.	4. Check for dirty, loose, or broken contacts and repair, or replace switch.
	5. Dirty record head, or worn head.	5. Clean and re-record; replace worn head.
	6. Loose pressure pads.	6. Re-cement new pads.
	7. Defective input connector.	7. Check for loose or bent contacts and repair.
	8. Level indicator defective.	8. Check operation with new unit.
O. Improper high-frequency response	1. Dirty, worn, or misaligned record/playback head.	1. Clean; repair or replace defective head.
	2. Bias too high or too low.	2. Check biasing circuitry and oscillator and repair or replace as necessary.
	3. Magnetized heads.	3. Demagnetize.
	4. Pressure pads worn or loose.	4. Re-cement new pads.
P. Incomplete or no "Erase"	1. Dirty, worn, open, or misaligned head.	1. Check and repair or replace.
	2. Faulty erase circuitry.	2. Replace oscillator; check surrounding circuits for defective part.
	3. Erase pressure pads dirty, worn, or loose.	3. Clean or re-cement new pads.
	4. Open coupling capacitor, erase-to-oscillator.	4. Replace defective part.
Q. Low output level	1. Defective bias oscillator.	1. Replace oscillator; check surrounding circuits for defective part.
	2. Worn, dirty, or misaligned record/playback head.	2. Check and repair or replace.
	3. Dirty, worn, or loose pressure pads.	3. Clean or re-cement new pads.
	4. Weak tube or defective component in amplifier.	4. Check and replace defective parts.
	5. Record-level indicator not functioning.	5. Check operation with new unit.
R. Distorted output	1. Bias oscillator defective.	1. Replace tube; check surrounding circuits for defective part.
	2. Record-level indicator functioning improperly.	2. Check operation with new unit.
	3. Heads magnetized.	3. Demagnetize.
	4. Worn or misaligned record/playback head.	4. Check and repair or replace.
	5. Defective equalizing network.	5. Check equalizing network and replace defective parts; entire amplifier response must then be checked.
	6. Defective amplifier.	6. Check by frequency and gain runs, and replace weak or defective parts.
	7. Dirty or loose switch contacts.	7. Check, and repair or replace switch.
	8. Weak erase.	8. See Incomplete or no "Erase."
S. Noise; Hum	1. Improper bias.	1. Check oscillator circuit and replace weak or defective parts.
	2. Noisy tubes, transistors.	2. Replace tubes; check transistors on 'scope.
	3. Noisy controls.	3. Clean all controls, switch contacts.
	4. Loose grounds or shields.	4. Check and repair.
	5. Power supply filter defective.	5. Check and replace filter components.
	6. Shorted tube.	6. Check and replace.
	7. Magnetized heads.	7. Demagnetize.
	8. Low record current because of defective level indicator.	8. Check operation with new unit.

Table 3-3. Troubleshooting Chart: Cartridge Recorders

SYMPTOM	POSSIBLE CAUSE AND REMEDY
A. Tape winds unevenly in cartridge	1. Plastic flash, notably around knockout-pin marks on inside of flat surface of cartridge case, in area where tape winds, interferes with tape winding.
	2. Poor guiding evidenced by "curling" of tape. (See G)
	3. Cartridge not fully seated.
	4. Tape not falling into guides. Check for cartridge mold flash on inside of guide-post holes.
	5. Pressure-roller yoke not pivoting freely. This causes a delay in equalization of pressure between top and bottom of pressure roller and capstan, which in turn may cause a stepping in the tape winding. The binding of this pivot can be relieved by prying the fork of the yoke apart slightly with a screwdriver.
	6. Check for bent pins.

Table 3-3. Troubleshooting Chart: Cartridge Recorders (Cont'd)

SYMPTOM	POSSIBLE CAUSE AND REMEDY
B. Cartridge climbs up during operation	1. Check for bent pins. 2. Uneven winding of tape in cartridge.
C. Groove worn in pressure roller by tape	1. Machine fails to shut off at end of play. (See D) 2. Excessive torque in take-up clutch. (See F) 3. Excessive drag on tape, causing creepage through capstan. Check freedom of turntable bearing and/or counter. 4. Insufficient pressure on pressure roller due to stretched spring or bent parts.
D. Machine fails to shut off automatically	1. Uneven winding of tape in cartridge. (See A) 2. Excessive drag in control mechanism (cam or levers). 3. Insufficient torque in clutch. (See F) 4. Excessive drag on tape. (See C3) 5. Insufficient pull on tape by capstan. (See C4)
E. Tape winds around capstan or pressure roller	1. Failure of take-up because of low torque in take-up clutch (see F), or poor winding of tape in cartridge causing excessive drag on take-up reel. (See A, B & F)
F. Torque of clutch	1. Clutch torque outside of limits, may be due to actual slippage of adjustment. (Locking screw or nut should be checked.) 2. Oil or loose particles, such as burrs, may contaminate clutch lining. (Torque may either increase or decrease.) 3. Lack of lubrication on end play bearing. 4. Unlubricated washer between pulley and take-up shaft bearing, or between turntable spring and shaft bearing.

G. Poor tape guiding	1. Poor tape guiding is evidenced by tape "curl" as it leaves the capstan. (Tape "curl" means that one edge of the tape is tighter than the other as it leaves the capstan. It may require very close observation to detect "curl".)
	   a. Cartridge must be fully seated and contain new (unstretched) tape.
	   b. Tape "curl" is usually due to misalignment of the capstan.
	   c. Tape "curl" may be due to the tape not operating in the guiding grooves of the tape guide posts. (See A1)
	   d. The operator may have failed to seat the cartridge properly.
	2. Piles of oxide built up on the heads.

H. Tape won't rewind	1. Binding of tape in the cartridge. (See A)
	2. If the capstan is not rotating and motor is stalled, drive system is probably overloaded.
	   a. Check to see that there is no excessive friction or binding.
	   b. Check that rewind turntable shaft is free and properly lubricated.
	   c. Check that idler bearing is properly lubricated.
	3. If the capstan is rotating.
	   a. Check if the idler is pressing the drive belt against the rewind pulley.
	   b. Check for friction or binding.
	   c. Check all staked or riveted parts.
	4. If capstan is not rotating but motor is running, check the belt tension; tension may be low, or the belt may have oil or grease on its surface.

I. Mechanical Squeal	1. Clutch torque high, causing belt slippage on take-up pulley. 2. Belt slipping on take-up pulley due to oil or grease on belt. 3. Insufficient rewind idler lubrication. 4. Tape rubbing over the heads; when this occurs the heads will usually have a pile or coating of oxide built up on their faces, which must be cleaned. (A tape which rubs off excessively on the heads should be discarded.)
J. Speed change won't operate	1. Check that change linkage is not bent and that its travel is not limited. 2. Inadequate lubrication of linkage. 3. Check that shift lever is not bent and that travel is not limited. 4. Oil or grease on belt. 5. Stretched belt. 6. If shift lever is in neutral position but touches belt in either speed, adjust centering spring. 7. Excessive end play in motor. 8. Excessive belt tension.
K. Two tracks heard at once	1. Check guiding (See G). 2. Check head height (slight misadjustment of head height may not be observed on playback only).
L. Difference in level of two heads	1. Heads should be cleaned to eliminate possibility of one core making better contact with tape than other core. 2. May be caused same as in "K," above.
M. Azimuth of head won't adjust properly	1. Adjustment screw may be overtight, bracket may be bent.
N. Pressure pads do not open sufficiently for loading of tape	1. Excessive drag in pressure-roller levers. 2. Improper spring tension. 3. Excessive lubrication under pressure pad mechanism. 4. Damaged pressure pads.
O. Play/Record switch won't operate	1. Bent linkage to Play/Record switch.

Part IV

Home Intercoms

1 – Introduction

1. The System

Today, the intercom system once restricted to offices and business use is becoming an essential part of many homes. The intercom system in the home is used to talk and listen from any room in the home to any other room. In addition, the home intercom system can be used to answer the door from any room in the home, to listen in on the children at any time from another room, and to call the family together. Many of the new home intercom systems also pipe soft background music throughout the house when the intercom is not being used for communicating. The home intercoms are usually housed in attractive plastic or metal cabinets that can be placed anywhere, or are provided with kits to be built into the walls of a home. Typical home intercom systems are shown in Figs. 1-1 to 1-7.

Types of Home Intercoms

The term *intercom* is actually a shortened version of

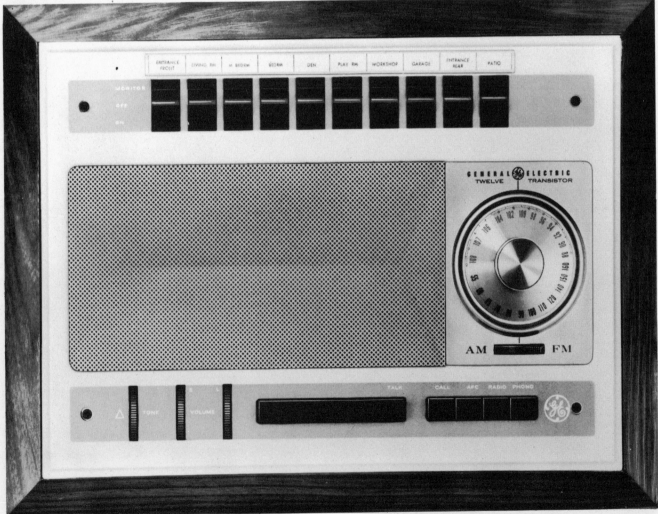

Fig. 1-1. Master station panel for General Electric model W330 includes an AM-FM radio. The master can handle up to ten remote stations. The unit is completely transistorized.

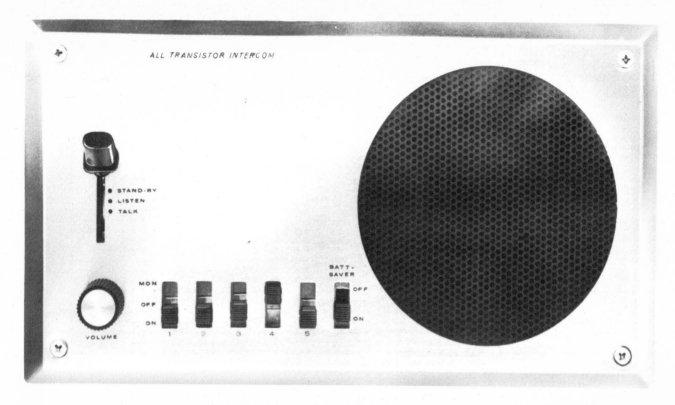

Fig. 1-2. Master station is fully transistorized and operates on a 9-volt battery. The master can converse with any or all of five remotes, and remotes can converse with each other if preset at master's switchboard. (Courtesy of Fanon-Masco)

*inter*office *com*munication or *inter*room *com*munication. Two types of intercoms are used for interroom communication in the home: the *wired* intercom and the *wireless* intercom. The wired intercom system consists of an amplifier and speaker circuit connected by simple cabling between units. AM or FM radio circuits may be added to the amplifier circuits to provide a source of background music. The speaker circuit may be weatherproof for outdoor mounting to converse with callers. The wireless intercom system consists of a combination transmitter-receiver, which broadcasts and receives over the regular a-c wiring in the home. The wireless intercom is simply plugged into the standard wall outlet. Although, the wireless intercom requires no cabling, it is limited to locations where a-c power is available, while the wired intercom can be placed anywhere, even outdoors. The wireless intercom is usually used for voice communication only, and does not send background music because of the restrictions on the frequency spectrum on which it can broadcast.

Arrangement of the Wired Intercom System

Each unit of an intercom system is called a *station*. For a wired intercom system, there are two types of stations: the *master* station and the *remote* station. The master station contains the switching circuits for activating and controlling the intercom system and the amplifier circuits. The master station is supplied with operating power, either ac from the home wiring or dc from batteries. The remote station contains extension speaker circuits and a call-in switching circuit. The remotes receive operating power

from the master. Two kinds of operation may be provided in the remote stations: *nonprivate* or *private*. A nonprivate remote can be listened to by the master at any time. This type of operation is used for baby-sitting, monitoring a room, or answering the door, and is the kind most frequently found. A private remote cannot be listened to by

Fig. 1-3. A transistorized wireless two-station intercom which requires no warm-up. Additional units may be added to system on the same power lines. (Courtesy of Fanon-Masco)

the master except when controlled by the remote. This type of operation is used for baths and other private rooms. Most remotes are only nonprivate, though some are private. Private remotes can be easily made nonprivate, however, when so desired.

Most home intercoms are arranged as *master-to-remote*

systems as shown in Fig. 1-8. This system consists of one master and the one or more remotes. In the simplest systems, the master calls all the remotes simultaneously, and any remote can call the master one at a time. If it is desired that the master call each remote privately, a multi-

remote switchboard system shown in Fig. 1-9 is used. This system is similar to the multistation master-to-remote system, except a switchboard is provided to preset the remotes so that they can communicate with each other. Any remote can also monitor any other station if preset at the master.

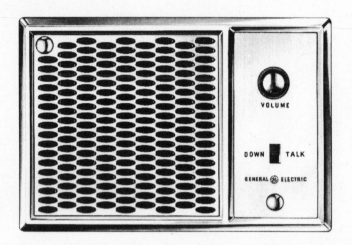

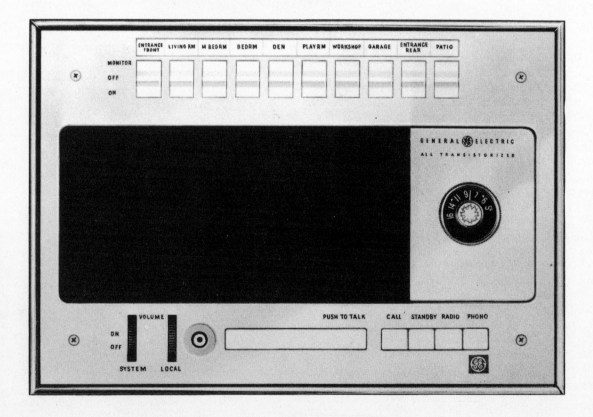

Fig. 1-4. Master station and remote station for General Electric model W320 includes an AM radio and input jack for record player. Master can converse with up to ten remotes.

station master that can individually select remotes to call must be used. However, in the simple master-to-remote system, the remotes cannot converse with each other. To allow the remotes to communicate with each other, the master-to-

In some homes, it is desirable that all stations be able to communicate with each other. If this is the case, the more complex *master-to-master* system shown in Fig. 1-10 is used. In this system, all the stations are multistation mas-

Fig. 1-5. Remote station for General Electric model W337.

Fig. 1-6. Master station for controlling eight remotes. Amplifier for system is included in separate housing. (Courtesy of the Bogen Communications Division of Lear Siegler, Inc.)

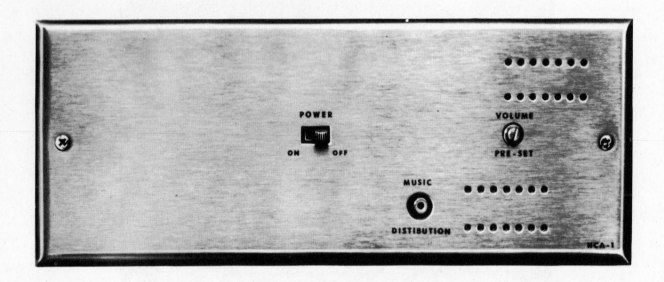

Fig. 1-7. Transistorized amplifier for home intercom. Music input jack is provided for connecting to source of background music, such as FM radio, record player, etc. (Courtesy of the Bogen Communications Division of Lear Siegler, Inc.)

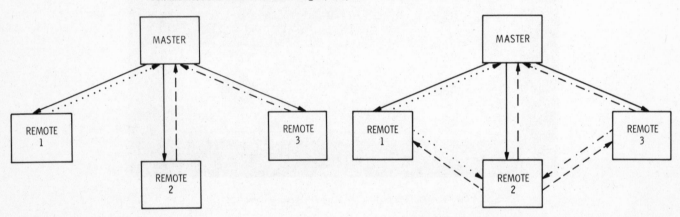

Fig. 1-8. Master-to-remote system. This master converses with all the remotes simultaneously; the remotes converse with the master, but not with each other.

Fig. 1-9. Master-to-remote switchboard system. The master converses with the remotes individually; the remotes converse with the master and, if preset, with other remotes.

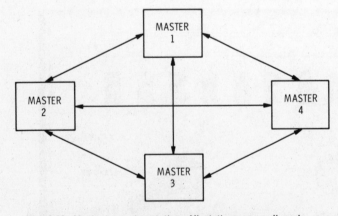

Fig. 1-10. Master-to-master station. All stations can call each other; several simultaneous two-way conversations are possible.

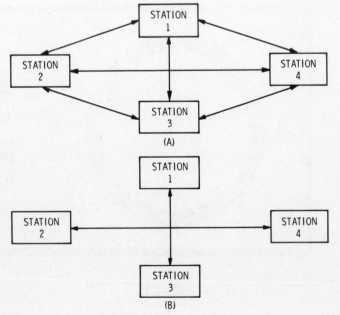

Fig. 1-11. Wireless intercom system. (A) all stations are on same frequency (1, 2, 3, and 4); and (B) stations are on different frequencies.

ters. Any station can talk to or monitor one or more of the other stations. Several two-way conversations can take place simultaneously in this system.

Arrangement of the Wireless Intercom System

In the wireless home intercom system, each station is identical. The individual station consists of a combination transmitter-receiver, which broadcasts and receives through the a-c wiring. In this system, a transmitting station calls all the receiving stations simultaneously, and any station can converse with all the other stations as shown in Fig. 1-11A. If it is desired that all stations are not to be on the same channel, sets of different frequencies can be used for certain stations as shown in Fig. 1-11B.

2 – Theory of Operation

1. Operation of the Wired Intercom System

The basic wired intercom system consists of a master station containing an audio amplifier and its power supply, a speaker-microphone, a *talk-listen* switch, and a *station selector* switch; and a remote station containing a *talk* switch and a speaker-microphone (see Fig. 2-1). To talk from the master, the talk-listen switch is placed to *talk* and the station selector switch is placed to the remote to be called. The master's speaker-microphone is connected to the input of the amplifier, and, at the same time, the output

Audio Amplifier

The audio amplifier (see Fig. 2-2) receives an input signal from the master or remote speaker-microphone connected for talking, and develops an amplified output signal for the master or remote speaker-microphones connected for listening. Present-day systems use both tubes (see Fig. 2-2) and transistors (see Fig. 2-3). Most of the tube units use the same tubes generally found in radios, TV's, and

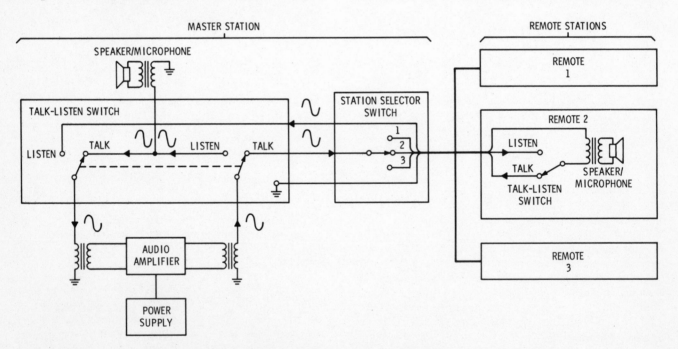

Fig. 2-1. The wired intercom system.

of the amplifier is connected to the line leading to the remote's speaker-microphone. To listen to a call at the master, the talk-listen switch is placed to *listen*. The master's speaker-microphone is connected to the output of the amplifier, and, at the same time, the input of the amplifier is connected to the line coming from the remote's speaker-microphone. To answer a call at the remote, the talk switch is placed to *talk* to connect the remote's speaker-microphone to the input of the amplifier. This switch is necessary to avoid having the master constantly listening to the sounds and noises from a live remote.

hi-fi's (for example, the 50C5, 12SC7, 12SL7, 12AT6, 12AT7, 12AV6, 12AX7, etc.). The tube amplifiers usually consist of one or two voltage amplifiers and a single-ended power amplifier. The transistor amplifiers normally consist of a voltage amplifier, a driver, and a push-pull output stage.

Power Supply

The power supply provides the d-c operating voltages and currents required by the audio amplifier. Both tubes

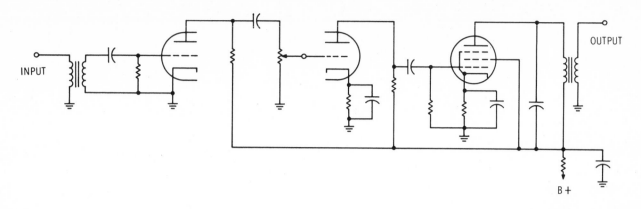

Fig. 2-2. Tube audio amplifier schematic.

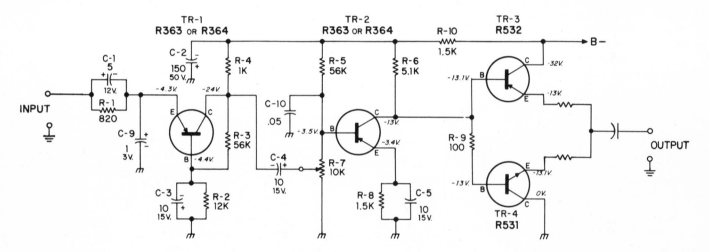

Fig. 2-3. Transistor audio amplifier schematic.

and semiconductors are used in the power supplies of home intercoms. For the low-powered intercoms, a half-wave ac-dc supply is usually provided. For the larger intercoms, especially those equipped for playing background music, a full-wave a-c supply is normally required. Filament power is either obtained from a series string across a-c line, or from the filament winding of the power transformer.

Speaker-Microphone

The speaker-microphone in an intercom performs a double duty; it acts as a speaker when the station is connected for listening, and as a microphone when the station is connected for talking. Because of the long run of cable between the master and remotes, it is desirable for the microphone to produce a low output current and a high output voltage to reduce transmission losses. When common speakers, having a voice coil impedance of 3 to 4 ohms, are used as microphones, the generated output voltage is very low. This results in low amplifier sensitivity and high amplification needed in the amplifier. To increase the voltage output from the speaker-microphone, high-impedance voice coils are required. Therefore, a special 45-ohm speaker is frequently used in home intercoms. However, with the increased use

of transistors, which are basically current amplifiers, more of the low-impedance speakers are coming into use.

Talk-Listen Switch

The talk-listen switch interchanges the two connections between the master and remote speaker-microphones with the two amplifier input and output connections. Thus, a double-pole double-throw switch is required. Generally, the switch is of the rotary type (see Fig. 2-4), although lever and pushbutton types are sometimes used. The switch usually has a center rest position, which is *listen*. From the listen position, the switch can be placed in a spring return position, *talk*, or a locked position, *lock*, which makes the same connections as *talk*.

Although many complicated switching schemes are possible, the operation of this switch can be simplified into two functions. In the listen position, the amplifier's input transformer is connected to receive calls from the remotes, while the amplifier's output transformer is connected to the master's speaker-microphone. This connection is made through the talk switch in the remote as was explained before to reduce unnecessary noise in the master's speaker. This position is also called standby in some intercoms. In the talk position, the amplifier's input transformer is connected to the master's speaker-microphone, while the amplifier's output transformer is connected to the remote's speaker-transformer to send a call. The switch also opens unnecessary connections, such as the remote's call wire.

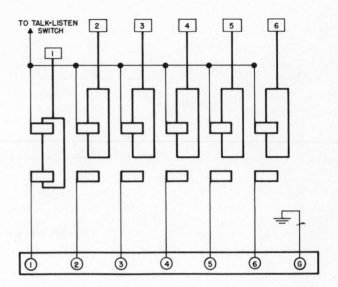

Fig. 2-5. Station selector switch wiring for six-station selector switch.

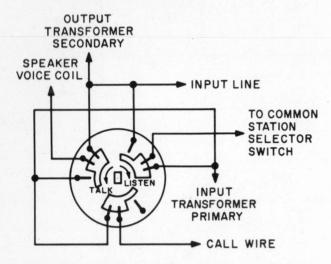

Fig. 2-4. Talk-listen switch wiring. Talk-listen switch in listen position with the common call wire connected to input transformer.

Station Selector Switch

The station selector switch chooses the remote station to converse with the master by connecting the talk-listen switch to the line to the selected remote. The station selector switch is generally the multiple pushbutton or lever type (see Fig. 2-5), although rotary switches are sometimes used in small systems of three or four stations. Only one wire is switched, since all stations have a common ground wire. For talking, the station selector switch connects the output transformer of the master to the line running to the selected remote's speaker-microphone. For listening, the input transformer of the amplifier is connected to the line coming from the selected remote's speaker-microphone through any closed contacts of the station selector switch.

Remote Talk Switch

Most intercom systems are arranged so that the remotes

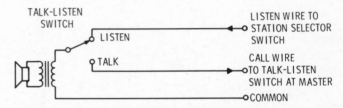

Fig. 2-6. Remote talk switch.

can call the master without being called through the use of a *call* wire. If this wire is not provided, the station selector switch connecting the remote into the circuit must be closed before any conversation can occur. Thus, the master must be left in *listen* for this remote, which results in noise being received at the master at all times. To avoid this, a two-way system is set up by using a call wire common to all remotes (see Fig. 2-6). A single-pole, single-throw normally-open switch of the pushbutton type is generally used as the *talk* switch. When a remote must call the master, the talk switch is set to *talk,* connecting the remote's speaker-microphone across the input transformer of the amplifier regardless of the setting of the station selector switch.

2. Operation of the Wireless Intercom System

The basic wireless intercom system consists of identical combination transmitter-receiver stations containing an r-f amplifier-oscillator, a diode detector, a squelch circuit, an audio amplifier, an audio output-modulator, and a speaker-microphone (see Fig. 2-7). The circuits in the wireless intercom serve a double duty: transmitting and receiving. The r-f amplifier-oscillator acts as an amplifier for received signals and as an oscillator to generate an r-f carrier for transmitted signals. The diode detector is used only in receiving to demodulate the received r-f signal. The squelch circuit reduces noise and interference during receiving. The

audio amplifier performs the same function in both transmitting and receiving; it amplifies audio signals. The audio output amplifier-modulator acts as an audio output amplifier during reception and as a modulator to vary the r-f carrier during transmission. The speaker-microphone acts as a speaker when the station is connected for receiving, and as a microphone when the station is connected for transmitting.

The circuits in the wireless intercom are arranged for either transmitting or receiving by a talk-listen switch. With the talk-listen switch set to *talk* for transmitting, the

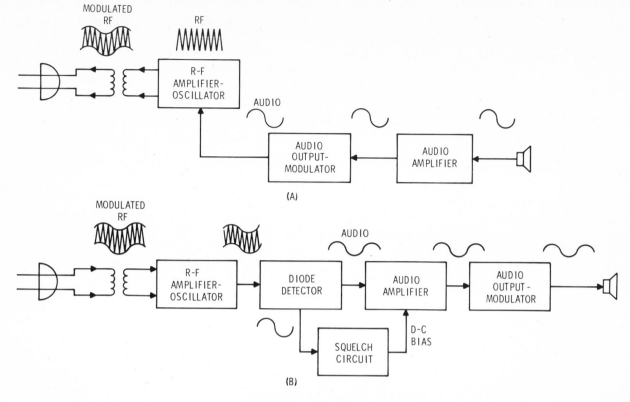

Fig. 2-7. The wireless intercom system.

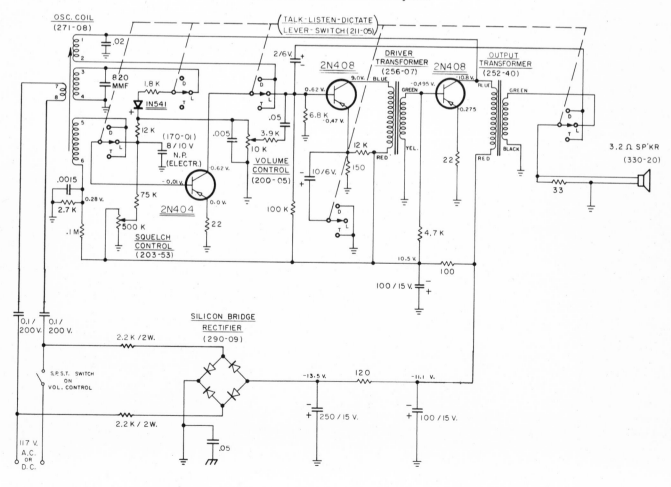

Fig. 2-8. Typical wireless intercom schematic of the Fanon-Masco wireless intercom FW-40.

speaker-microphone converts sound waves into electrical signals. These signals are coupled to the audio amplifier for amplification. The audio signal is coupled to the audio output-modulator, where it is further amplified. This amplified audio signal is fed to the r-f amplifier-oscillator, which is generating a constant-amplitude r-f carrier signal. The audio signal is mixed with the r-f carrier signal to produce an amplitude-modulated r-f signal that is transmitted over the a-c wiring through the line cord.

When the talk-listen switch is set to *listen* for receiving, the r-f signal from another station enters the intercom through the line cord, and is coupled to the r-f amplifier-oscillator for amplification. After amplification, the signal is coupled to the diode detector, which separates the audio signal from the r-f carrier signal. The detected audio signal is fed to both the audio amplifier and the squelch circuit. This detected signal causes the squelch circuit to conduct, which in turn biases the audio amplifier to the point of conduction. By proper adjustment of the squelch circuit, random noise can be blocked from reaching the audio amplifier during periods of no transmission. The audio signal fed to the properly biased audio amplifier is amplified and coupled to the audio output amplifier-modulator, where it is further amplified to drive the speaker-microphone.

The schematic of a typical wireless intercom is shown in Fig. 2-8. This intercom consists of an r-f oscillator, a diode detector, a squelch circuit, an audio amplifier and an audio output amplifier-modulator as described previously. The only difference is that there is no r-f amplifier.

3 - Maintenance and Servicing

1. Introduction

The maintenance and servicing of home intercoms is usually simple since the circuits are relatively straightforward. However, servicing can become difficult and time consuming if a logical systematic method of troubleshooting is not used. In this chapter, such a systematic approach to troubleshooting is given. The maintenance and servicing information contained in this chapter applies only to the actual intercom circuits and not to accessory circuits, such as FM radios and stereo. Information on these circuits is included in other parts of the book. As has been pointed out, there are two types of home intercoms: wired and wireless. The information contained in this chapter is equally applicable to both types.

2. Equipment Required

The general shop tools and test equipment available to TV technicians are usually all that are required for servicing home intercoms. In particular, the following test equipment is useful:

1. VOM, 20,000 ohms/volt meter, and/or VTVM.
2. Tube tester and complete stock of replacement tubes.
3. Transistor tester.
4. Signal generator, rf and audio (alignment of radio only).
5. Oscilloscope (alignment of radio only).

3. Troubleshooting Techniques

In troubleshooting a home intercom system, assume that there is only one trouble source. Try to isolate this trouble using an organized troubleshooting procedure. When the trouble is found and corrected, check the operation of the home intercom to ensure that there is no other trouble.

There are six basic steps in troubleshooting. Knowing these steps and how to use them is important in locating troubles in the shortest time. Equally important, however, is the sequence in which these six steps should be performed. Although, you could perform them in any order and probably still locate the trouble, it would take more time than by using them in a systematic manner. The six basic troubleshooting steps and order of use are:

1. Symptom analysis.
2. Equipment inspection.
3. Signal-tracing and signal injection.
4. Voltage and resistance measurements.
5. Tube and transistor testing.
6. Equipment performance tests.

Symptom Analysis

Symptom analysis is the study of trouble symptoms to isolate the trouble to as few components as possible. By simply studying and analyzing a trouble, you can frequently isolate the trouble to one stage and a few components. In some cases, you might find through symptom analysis that the intercom system is OK, and that the trouble is due to an external cause, such as interference from a nearby ham radio transmitter. However, before you can efficiently perform symptom analysis, you must first thoroughly understand how the defective intercom works. The first step, therefore, in symptom analysis, should be a review of the instruction or service manual for the particular intercom.

Intercom systems are basically multiunit equipments consisting of a number of stations. Thus, the second step in symptom analysis should be the isolation of the trouble to one station of the system by a simple check of each unit. The easiest and quickest way to do this is by talking and listening at each station. For example, assume that you find that the master station in a wired system can talk to all the remote stations, but one remote cannot talk to the master. Since all other stations can talk, all the common circuits in the master and in the cabling are OK. The only place left then for the trouble is in the dead remote.

The third step in symptom analysis should be the isolation of the trouble to the defective stage. The prior system check reveals a number of facts about the trouble. First, the speaker-microphone in the remote must be OK, since it can receive from the master. Secondly, the call wire circuit from the remote must be OK, since this wire is common to all remotes and some of the remotes can talk to the master. The only part left in the remote is the call switch, which must be defective. By reasoning and logic, the technician can frequently isolate many other troubles to one part of the equipment. For instance, if a wired intercom system works in one direction, the amplifier in the master and the speaker-microphones in the master and the remotes must be OK. The trouble then lies somewhere in the switching circuits, since that is all that is left.

Another important step in symptom analysis is the varying of the equipment controls to see how they affect the trouble symptoms. For example, the trouble might be a 60-cycle hum in the output of the intercom system. If varying the volume control changes the level of the hum, the source of trouble is isolated to somewhere before the volume control.

Equipment Inspection

Equipment inspection uses the senses, i.e., sight, smell, hearing, and touch, to locate the trouble. To waste little time, the technician must perform symptom analysis first to isolate the trouble to as few components as possible. Equipment inspection can be used to locate such troubles as charred and burnt-out resistors, leaky transformers and capacitors, arcing, smoke, loose tubes and plugs, broken and damaged leads and cables, short circuits in wiring, and unlit tubes. By careful examination of the equipment using the senses, you can sometimes save much time in locating troubles.

Signal-Tracing And Signal Injection

Signal-tracing and signal injection are similar methods of troubleshooting equipment. Signal-tracing is tracing the path of a normal input signal at various points through an equipment to locate the stage of the equipment where the trouble has developed. Signal injection is injecting of signals in place of the normal signals at various points in an equipment and observing the resulting output to locate the stage of the equipment where the trouble has developed. Each method has some advantages over the other, depending on the characteristics of the equipment under test. Usually signal-tracing is favored, since the circuit cannot be overloaded as is possible during signal injection. However, you cannot use signal-tracing if the normal input signal to the equipment is not available or cannot be observed accurately because of its amplitude or frequency. With both methods, you should begin at the functional midpoint of the equipment. This saves time because you immediately isolate the trouble to approximately half of the equipment. For this reason, subsequent measurements should also be made at the functional midpoint of the remaining part.

Voltage And Resistance Measurements

The main objective for the first three steps in troubleshooting is the isolation of the trouble to a defective stage in the equipment. Once you have succeeded in locating the defective stage, you should perform voltage and resistance measurements to isolate the defective components within the stage. Considering the numerous measurements possible and the time required to make them, the technician should not make voltage and resistance measurements until the defective stage is located. Before making any measure-

ments, you should determine the type of meter to be used, the settings of all controls, and the expected tolerances. Measurements may vary as much as $\pm$ 20% and still be considered within tolerance.

Tube and Transistor Testing

Of all the troubleshooting steps, tube testing is the best known and probably the most misused. Frequently, a technician will test the tubes as the first step in troubleshooting. This often results in a waste of time, since many tubes are tested when possibly only one or maybe even none of the tubes is defective. Besides the time wasted, tubes sometimes test good in a tube tester and yet do not operate properly in the circuit due to the failure of the tube tester to check the tube under its exact working conditions. To avoid this problem, tubes could be tested by substituting them one at a time with known good tubes of the same type. However, this requires even more time than testing the tubes in a tube tester. In certain critical circuits moreover, you may have to substitute several tubes before one is found that will work saisfactorily. This further increases the time required.

In addition to the time wasted, two other considerations require that previous troubleshooting be performed before testing tubes. In many instances, tubes become defective as a result of a defective component in that circuit. For example, a bypass capacitor can short circuit, resulting in a heavy plate current and a burnt-out tube. If a new tube is substituted on the basis of a tube test, it too will quickly burn out. In other instances, changes in the value of circuit components can make an old tube appear marginal before its life is exhausted. Replacing the old tube with a new one only cures the trouble for a while. As this tube ages, it too will appear to be marginal in performance and require an early replacement.

Transistors, like tubes, may be tested by substitution or in a transistor tester. However, while tube failure is a common trouble, transistor failure is a relatively rare occurrence. Because of this, it is even more important not to test transistors until the trouble has been isolated to one stage by previous troubleshooting steps.

Equipment Performance Tests

After locating and correcting a trouble, the technician should run an equipment performance test to ensure that the trouble has actually been corrected, and that the intercom system is again operating exactly as intended. Equipment performance tests may range from a simple check of the entire system to complex procedures for testing frequency response, sensitivity, distortion, etc. The types of tests to be performed and the procedures to be used are usually given in the service or instruction manual for the particular intercom. For example, wireless intercoms must usually be retuned for maximum received volume in both directions after maintenance and servicing.

In addition to providing an equipment check after a trouble has been repaired, the technician frequently uses the equipment performance tests in conjunction with the troubleshooting charts normally provided in many service or instruction manuals. Since troubleshooting charts for intercoms are usually given in these manuals, you may wonder why so much emphasis is placed on systematic troubleshooting and not on troubleshooting charts. First of all, most troubleshooting charts must be started at the beginning and then followed step-by-step through many various tests, such as frequency response, sensitivity, distortion, etc., until the trouble is finally isolated. This process is time consuming. By knowing exactly how the equipment works and by applying systematic troubleshooting procedures, the technician *normally* can locate a trouble faster than if he depended solely on a troubleshooting chart. If troubeshooting charts were the answer to maintenance problems, there would be no need for theory of operation in each service or instruction manual. Secondly, troubleshooting charts cannot include all possible troubles that may occur. This is where knowing exactly how an equipment works and how to apply systematic troubleshooting procedures really pays off for the technician. However, the intercom manual is helpful in locating the trouble.

4. Parts Replacement Requirements

In replacing a defective part, the technician should use an exact replacement. This is especially important in certain critical circuits, such as the r-f amplifier-oscillator in wireless intercoms. To identify the part, the parts list usually included as part of the manufacturer's service or operation manual should be consulted. Each part is normally designated with a specific code number that makes ordering easy.

If an exact replacement for a defective part is not available, an equivalent part should be used. Generally, the equivalent part should have the exact electrical characteristics as the part it is replacing. If possible, it should be the same physical size, and shape and have the same mounting features. Occasionally, it may be necessary to make some physical changes to utilize the equivalent part.

When replacing certain parts, such as shorted bypass capacitors, it is also desirable to replace associated parts, such as the bypass resistor. This is good preventive maintenance, since the resistor was probably carrying a current above its rated maximum value. Replaced parts, such as resistors and capacitors, should be mounted in the same position as the original part, and leads should be dressed in the same manner to prevent possible interactions and oscillations.

Part V

Combination Receivers

1 – Operation

1. Introduction

Many home combination receivers consist of five individual units: a television receiver, an AM-FM stereo tuner, a stereo record changer, a stereo amplifier, and a tape recorder. See Fig. 1-1. The operation, maintenance, and servicing of these individual units are covered in other parts of this book. This part describes the operation of the first four of these units as an integrated set and discusses the circuits common to these units when used in a home combination receiver. Servicing and maintenance information applicable to these units when they are arranged in a home combination receiver is included in this part.

The home combination receiver's operation is dependent to some extent on the common circuits in the set. In most combination receivers, the a-c power input and the audio sound output circuits are common to all units of the set. Usually, the B+ output of the stereo audio amplifier is common to both the amplifier and the AM-FM tuner.

Fig. 1-1. The home combination receiver provides a complete home entertainment center in one cabinet.

2. Circuit Arrangements

Arrangement of the Common Circuits

The a-c input power to the individual units of the home combination receiver is controlled by a *function* switch (see Fig. 1-2). This switch selects either AM radio, FM radio, FM stereo, phonograph, or television operation. The function switch also controls the B+ power supplied to the AM-FM tuner by the stereo audio amplifier to provide either an AM, FM or FM multiplex output. In some combination receivers, the function switch also controls the speaker system, connecting it to either the audio output stage of the television, or to the left- and right-channel out-

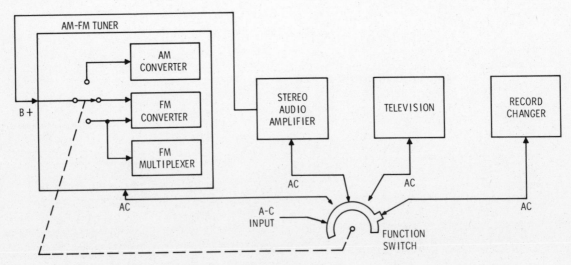

Fig. 1-2. Arrangement of the a-c power input and B+ tuner input circuits in home combination receivers.

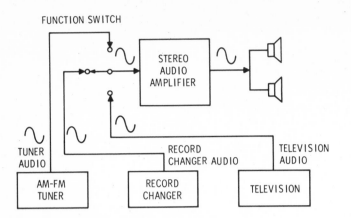

Fig. 1-3. Arrangement of common audio output circuits in home combination receivers.

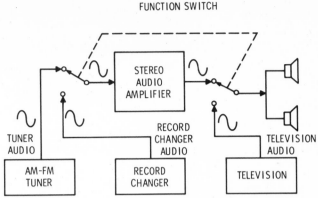

Fig. 1-4. Arrangement of independent audio output circuits found in some home combination receivers.

puts of the stereo audio amplifier.

The audio output is usually common to all units of the combination home receiver. The audio output from the television, AM-FM tuner, or record changer is fed to the common stereo audio amplifier for amplification and for coupling to the speaker system (see Fig. 1-3). With the stereo audio amplifier removed, the combination receiver does not work in any model. However, in certain sets, such as the Admiral D11 series, the RCA-CTC-15 and KC5136Z series, and the Philco M492 and M493 series, the television set is provided with an integral audio system as found in the regular TV chassis. The audio signal to be coupled to the speaker system is selected by the function switch (Fig. 1-4). In this case, removing the stereo audio amplifier only cuts off the AM-FM tuner and the record changer.

Arrangement of Television Circuits

The television receiver circuits used in home combination receiver are the same as the standard circuits used in console televisions, except there is usually no a-c power switch, no audio output tube and transformer, and no

speaker. The a-c switching is performed by the function switch located on the control panel.

The audio output from the television is usually taken off the plate circuit of the audio detector and coupled through a divider network to the input of the stereo audio amplifier (see Fig. 1-5). The GE M782, M784, M786, and M788 series, the Magnavox C36 and C45 series, and the Sylvania 575-9 series use this arrangement. In certain sets, such as the GE series, the audio output tube is left in the set to provide the proper filament load and the correct loading for the B+ power supply of the TV chassis. In this case, the audio output tube is biased to a point to provide the desired B+ load.

Other sets such as the Admiral D11 series, the RCA CTC-15 and KCS136Z series, and the Philco M492 and M493 series, have television circuits identical to those found in the standard circuits. The a-c switching is performed by the volume control, as is usual, and the television audio output is provided by the audio output tube and transformer. As discussed previously, the function switch connects the speaker system to either the output transformer of the television or the left- and right-channel outputs of the stereo amplifier.

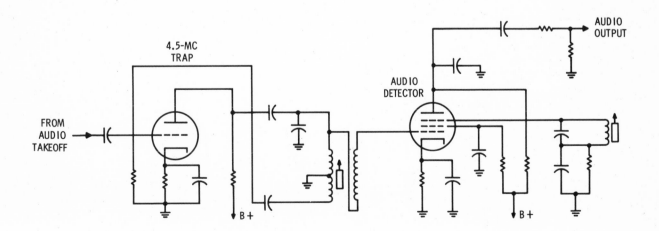

Fig. 1-5. Arrangement of audio output circuits in televisions used in home combination receivers.

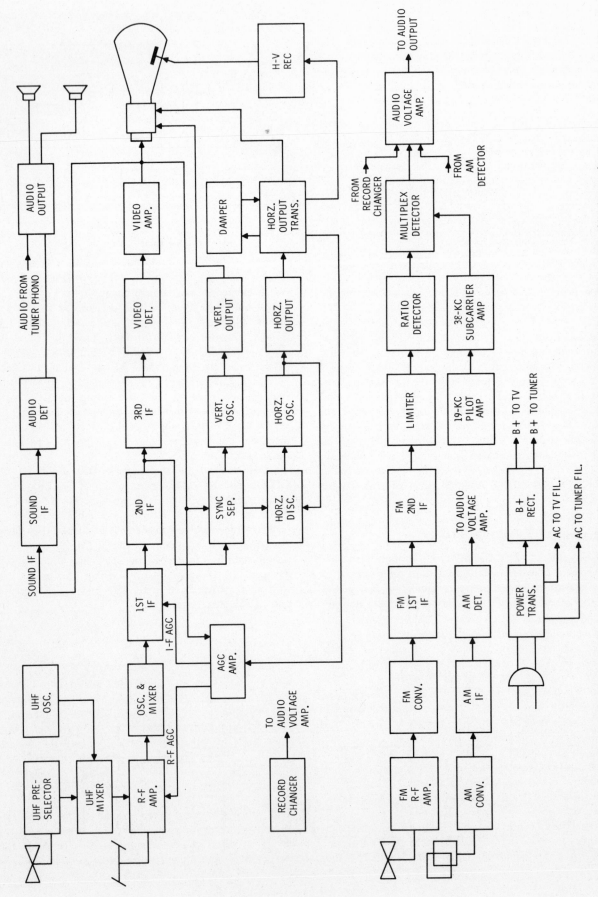

Fig. 1-6. Arrangement of integrated power supply and audio sound output circuits in some televisions and in home combination receivers.

Certain sets use integrated power supply and audio output circuits (see Fig. 1-6). The television power supply provides the B+ and filament ac to a separate tuner. The stereo amplifier is integral with the television circuits. The audio output stage on the television provides a right- and left-channel output to the speaker system.

stereo amplifier integral with the television for amplification and coupling to the speaker system.

Arrangement of Stereo Amplifier Circuits

The stereo audio amplifier circuits used in combination

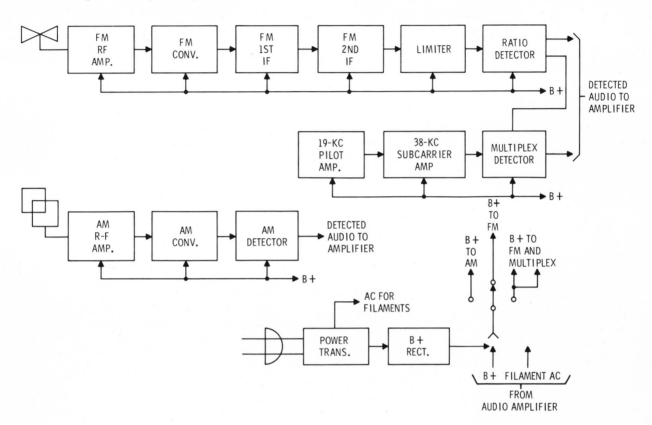

Fig. 1-7. Arrangement of AM-FM tuner circuits used in home combination receivers.

Arrangement of AM-FM Tuner Circuits

The AM-FM tuner circuits used in combination receivers are the same as the standard circuits, except that there is usually no a-c power switch and no audio output circuits. In some cases, there is no power supply in the tuner, but the a-c power required for the filaments and the B+ power is provided by the stereo amplifier or the television.

The a-c switching for the tuner is performed by the function switch located on the cabinet. This switch also controls the B+ power supplied to the tuner circuits to provide power to either the AM circuits, the FM converter, or the FM circuits with the multiplex circuit (see Fig. 1-7). The detected audio signals from the tuner are usually fed to the stereo audio amplifier for amplification and coupling to the speaker systems.

Certain sets, such as the Zenith 16224 and 16M24 series, discussed previously, use integrated power supply and audio sound output circuits. In this case, the television power supply provides the B+ and filament ac to the tuner. The detected audio signals from the tuner are fed to the

receivers are the same as the standard circuits, except there is usually no a-c power switch, and the amplifier receives an input from the television in addition to the usual inputs from an AM-FM tuner and record changer. In most cases, the amplifier also supplies B+ and filament ac to the AM-FM tuner. The a-c switching for the amplifier is performed by the function switch located on the chassis. This switch also controls the audio signal to be coupled to the speaker system for certain sets, such as the Admiral 11 series, the RCA CTC-15 and KCS136Z series, and the Philco M492 and M493 series discussed previously. In these cases, the speakers are connected in parallel groups for the AM-FM tuner and record changer and in series for the television.

Arrangement of Record Changer Circuits

The record changer circuits used in home combination receivers are identical to the standard record changer circuits found in hi-fi and stereo sets. A-c wiring is different in that it must interconnect with the junction switch.

2 – Maintenance and Servicing

1. Introduction

Maintenance and servicing information for the home combination receiver considered as a unit is given in this chapter. Troubleshooting information required to isolate the trouble to one unit of the set is described. Once the trouble has been isolated to one unit, the maintenance and servicing information described in other parts of the book for the individual units should be consulted to locate the trouble.

2. Equipment Required

The same general shop tools and test equipment listed in other parts of this book are usually all that are required for servicing home combination receivers. Consult the part covering specific units found in the combination receiver for the equipment to service that particular unit.

3. Troubleshooting Techniques

Introduction

In troubleshooting a home combination receiver, assume that there is only one source of trouble. Try to isolate this trouble to one unit of the home combination receiver using an organized troubleshooting procedure. When the trouble is isolated to one unit, use the troubleshooting information contained in other parts of the book to locate the defective part or parts. After the trouble is corrected, check the operation of the complete home combination receiver to ensure that there is no other trouble source.

There are 5 basic steps in troubleshooting. Knowing these steps and how to use them is important in locating troubles in the shortest time possible. Equally important, however, is the sequence in which the 5 steps should be performed. Although, you could perform them in any order and probably still locate the trouble, it would take considerably longer than if you used them in a systematic manner. The 5 basic troubleshooting steps and order of use are:
1. Symptom analysis.
2. Equipment inspection.
3. Signal-tracing and signal injection.
4. Voltage and resistance measurements.
5. Equipment performance tests.

Symptom Analysis

Symptom analysis is the study of trouble symptoms to isolate the trouble to as few components as possible. By simply studying and analyzing a trouble, you can frequently isolate the trouble to one unit of the combination receiver, and sometimes even to the defective stage within the unit. In some cases, you might find through symptom analysis that the home combination receiver is OK, and that the trouble is due to an external cause, such as a defective antenna or lead-in wire. However, before you can efficiently perform symptom analysis, you must first thoroughly understand how the defective home combination receiver works. The first step, therefore, in symptom analysis, should be a review of the service manual for the particular unit.

Home combination receivers are basically multiunit equipments consisting of a number of individual units. Thus, the second step in symptom analysis should be the isolation of the trouble to one unit of the set by a simple check of the set. For example, assume that you find that the TV and record player work, but the AM-FM tuner works only on FM. Since there is sound output for the television, stereo, and FM tuner, the common audio circuits and speakers are OK. The only place left then for the trouble is in the AM-FM tuner.

The third step in symptom analysis should be the isolating of the trouble to the defective stage in the individual unit. The prior system check reveals a number of facts about the trouble. First, the interconnecting cabling between the tuner and the stereo amplifier must be OK, since the detected AM and FM signals are connected through the same wiring. Secondly, the common tuner circuits, such as the power supply, the AM-FM i-f stages, and a portion of the switching circuits are OK, since the tuner works for FM. The only stages left are the AM converter, AM if (if separate), and the AM detector. By reasoning and logic, the technician can frequently isolate many other troubles to one part of a unit in the set.

Another important step in symptom analysis is the varying of the equipment controls to see how they affect the trouble symptoms. For example, if varying the tuning control changes the pitch of the signal heard in the loudspeakers, the source of trouble is isolated to the converter, or somewhere before this stage.

Equipment Inspection

Equipment inspection uses the senses, i.e., sight, smell, hearing, and touch, to locate the trouble. To waste little time, the technician must perform symptom analysis first to isolate the trouble to as few components as possible. Equipment inspection can be used to locate such troubles as incorrect interconnecting cabling, broken and damaged leads and cabling, charred and burnt-out resistors, leaky transformers and capacitors, arcing, smoke, loose tubes and plugs, short circuits in wiring, and unlit tubes. By careful examination of the equipment using the senses, you can sometimes save much time in locating troubles.

Signal-Tracing and Signal Injection

Signal-tracing and signal injection are similar methods of troubleshooting equipment. Signal-tracing is tracing the path of a normal input signal at various points through the equipment to locate the stage of the equipment where the trouble has developed. Signal injection is injecting of signals in place of the normal signals at various points in the equipment, and observing the resulting output to locate the stage of the equipment where the trouble has developed. Each method has some advantages over the other, depending on the characteristics of the equipment under test. Usually signal-tracing is favored, since the circuit cannot be overloaded as is possible during signal injection. However, you cannot use signal-tracing if the normal signal input to the equipment is not available or cannot be observed accurately because of its amplitude or frequency. With both methods, you should begin at the functional midpoint of the unit under test. This saves time because you immediately isolate the trouble to approximately half of the unit. For this reason, subsequent measurements should also be made at the functional midpoint of the remaining part.

Voltage and Resistance Measurements

The main objective of the first three steps in troubleshooting is the isolation of the trouble to a defective unit of the home combination receiver, and then isolating of the trouble to a defective stage within the unit. Once you have succeeded in locating the defective stage, you should perform voltage and resistance measurements to isolate the defective component within the stage. Considering the numerous measurements possible and the time required to make them, the technician should not make voltage and resistance measurements until the defective stage is located. Before making any measurements, he should determine the type of meter to be used, the settings of all controls, and the expected tolerances. Measurements may vary as much as ± 20% and still be considered within tolerance.

Equipment Performance Tests

After locating and correcting a trouble, the technician should perform an equipment performance test to insure that the trouble has actually been corrected, and that the units of the home combination receiver are again operating exactly as intended. Equipment performance tests may range from a simple check of the entire set to complex procedures for testing the frequency response, sensitivity, bandwidth, distortion, etc. of the individual units. The type of tests to be performed and the procedures to be used are usually given in the service manual for the particular combination receiver. For example, AM-FM tuners must usually be retuned if the r-f and i-f tubes are changed during maintenance and servicing.

In addition to providing for an equipment check after a trouble has been repaired, the technician frequently uses the equipment performance tests in conjunction with the troubleshooting charts normally provided in the service manuals for the individual units. Since troubleshooting charts are usually given in these manuals, you may wonder why so much emphasis is placed on systematic troubleshooting in this section. First of all, most troubleshooting charts must be started at the beginning and then followed step by step through many various tests, such as frequency response, sensitivity, alignment, etc., until the trouble is finally isolated. The process is time consuming. By knowing exactly how the equipment works, and by applying systematic troubleshooting, you normally can locate a trouble faster than if you depended solely on the chart. That is the reason why a theory of operation is included in most service manuals. Secondly troubleshooting charts cannot list all the possible troubles that may occur. This is the time where knowing exactly how an equipment works, and how to apply systematic troubleshooting procedures pays off for the technician. However, the valuable troubleshooting information given in the service manual will be of invaluable help in locating the trouble.

4. Servicing Hints

The following servicing hints are applicable to the individual units of the home combination reeciver, and are provided here to assist the technician in servicing the set.

Audio Amplifier

1. The a-c supply lead to the audio amplifier is sometimes polarized for minimum hum. To polarize the a-c line into the audio amplifier with no signal applied, turn the audio amplifier ON and the volume control fully up. Reverse the a-c lead to the amplifier, and note any change in background hum. Select the position of the plug with the least noticeable hum.

2. Do not operate the audio amplifier without rated speaker load, especially transistor amplifiers directly coupled to the speakers.

3. Do not short the audio output of either channel while the amplifier is operating.

4. If a power transistor shorts, replace the emitter resistor and check the condition of the silicon diode rectifiers. If either output power transistor fails, replace both transistors since the amplifier will not function properly unless a matched pair is used.

5. When a power transistor is replaced, the insulator between the transistor and the heat sink should also be replaced.

6. Be sure the coded speaker leads are connected to the like coded terminals on the speakers for proper polarity, and check that the speaker groups are in phase with each other.

AM-FM Tuner

1. If the tuner works in one mode and not the other, the common circuits, such as the AM-FM i-f amplifiers, the audio preamplifiers, and the power supply are probably OK, and should be checked last.

2. To isolate the trouble to the r-f, i-f, limiter, and ratio detector portions of the receiver, or to the multiplex portion, a multiplex generator can be used as a signal tracer to determine if the multiplex section of the receiver is functioning properly. The composite output of the multiplex generator should be injected at the output of the ratio detector.

Television

1. Loss of sound can be due to trouble in the sound sections of the television or in the common audio amplifier circuits. Isolate the trouble by operating the home combination receiver in all functions to check the audio amplifier.

2. When removing the TV chassis for service, check to see if the other units of the home combination can be interconnected to provide AM-FM tuner and record changer operation. In most cases, removing the TV chassis does not affect the operation of the other units.

Index